Raisa Borovsky

Siberian Summer

or

The World Upside Down

Boston · 2019

Raisa Borovsky
Siberian Summer or The World Upside Down. *Novel*

ISBN 978-1940220970
Library of Congress Control Number: 2018966915

Published by M•Graphics
www.mgraphics-publishing.com
mgraphics.books@gmail.com

Book Layout by M•Graphics © 2019

Printed in the United States of America

To my mother and father, blessed be their memory,
who passed peacefully of old age;
and to the two dearest friends of my youth,
who will never grow old...

Having written a novel in a language that is not my own,
I want to express my deep gratitude to my husband Wayne,
who always had patience—and found the time—
to help me with editing.

Contents

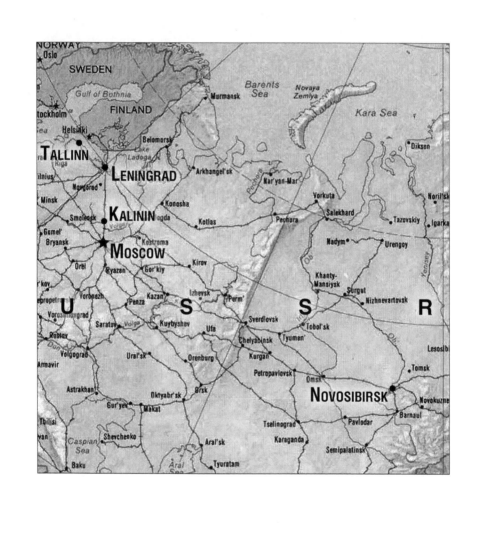

PREFACE

I FIRST LEARNED THAT THE WORLD is round when I was about four years old.

I kept struggling for several days trying to imagine: how can people live on the *other side?* Are they walking upside down? How come they don't fall?

Finally, I came to my mother for the explanation.

She thought for a while, not sure how to answer my question, and finally said:

"Those people don't even know that they walk upside down. It feels just right for them. Actually, they think that it is we who are upside-down..."

* * *

A quarter of a century later, I found myself living in that upside-down world. All around me were Martians, although they often disguised themselves as humans. It sure felt uncomfortable, not to say awful. I felt dizzy most of the time, often about to fall and never get up—but got no empathy from anyone...

Everybody around me considered themselves perfectly fine, and kept assuring me that I must feel great! Especially in comparison to that terrible life that I—they knew it for sure—had lived on the other side of our planet, where everybody walks upside down...

But the worst was that eventually I started believing them, or at least pretended to believe, and somewhat adapted—although I no longer could tell the top from the bottom or right from wrong...

* * *

It was in mid-1990s when I dared to come back for the first time— a freshly baked American citizen on a honeymoon, with an American husband who had worked all over the world and thought nothing of adding Russia to the list of weird countries he'd been to.

An old Aeroflot airplane landed. We made it from St. Petersburg to Novosibirsk in less than four hours, which seemed an eternity. The plane was not as comfortable as I remembered it: too stuffy, unsmiling attendants, lousy lunch… In any case, we did not crash and arrived on time, tired but excited. I knew my father would be waiting for us in the arrival hall, as he had always done throughout all the years.

Nadia, my teenage daughter, and I were standing on the tarmac, waiting for my husband to emerge from the plane. It must have been around a hundred degrees (if you measure in Fahrenheit, which Russians don't use). The afternoon sun was burning mercilessly, the asphalt under our feet radiated heat like a kitchen stove, and the air itself was trembling as if it was about to start melting.

Walter finally came out—an experienced traveler with strong opinions about everything in the world, including countries he had visited. He looked around him in astonishment, frantically searching for his sunglasses, so helpless that I wanted to laugh: he must have been wondering if somehow we had taken the wrong airplane, and landed in the tropics instead of the latitude of the middle of Canada.

I took him by the hand and said with a smile:

"Welcome to Siberia."

Chapter One

SIBERIA

I WAS BORN IN LENINGRAD, USSR, a city and country that no longer can be found on the world map. Sometimes I feel that my very birth was a mistake—God playing his (or her?) giant roulette that randomly stopped spinning in the wrong place at the wrong time.

My mother had an easy labor—so easy that she lived the rest of her life convinced that talk of childbirth pain was a myth made up by women who wanted attention. My father had dropped her off at the hospital around 10 PM, when the sun was just setting. I was born at 3 AM, a few minutes before sunrise. It was one of the shortest nights of the year, around summer solstice. Maybe that is why I have always been depressed by darkness, especially by early winter darkness, which feels like death.

From the corner of the window of her hospital ward, my mother could see the spike of the Peter Paul Fortress catching the last and first rays of sunshine while the sky never got completely dark... For many years, I believed that the pinkish glitter on the ever-murky waters of the Neva River was the first thing I saw upon coming to this world— until I learned that newborns cannot see farther than the length of their own arm, just enough to locate their mom's nipple when feeding. Except that, in my case, the nipple was rubber, with milk coming from a bottle: as most girls whose sexual maturity fell during the famine of the World War Two, my mom did not have enough breast milk to sustain a healthy baby.

Judging from the bits and pieces that I learned about my parents' childhood years, both of their families were exceptionally lucky in avoiding Stalinist political repressions or being killed at war, never mind perishing in the Holocaust. All of my four grandparents sailed through the many turmoils of the twentieth century relatively uns- carred. Mom's father, a very talented and successful engineer, was briefly arrested sometime at the end of 1940, on the accusation of having been a spy while visiting (for work, mind you) then capitalist Estonia. He was released after only a few months, with apologies for the mistake... Or at least that is the way the family legend goes: of all things the KGB is known for, apologizing for anything was not one of them...

My mom, who always spoke about her pre-war childhood as of an exciting fairy-tale, told me that her father was never the same after his arrest. On the other hand, the war started soon afterwards, so nobody and nothing was ever the same. My grandfather Alexandr Vasilyevich Staheyev, already in his fifties and a valuable specialist, instead of being enlisted in the Red Army, was commandeered to the Ural Mountains to supervise relocation and launching of the plants hurriedly evacuated from the European parts of Russia. My mom's family, however, remained in Leningrad long enough to experience the first bombing by German warplanes, and left on the very last cargo train that escaped the city just hours before the 900-days-long siege closed its deadly ring around it.

By some weird coincidence, my dad's family spent the war in that same city in the Urals, my future parents living only a mile away from each other; however, as children they never met. Or maybe they had, accidentally, but took no notice of each other, my mom being two years older, a tall and shy Russian teenage girl, and my father a rambunctious Jewish boy in perpetually ripped trousers, whose family tried its best to forget their Jewishness and blend in with the locals...

My mom and dad met many years later in Leningrad, a young school teacher and a brilliant doctorate student, and that is probably where I should start the story of my life—if only it could be separated from the story of my country—or, better said, the country where I was born but that is no longer mine... The country that now exists under a different name, different flag, and different slogans—but which might, after all, have not changed that much...

1

The best part of any travel is knowing that one day you will return home. But what embassy gives visas to your childhood?

During a bumpy ride through my life—daring, exciting, terrifying, sometimes full of dreams and hopes, at other times dull and hopeless,

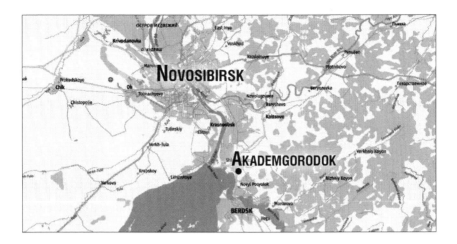

filled with loneliness and despair—I never stopped looking back, to where I had come from... In spite of all logic and science, I could never fully accept the concept of *no return*. One-way road... Always one-way, no matter how much you regret the turns you have made, or scared of a twist that lies ahead...

We grew up together—my town and I.

My first vivid memories of it would relate to everyone's image of Siberia. I must have been three and a half years old (and so was the town), and it was winter. There were huge snow banks around me, some over two meters high, and I was digging a cave with a little plastic shovel. It was an exciting job: I wanted to dig a cave big enough for me and my teddy-bear to hide in. I almost forgot that just an hour ago I had felt very lonely. And then I saw that girl. She was about my age, dressed like myself, in a fur coat, fur hat, and *valenki*—traditional Siberian boots made of thickly pressed wool. She watched me silently for a while, and I did not dare to speak.

Then she asked, matter-of-factly, "May I play with your teddy?"

That very evening, the girl's father brought her over to my parents' apartment for a "play night". The father, Yuri Ivanovich Kotov (lovingly shortened to *Yurivanych* by people who knew him well) was a young physicist, who, like my father, had recently defended his first dissertation, and moved his family to Siberia from the European part of Russia, following his love for the unknown and for adventure, lured by the promise of luxurious living conditions (by Soviet standards, at least), and infinitely better opportunities for scientific research. He and his wife soon became my parents' closest friends, and more stories (this time "adult" stories") came from that—but to all its turn... The girl's name was Alla, nicknamed *Allochka,* (with the stress on the first syllable, please), and she was four-and-a-half years old, a full year older than me. She became my very first friend—and, as an older and more boisterous girl, was always a leader in our little duet.

* * *

Our town, known as Academic Town, or simply *Akademgorodok* (one can still find a fair amount of Google entries describing the place, including a descent Wikipedia article) was a strange place to grow up in— a small and exclusive island, which suddenly appeared in the middle of the Siberian woods almost as if in a fairy tale. About twenty miles from the big industrial city of Novosibirsk, it was brought to life by a single decree of the Soviet government, which wanted to create a scientific center outside the thickly populated and strategically vulnerable European part of Russia. It was designed and built for scientists, and scientists became its major inhabitants and creators.

The scientists who moved in first were mostly young men, adventurous and enthusiastic enough to be willing to relocate thousands of miles from places where they had grown up and worked, talented enough to turn its thirty-something scientific institutes into centers of the world's science, and brave enough to dare to start their careers—in many cases already quite established—from scratch, believing that they would achieve more. My father was one of them, an ambitious twenty-eight-year-old graduate of a post-doc program of the Leningrad University. He began his work in Akademgorodok before it was actually built. All the town's pioneers (among them a few of my father's former university classmates and later his life-time friends) lived in temporary log cabins while their future apartments were being built.

My mother and I joined my dad a year later, as soon as our apartment complex, one of the first residential buildings in town, was completed. I was fascinated by the airplane and slept in a taxi most of the way from the airport. I woke up while my mother was putting me down on the couch in my new room, saying,

"We are home now."

* * *

The most memorable and distinctive sounds of my early childhood were the voices of thousands of birds calling each other from the trees outside my window, and happy voices of children playing in the yard. I used to wake up to those sounds every morning of my preschool childhood. The next sound was usually a knock on the door (it was many years before my parents got around to buying a door bell), and a child's voice (it was usually a girl, but not always)—or sometimes the voices of several children—asking my mother:

"Is Anya coming out?"

And then I would jump up from whatever I had been doing (drawing, building, making a doll house)—and shriek: "Yes, yes!!!"

* * *

In late spring and early summer, carpets of flowers in the woods were so thick that one could not see the ground. They were snowdrops, first ambassadors of spring, white as the melting snow that gave them their name. A bit later came violets, blue as the spring sky before the sunset; in June they all gave way to bright orange ball-shaped flowers called "little fires". And indeed, in spots where the sun managed to make its way through the canopy of leaves and needles, the ground seemed as if it were burning. Later in summer, even preschoolers could pick up enough mushrooms for the family supper, not leaving the safety of their "back yard."

Summers were short, but often very hot—so hot that it was hard to sleep at night, even with all the windows and balcony doors wide open. During the day, children under ten, boys and girls alike, did not bother wearing any clothes at all except cotton underpants. They ran barefoot around town, becoming very unhappy when, on cooler days, the parents made them put on sandals and shirts.

* * *

Everything was *different* in Akademgorodok. The real master and boss of the town—which included all scientific institutes, its economic and social backbone—was not the local Communist Party boss, as everywhere else in the country, but the Chairman of the Siberian Division of the USSR, Mikhail Lavrentiev, a world-famous mathematician. He was our absolute monarch, who reported only to Moscow, not to the regional Party boss.

"Power corrupts, and absolute power corrupts absolutely." I am not sure that those words could be fully applicable to Lavrentiev—although there almost certainly was some truth to them.

A person in power inevitably invites harsh criticism and even envy—so all of that must be taken into account. Growing up, I heard Lavrentiev's name an infinite number of times, much more often than the name of Brezhnev, then the head of the Soviet Government—but I can't recall either much love or much hatred. As a very young girl, I remember one widely discussed episode, which gained popular approval.

As far as the story goes, a young scientist—for mere entertainment—shot with a hunting gun a mother squirrel and her babies, who lived in the town's woods. When President Lavrentiev learned about that, he ordered the man to be expelled from the town *within twenty-four hours* (which for the latter obviously meant losing his prestigious job and government-subsidized apartment). The order was carried out promptly. No courts, no lawyers, no appeal. We lived in a totalitarian society, after all.

* * *

As for the far-away Moscow government, it treated our baby-town as their beloved spoiled child. At least for a while, its cultural and social life went almost uncontrolled. The very popular amateur drama club *Integral* staged plays by dissident authors that even in those relatively liberal times were forbidden in capital cities. The House of Scientists housed numerous clubs, where people openly said and discussed things that would have gotten their Moscow and Leningrad colleagues into big trouble.

While the child was growing up, however, its parent became stricter. Clubs had to become more cautious in their programs and discussions. *Integral*, which refused to conform, was simply closed down. As everywhere else in the country, the most interesting events gradually moved from the scientific institutes and halls of the House of Scientists into residential homes. The most fascinating lectures, slide demonstrations, and poetry readings were taking place in our parents' kitchens and living rooms.

Nevertheless, there was plenty of demand for "official" culture. The big halls of the House of Scientists were rarely vacant. Of course, the main purpose of the institution was to house international conferences in a variety of scientific disciplines—but most of the days of the year the premises were occupied by "less serious" events. Russia's leading drama productions, which were permanently sold out in Moscow and Leningrad, were much more accessible when performed in Akademgorodok. Famous orchestras and soloists from all over the world loved to play there. Presentations and lectures of various kinds, from art slide shows to new discoveries in history and popular science, gathered a full house. The art gallery, with its constantly changing exhibitions, was a great place to meet interesting people.

To complete the picture, I should stress the most distinguishing feature of Akademgorodok, compared to the rest of the country: its openness to the world. Growing up in the middle of *the Cold War*, none of us children ever heard the term. Science was as it should be—above politics; it extended over state boundaries and language barriers. And our town was the center of the *world's* science.

That is the place I was lucky and privileged to grow up in. My first ideas of the world were shaped by belief that the only honorable occupation of a man was to be a scientist, solving mysteries of the Universe. That discussing books, listening to classical music, and skiing in the woods were the main leisurely activities outside work—and, most importantly, that foreigners were sincerely interested in history and culture of my country and that everyone in the world lived in awe of the Russian science, and hugely respected the country that had sent the first man and the first woman into space, not to mention having won the Second World War...

At the same time, the vicious capitalist world that most of the country hated and feared, appeared to us as flowing with milk and honey, where talented scientists, artists, and writers had no restrictions on what they worked on and how they expressed themselves.

Later I had to pay dearly for those beliefs, which were, at the very minimum, over-optimistic—if not outright wrong. Is it possible that my current book is a way of contesting knowledge received a super-hard way, which my heart still refuses to accept? Not all questions need to be (or can be) answered—so I will let my readers to find out for themselves...

2

What are my most vivid memories?

I close my eyes, and see the wooded area behind our house on a winter evening. It is completely dark by five o'clock, but as late as eight there are still at least two dozen children, preschoolers to preteens, playing around big ice-covered slides. We are sliding again and again, falling into fresh snow at the end of every ride and then running and climbing back to be the first for the next one. Our laughter and happy screams are lost among hundred-year-old pine trees. There are almost certainly no adults (very young children, who require parents' supervision, have already gone home), and the only light comes from apartment windows, glowing behind the bare trees.

I am finally getting hungry, and probably need to use the bathroom. I run to my house, and three minutes later knock at the door of my apartment. But there is no answer: nobody is home. I may be slightly disappointed, but not a bit scared. I know that the next-door neighbor is home, and am looking forward to playing with her three children. But she is not answering the door either. I do not have time to start crying, for a door opens on the floor below, and another neighbor is calling:

"Anechka, come over here! Your mom will be home soon!"

A minute later she is shaking the half-melted snow out of my *valenki*, taking off my coat and bringing me to the kitchen. Her family has already finished supper, and the table is cleaned, but she is asking, "What would you like to eat?"

While I am finishing the second bologna sandwich with a cup of hot tea mixed with sweetened condensed milk, my next-door neighbor from upstairs shows up.

"Ah! You are here! Would you like to come and play with my kids for now, while your mom is doing her shopping?" In a confirmation of her invitation, she has dry slippers for me.

Of course, I do want to play with her two sons, and even more, with her daughter. I run up the stairs leaving my fur coat and *valenki* behind, and probably even forgetting to say thank you to my kind hostess (never mind—my mom will fix both mistakes when she returns). When my mother arrives half an hour later, I don't even want to go home. It is almost certainly OK, since she will be chatting with her neighbor for a while anyway.

Another one of my brightest memories was going skiing alone, as soon as I was old enough to go outside our yard. I must have been five and a half when my mother first suggested that I ski up to the university—maybe three-quarters of a mile by semi-wooded alley. I remember the sun so bright it hurt my eyes, and adult skiers smiling and giving way to me on the trail, and me feeling very independent and very proud...

Now, here is a sad memory. I am in bed sick, with a sore throat and fever, but that is not what creates the tense and somber atmosphere at home. My father, together with all our male neighbors, is participating in a search party looking for a lost fifteen-year-old boy who had somehow separated from his older friends while skiing outside town. Mom is home, worried sick, although she does not personally know the family. The ground search goes on for several days. Each day a few institutes stop their work to allow hundreds of scientists to join the search party. (After a week of unsuccessful searching, skiers were replaced by military helicopters—all in vain. The boy must have taken a wrong turn and then lost the trail that was quickly disappearing under fresh snow; his body was found in the spring by peasants of some village, ten miles away from the place he had been last seen. I did not even know the boy's name, but I will never forget the strong feeling that his disappearance was *everyone's problem*. Every family in town was anxious to find him, and when the search failed, grieved as if he were their own son...)

* * *

And then, a completely different memory—a life-turning event for an almost-six-year-old. It must be late April, or maybe cool early May. The ground, just liberated from the five-months-long snow blanket, is breathing freely and happily, smelling of wet soil ready to give birth to grass and flowers, to send its juices up the tree trunks, to help produce leaves and fruit. But the world is not a safe place...

The ground under my feet is alive—full of earth worms, the first laborers of the spring. And I fear nothing more than those squirming sleazy little creatures, imagining one crawling on me, touching my arm, my neck, maybe even making its way under my coat, trapped there...

Imagination is much worse than reality—but how on earth have local boys found out about my imagined fears? Did I give them away by some scream, gesture of disgust, running away from a curious worm who dared to appear on the surface? None of that matters now. What matters is that the pack of five to seven-years old male friends inhabiting my neighborhood have found a hunting victim—and that hunting victim is me. (Those very boys, when mixed with my girl-friends, are perfectly peaceful creatures, great partners in playing ball, hide-and-seek, and drawing with chalk on asphalt driveways; they are only dangerous when they get all together to form a male gang—and as any gang, they immediately start looking for a prey).

Every day, walking into the yard, I first look around me to assess the situation: if my enemies are playing with other girls, I am safe. I can join in their game, or go look for another group. But if I can see no one, then I have to be on high alert. The gang may appear at any moment, from anywhere—there are plenty of thick tree groves and buildings around, to hide behind. Retreating back home wouldn't do that—my parents will make me go outside anyway, and they have no empathy for my fear of worms, or of boys: Life is full of difficult situations, you better learn to navigate and manage them as early as possible...

But I can't manage. Neither can I imagine a situation more terrifying than a gang of boys (yesterday's peaceful playmates), chasing after me with a squirming worm in the leader's hands, with exciting hunting screams... My heart beats in my throat at the very thought of that, and my legs—my saviors—feel weak... I look for a group of girls to join—although that doesn't always provide protection: sometimes, the girls conveniently disappear when the gang appears on the horizon.

This day, the scene repeats again, as in a horror movie—the one hundredth time, it seems. The gang floating around the yard, bored until they see me, quickly digs out a worm from the ground, waves it to show me, and takes up running towards me, their screams anticipating an exciting chase. I run, as usual, with my heart jumping out of my chest. For some miraculous reason, I manage to leave them behind far enough to find a refuge behind an electrical power booth; my pursuers can't see me—but I know that it is just a minute of respite. I look around me for the next place I could hide—if I can run fast enough to make it there. Nearby bare bushes provide no protection, and the forest is too far away.

Despair overwhelms me, my breath all but stops. But suddenly something amazing happens. Like a cornered wild animal who has no way to escape, I make a leap forward. That is not a conscious decision, no logical calculation—that is just an instinct, so swift that I have no time to weigh its consequences. The game steps out of its hiding place to face the hunters. For a few seconds they resume their wild run, and their wild screams. The victim does not move. The pursuers slow down. Their excitement diminishes, but they still attempt to recover, not giving in to disappointment because of the sudden turn of events that none of them can understand. The leader is waving the worm, which is probably also scared to death, so high, so far from its native mother earth—just a few meters away from my face. I don't move. I am not sure that I *can* move, even if I want. I just look at it, then at the leader's face. Something inside me tells me to not avert my gaze. Look. Keep looking. No expression of fear.

Suddenly, I feel not just calm, but amazingly powerful. That feeling of power overwhelms me, even more than fear and helplessness did just a few minutes earlier. Before there is any time to think, I *know* that I own the situation. For the first time in my life, I am in charge. I continue looking straight at the leader's face, and I see that something very subtle changes in him. Then I shrug my shoulders. As in a dream, I see him dropping the worm on the ground, and turning away, astonishment in his face mixed with some other feeling that I cannot yet define. The gang follows their leader, disappointed but obedient.

Almost subconsciously, I understand what has changed: I am safe. Not just for today, but forever. The danger is gone from the world. I can play wherever I want, with whomever I want; I don't need to be on perpetual watch. I don't think I have told anyone of what happened, certainly not my parents. It would have been too hard to explain, but I return home a different person. I am prepared to become a six-year-old, too old to be manipulated by boys in my yard...

A few weeks later I receive an invitation to the leader's seventh birthday party. His name is Vovka (nickname for Vladimir), and he becomes my first childhood love. We never talk about it, but he always appears nearby when I play with my group of girls. And, when I finally start school, he, a 3rd grader, hangs out outside until I emerge from the house—and, pretending that we had met by coincidence, walks with me to school.

3

Kamen-na-Obi (meaning "the Rock on the River Ob") in the 1960s was a town of 30 thousand, lost somewhere on the border of southwestern Siberia and Altai district, about 200 kilometers from Novosibirsk, if you are a bird and can fly. We, however, were bound to earth travel, so it took a train and a ferry to reach the town, and another two hours on dilapidated all-wheel-drive station wagon with tarpaulin top (lovingly called *gazik* by country dwellers) that we had to take to get to our final destination, a village with an unremarkable name, *Ivanovka*.

When we first arrived in the town, it was late afternoon, sun setting and summer temperatures finally lowering to a bearable level. We spent the night in a local inn, whose windows were facing the river and a floating zoo, which happened to park there that night. The only animal I remember from that zoo was a male lion with a huge wet mane, trapped in a tiny cage; his desperate roar seemed to shake the walls of nearby buildings for at least a mile around.

"Much worse than an earthquake," I thought.

Because it was the earthquake that had occurred a few months earlier, back in winter, that brought my family—together with a dozen other folks from Akademgorodok: scientists, university students, and lay people like my mom hired by our Institute of Geology—to spend the summer in that god-forsaken place, researching and calculating, trying to figure out why Mother Earth had decided to misbehave... Earthquakes are not unusual in and around the Altai Mountains, and can sometimes be felt on the West Siberian Plain. The one under research, barely noticed up north in Novosibirsk, had its epicenter in Ivanovka—that is why the village no one had ever heard of, suddenly became a place of scientific significance. It had an even greater significance for my family: my life could have ended there—but apparently God had a different plan for me...

* * *

Can I go a few weeks back?

Due to the work start date in mid-June, my mom had decided to celebrate my seventh birthday a week earlier—a decision that she later regretted bitterly. But at that point there seemed to be no choice: seven was a big date for a child; in the fall I was supposed to start school. Besides, so much preparation had been put into that party, with a new lace dress made by a seamstress just for the occasion, long poems learned by heart, dances rehearsed... It just had to happen.

Back then there were three schools in Akademgorodok, all teaching kids from grade one through tenth (and 10 years was all we had to do at school). Being the center of Soviet science, Akademgorodok had an excellent school system. Still, not all schools were equal. The so-called English school was the privileged one, and the hardest to get into: it required an entry exam from all prospective students. Allochka was in that school, and so was Vovka, and so were most children I knew. Students started learning English in second grade, five days a week. By sixth grade students had some subjects, such as geography and history, taught in English. All was crowned by a year-long course in English literature, also taught in its original language. So, graduates would be bilingual (no one had yet graduated from that very new and experimental school), well equipped for success in the rapidly developing world of Soviet science...

Entry exams were not easy—certainly not for seven-year-olds; they required significant preparation. Some preschool centers were formed, to do just that. Since I was a "home child" and did not go to a pre-school, it was my mother, a former school teacher, who tutored me personally (occasionally using a belt when I got defiant). After a winter of hard labor, I went for my exam well versed in reading, retelling stories, and doing simple math problems. Unfortunately, I also had test anxiety, and possibly some attention deficit. So, I failed in my strongest field, math, having misunderstood the problem and therefore solving it incorrectly.

My father was furious, my mother heartbroken. I got a little scolding, but then mom turned to blaming herself, and putting pressure on my father to go to the school principal and appeal the decision in person. My dad, completely incapable of any kind of manipulating people, even in the most innocent ways, could not understand what he could do. But mom did not give up. She found an acquaintance who personally knew the school principal; a teacher was dispatched to our home to test me one-on-one, rather informally. After about an hour of what I experienced as a friendly conversation, the teacher left with a smile, having assured my mother that her daughter was perfectly fit for the English school, both in terms of general intelligence and preparedness. So, there was something to celebrate, in addition to being one week short of the magic age seven—and the typical "Akademgorodok birthday party," with a five-course dinner and all children presenting performances and winning prizes, ensued.

* * *

"Don't tell the village kids that you are going to English school," warned my mother.

I could not understand why. Wasn't it something I had achieved through hard work and should have been proud of? Mom failed to explain.

Summer in the village Ivanovka was a weird one, although certainly not deprived of fun. My mom spent most of the days in the office with other young men and women, looking very serious and busy. Dad, as usual, preferred to hang out on his own, taking long walks in the fields and forests. We always met for lunch and dinner, carefully prepared by a local cook and served just for the "scientists," as we were known in the village, in a long shed with ceiling fans, transferred into our special dining room and a club for the summer. During the rest of the day, I ran around with other kids, chasing chicken and geese, petting stray cats, watching goats and cows. City kids as we were, most of us saw a cow or a goat being milked, or picked up eggs still warm from a hen, for the first time in our lives.

Two major inconveniences were the "dress code" (cover the top of your body if you are a girl—no matter how hot the weather), and absolutely no swimming in the pond, even though all the local kids did it—together with every kind of domestic animal that roamed the village. Other than that, we were free to run around barefoot on dirt roads, have our faces and clothes covered with dust, and play with whomever and whatever we wanted. And most importantly, we had almost nightly (daily on Sundays) trips to the Ob River, exploring various wild beaches and splashing, submerging, swimming in pristine crystal-clear water...

We used to travel in the open trunk of a truck, children and adults together, watching the quickly changing landscape around us, telling stories, singing, laughing, and not worrying about seat belts, car accidents, vicious ticks that carried encephalitis, or the possibility of drowning in unknown waters—or about any unpleasant things whatsoever...

Later at home (or whatever was "home" for us that summer), I took to drawing sceneries we had seen. I dreamed of having a camera to catch all the beauties of the wild—but of course only adults had cameras, and by far not everyone (my parents didn't). Besides, black-and-white photographs would have been useless for relating the rich colors of various shades of green and blue, occasionally spotted with bright orange spots of *oblepiha* (sea buckthorn) plantations; those fragrant berries, unique to Siberia, were believed to have as many health benefits as they were hard to be picked up from their horny bushes growing on hill slopes.

Akademgorodok kids, mostly younger than seven, eventually started to bore me. If only Allochka had been there... That was the first summer that our parents decided to spend differently—I was so used to having her around... Fortunately, with plenty of local kids, it was not hard to befriend a few older village girls. They had already started school, and probably knew things that a city girl from a good family was not supposed to know. They occasionally tried to put me down (either because I was still a "preschooler", or because they instinctively defied that brighter and far more prosperous world I had come from)—and of course, the less those girls appeared to want me, the more I wanted them. My parents watched me with some anxiety but stopped short of attempting to control my social life.

Once I asked one of my new friends (I think her name was Lena), who was supposed to start third grade in the fall, whether she had learned some English. She raised her eyebrows and replied that kids don't start learning foreign language until grade six. I argued that in my future school we'll be learning English as early as in second grade. Lena called me a liar; I probably got upset and left shortly thereafter. Once I reached the one-room log cabin my family rented from an old peasant woman for the summer, I got distracted by reading and drawing and forgot about the incident.

The next day we all played together as usual; I watched the girls swim in the village pond, envying them as usual, but anticipating an evening trip to the river. Then the group of us decided to go to the swing. Or, more exactly, the girls wanted to swing, and I just went along: I had never been a fan of heights, and the makeshift wooden board tied by two ropes to a big tree did not look particularly appealing.

I hesitated for a few minutes before getting on; the girls assured me that there was nothing to fear and that we would all have great fun. I made them promise that we would not go very fast, and reluctantly climbed on the shaky board. At first it did seem like fun: I finally felt fully belonging to the group. But soon the swing went faster, and higher. I stopped chattering, then screamed. The girls laughed and threw the swing into a 180-degrees circle. I begged them to stop, but they just continued laughing. I no longer knew which way the earth was; the world was spinning, one second the ground rushed toward me threatening to smash me dead, the next second it disappeared completely, as if we were lost in space, far, far from anything to hold on to... I had never been that terrified in all seven years of my life: the eternity must have passed since I was standing on the ground on my feet—and I was unsure that I would live to experience it again... I was crying, beg-

28

ging, howling like an animal; nothing made the girls to slow our insane flight through the air.

"Jump!" screamed Lena, laughing; "If you are such a pissy-pussy, just jump!.."

"Jump, Jump!" echoed the other girls.

"Jump!" cried the blue sky—I won't be able to save you...

There was nothing to be done. It took a fraction of a second, if not less—a spring of leg muscles, letting go of the rope, separating myself from the flaky wooden board, flying into space...

Warm sand under the tree smashed but did not kill me. I was back on earth, glued to it, hurting all over, not sure whether I was alive, the world still spinning around. Like in a dream, I heard the girls' scared screams coming from above; the swing slowed down swiftly ("how simple it is" I thought; "they could have stopped it like that at any time...").

I saw the girls circling me, leaning toward me, pulling on my arms.

"I didn't think you would really do that," said Lena apologetically. "Can you get up now?"

Surprisingly, I did. Still not sure whether the earth was above or below me—but I felt my legs holding me.

"Want to play something else?" asked Lena. "We will do what you like..."

I shook my head.

"Can you help me home?"

I slept for a few hours on my little couch in the only room of the cabin. No one was there to disturb me, and it was just as well. When my parents got home in the evening, they found me at the table, drawing. There wouldn't be a trip to the river tonight, they said. The truck is needed for something else. But look what we have brought you!

Dad was holding a cantaloupe. Yellow, round, fragrant. The first one of the season. My mom cut it, and my parents watched me devouring nearly half of the fruit, with tenderness only parents can feel. Later that evening I threw up. Too much cantaloupe, said my mom. The evening was otherwise uneventful, and, as soon as it got dark, we all went to bed.

I did not get up the next morning. Or the following morning.

All I knew was that I was lying in the cabin in my bed, but the world turned upside down, the floor being on top of me and my parents with worried faces hanging from it, their heads below their bodies, faces close to mine, their worried voices making little sense.

When mom tried to help me sit up, the world started spinning faster, and I threw up. I kept throwing up for the rest of that day, following each attempt to move my head even a tiny bit. Mom tried to spoon-feed me, but it appeared impossible without propping me up—and that was exactly what I could not bear.

The local village paramedic called to my side shrugged her shoulders and recommended hospitalization. Akademgorodok guys made a makeshift stretcher, and with moans and more throwing up I was loaded into a truck one last time, and transported to the town where a few weeks earlier we had started our summer adventure. Kamen-na-Obi. The Rock-on-the-River Ob. At night, I expected to hear the lion roaring, but mom said that the floating zoo was gone. I also remember her saying to my father, over and over again: "It is because we celebrated her birthday too early. I knew, I knew, it was a no-no thing!—why, why did we do that?.."

* * *

Doctors in the local hospital had no idea what had befallen me, or how to treat me. I told no one about the swing episode; in fact, I think I forgot about it for the time being. But I clearly remember overhearing a woman in white coat telling my mother that she was still young and should just have another child: this girl won't make it, she said.

That was the only interesting thing I heard from the adults' talk. I thought it would be cool if my mom had a baby: I always envied kids who had siblings. The thought of dying did not worry me: at seven, death was too abstract to be scary. I just hated the room—with the merciless sun always shining through the window, and no way to hide from it. And I was horrified that my mom might step out, leaving me with those scary stranger women in white coats, who would—as they had threated more than once—move my head "in all directions." Thankfully, mom never left the room.

If she cried, I didn't see it.

* * *

Now, thinking back to those days, I don't blame the doctors. After all, they did everything they could: they placed me and my mom in a private room in the hospital, they provided her with regular meals; and they almost certainly gave me an IV—the only way I could have survived without food or water, which my body refused to accept.

Meanwhile, my dad was frantically calling Academgorodok, arranging medical evacuation. Two days later we were back on the ferry, only this time I was on a stretcher, and there were no merry workmates of my mom, just some strangers around us. At the pier near Novosibirsk, the ambulance was waiting at the dock upon our arrival. The room in the new hospital was cool, with tall trees providing ample shade from the summer sun. I shared it with a two-year-old boy who was surprisingly quiet. His mom sat next to him all the time, while my mom finally was able to go home and get some rest. The doctors assured her that they would not move my head, and somehow even I believed them. The medicine in the IV was changed, and they gave me shots—so many shots that I stopped feeling needles poking my skin. Those doctors did not know the name of my mysterious sickness either. They just tried whatever medicine was available, hoping something would work. And something did work.

Very slowly and carefully, I began moving my head, still afraid to lift it from the pillow. Soon I was able to swallow a few spoons of liquid food and keep it down. One morning I woke up and did not see the boy's mother next to his bed. It was a while until I realized that the boy was not there either. The room was empty, I was alone. When my mom came, I asked her about the two-year-old boy. She started crying and said that the boy had died last night. I did not understand why my mom was crying now, when I was getting better; I asked if the boy's mom would now have another child. My mom said that she already had another child, a seven-year-old who had just started school. It sounded reassuring to me: the mother of the dead boy should be OK then. I still was wondering if she would want to replace the lost baby by having a new one. Mom said she wouldn't be able to: she did not have a husband any more, the baby's father had left her for another woman while she was in the hospital with the sick child. The story didn't impress me then, so I have no idea why I still remember it... Or why my mom had decided to share it with me, for that matter...

The leaves outside my window started turning yellow, red, orange. I was moved to a bigger ward, sharing it with a few other children who were not going to die. I now could sit up in bed, ate with appetite, and started worrying about the beginning of the school year I had already missed. In late afternoon a smiling nurse would bring each of us a large platter with fruits: honey-smelling pears, golden bananas, sweet purple plums, grapes so transparent that you could see seeds in their middle. The only fruit consistently missing from my platter was everyone's favorite cantaloupe: I didn't think I would ever eat it again. The fruits were gifts from homes, in addition to three hot meals provided by the hospital—and they were the best part of the day. Meanwhile, I began to envy other girls who walked around the room freely, and even left it; I was still bound to my bed.

One day, when my mom was visiting, a nurse came and ordered me to get up. I resisted for as long as I could, but in the end had no choice but to comply. My fears turned out to be justified: as soon as I separated my bottom from the familiar safety of the bed, my body dropped on the floor like a sack of sand; my legs seemed to have lost all their muscles, provided that there still were legs: at least, I could not feel them at all!

"That's all right," said the nurse, "your strength will come back shortly." I cried and tried to get back into bed. The nurse and my mom grabbed me under both arms, and walked with me into a long hospital corridor, dragging me between them, farther and farther from the ward. At first, I felt dizzy, then it got better. Still, given a choice, I would have stayed in bed.

I wasn't given a choice, though. Adults continued making me walk several times each day, until I could do it on my own, without being held. Then it was hard to keep me in one place; I became "a discipline problem" in the children's department.

Allochka came almost every day after school; as all other visitors, she could only stand outside my window and call my name, waiting for me to hear her, climb on the windowsill, and wave at her; if we lucked out and no medical personal was around, we could open the window and scream back. Only parents were allowed inside the hospital.

The confinement began to bother me; I missed playing in the yard, missed my home, my toys, the privacy of my room. Worst of all, I could not stop thinking that my best friend was already in second grade at school, while I still had not started my first...

4

I spent that winter at home, and, if I wasn't reading, I was drawing lions. They were mostly in cages, but occasionally roamed around freely in some kinds of woods. I had seen many palm trees during vacations on the Black Sea, so those were easy to draw. Once in a while I added monkeys hanging from trees, and colorful parrots (which I had seen only in the zoo). But I kept returning to drawing a lion trapped in a cage, following some dark attraction to a creature desperately trying to break free, but failing. It was a strange feeling that I couldn't put in words...

Upon my discharge from the hospital in late autumn, my mom was told that she could consider sending me to school in January, but certainly not sooner. For whatever reason, she decided that starting first grade in mid-year was not a good idea. (I disagreed with her strongly, but it did not make any difference). I would start school in September next year, observing, like all other kids, one of Russia's favorite holidays: September First. That was the day when children ages seven to seventeen from all over the country started their school year, whether it was the first grade or the tenth. Dressed in gala uniforms (white shirts for boys, white aprons for girls) and carrying huge bouquets of flowers to be presented to their teachers, millions of kids walked to their schools to attend the festive new-school-year assembly. Music played everywhere. Parents were allowed, even expected, to be late for their jobs, and many took a day off.

"You can't miss a day like that," Mom kept saying. "You only start the first grade once in your lifetime..."

She didn't seem to notice that I was already too tall for my age or worry that the body size difference added to the age difference might create unexpected problems for her daughter. Or that I felt lost and confused, not to say unhappy.

That was the first winter when I began reading for pleasure, not because I was forced. I swallowed book after book: fairy tales, books about wild animals, stories about American Indians, pirates, medieval knights, adventure novels. Popular books were in short supply, but Mom always managed to get me new ones. Our home library, already quite substantial, became even more voluminous. (It increased dramatically during subsequent years after my mom accepted a part-time position as head of acquisition in the town's main book store, and thus acquired access to books unavailable to regular mortals).

For the November holidays (the widely celebrated anniversary of the Socialist Revolution), I received an early New Year present, a pair of skates; Mom wanted to encourage me to go outside as much as possible. At first, I was overjoyed; the next thing I knew, skating turned out to be much more difficult than it had appeared on TV. I was falling far more than sliding on ice; however, there was something at the rink that made me come back and keep trying. The harder I fell and hit the ice, the more I yearned to master the skill.

And that is how I first met Anyuta.

Her full name was Anna, like mine—but while my nicknames were *Ánia, Ánechka*, or occasionally *Ánnushka* (by close friends of my mom or family members—stress on the first "A", please!), the girl called herself *Anyuta*. She was only a few months younger than me, but had already started the first grade. She used to come to the rink after school, often accompanied by her mom, to practice for her figure skating classes.

Yes, in addition to going to school, Anyuta took formal figure skating lessons. She could skate forward and backwards, and even make turns on ice. But that was not what attracted me to her: she was the most beautiful child I had ever seen in my life. Not in movies, not on pictures had I seen a face so lovely, eyes that shiny, movements that graceful. Her curly hair, stubbornly refusing to stay under her white fur hat, was an unusual black color; her cheeks were rosy; her huge deep brown eyes, lined with long dark eyelashes, shined like stars in the bright winter night (at least those were the words I used to think about her)—and her smile... she was mostly serious, but when she did smile, the whole world seemed brighter.

We first met on a cloudy afternoon, with temperatures lingering only a few degrees below freezing, a calm and lazy day—and there were only two of us at the rink. Before we knew it, we were skating together, and Anyuta tried her best to teach me how not to fall. On the following days, I was looking for her and she for me. Anyuta's mother was the first one who commented on my skates: instead of figure skates that hold ankles, I had ones made for hockey-players, with low-cut boots and therefore much harder to stand in. The next day, Anyuta's mother brought from home an extra pair of figure skates, which were still too big for Anyuta. I tried them on and felt the difference immediately. From then on, my skating started improving swiftly.

At home, my mom scolded me for "imposing on other people" and "not understanding when to leave other kids alone." She did not think I should have accepted the skates, even if they were offered on loan. That episode, however, prompted her to walk with me to the rink and meet Anyuta's mom, to personally thank her. The two women exchanged phone numbers, and I finally began to believe that Anyuta was real, not some beautiful dream—and moreover, that she might some day become a part of my life, and I of hers. It was stronger than falling in love, stronger than any feeling I had experienced so far—an overwhelming desire to see her, to be with her, to follow her around…

And then Anyuta stopped coming to the rink.

I had not been in her home and did not know where she lived, so I could do nothing, except wait and hope that she would reappear. I was at the skating rink every day from the time school ended till dark—and I met many other kids, but Anyuta was not among them. My mom suggested that Anyuta could be busy with school work, or maybe that she decided to practice on a different rink—and, in any case, I should leave her alone: she was not my type. I had no idea what mom meant by "my type…" Was Allochka "my type"? Well, Allochka kept complaining about the amount of homework, had no passion for skating and appeared to be more interested in her new friends from school than in me. She was not living next door any more: after Alochka's mom gave birth to her little brother, the family moved into a bigger apartment, a few blocks away from us. Still, her parents visited often, and Allochka usually came with them. Those were almost the only times we saw each other.

The New Year came, and with it the two-week-long winter vacation. All kids were out now, our yard divided by snow fortresses and discarded fir trees, still glittering with forgotten ornaments, stuck upright in snow banks forming miniature forests. Grown-ups had to watch out not to be hit in the head by a snow ball or knocked off by sleds rolling down a nearby hill.

In spite of my mom's protests (she still wanted me close to home, where she could see me from the window), I used every opportunity to hang out in the town center, where the square in front of the movie theater was closed to traffic; thirty-foot-high ice figures of *Ded Moroz* (Grandfather Frost, the Russian counterpart of Santa Claus) and several ice animals from our favorite fairy tales, surrounded the giant New Year tree decorated with giant ornaments. Blue, green, and red lights lit the square after dark, music played all day long, and older kids competed with young adults in getting access to a two-story-high wooden slides. I went sliding too, but mostly I was there looking for Anyuta: after all, every child in town spent at least some time at the square. I ran into every single friend of mine more than once; Vovka always left his group of boys to slide with me; but Anyuta never appeared. I was heartbroken, the world making even less sense than before.

When school vacation was over and Anyuta did not reappear at the rink, my mom finally gave in to my pleas and dug out the phone number of Anyuta's mom. It turned out that Anyuta had been sick with pneumonia, had had to spend two weeks in the hospital, and was now home, recovering. She was not going to school, and her mom promised to let me know as soon as she felt well enough to accept visitors. There were no talks of her returning to skating that winter, so I quickly lost interest in the ice rink.

* * *

If was late February when I was finally allowed to visit Anyuta. The long Siberian winter was living its last weeks: days were getting longer; the sun shone less often, but light-gray clouds in the sky seemed to protect the earth from bitter cold; the air was getting softer and acquired some fragrance that only late winter air has. In open spaces, where the sun hit the most, previously soft white snow was becoming harder and darker, occasionally covered with a thin film of ice.

I found my friend in a small apartment where she had to share the bedroom with her parents; there were surprisingly few toys.

"I don't live here when I am at school," she explained. "I am only here when I am sick and sometimes on weekends; generally, I stay with my grandparents, they live close to school."

It turned out that Anyuta's grandparents occupied one of the single-family homes, lovingly called "cottages" in Akademgorodok, which were given to the most prominent scientists (or—on some rare occasions—to good friends of Lavrentiev, the Siberian Academy of Science president). There she had most of her toys, her bicycle, her very own swing set, and her lovely Airedale Terrier, who she missed the most. She added that her mother rarely visited her there: the grandparents were her dad's mother and father, and they did not like her mom.

Amazed with the story, I shared it at home.

"You have no business visiting that girl in her grandfather's house," was my dad's remark. "He is a known son-of-a-bitch and a careerist."

Before I had a chance to ask what "careerist" meant, Mom began to scold Dad for using inappropriate language in front of the child. That was an argument all too familiar for me to listen to, so I retreated to my room, and in a few minutes was back to drawing. That time, I drew two girls on skates, holding hands. Then I added a lavishly decorated fir tree and many, many lights around. Neither of the girls was smiling.

I was beginning to get used to living without Anyuta in my life. After all, winter was coming to an end and nothing could spoil the magic of returning spring...

5

My mom and I spent most of the summer in Leningrad, visiting various relatives and friends.

Mom and Dad's sides of the family comprised two separate worlds, different as they could be. My mom had no siblings, and only one first cousin; the first cousin was a quiet serious woman with a much older husband, a disabled war veteran, and a quiet serious daughter named Natasha, a few years older than me. Mom's two girlfriends from her early childhood called me their "niece." In return, I called them—and thought of them—as my "aunts;" I was friends with their children, notwithstanding differences in our ages. They were all ethnic Russians and atheists. As far as I was concerned, they were my extended family.

Among my dad's relatives, on the other hand, everyone was closely related to everyone else. Dad's numerous aunts, uncles, first and second cousins and their kids, of all ages and sizes, comprised what I would later call *mishpucha*: they were loud, opinionated, forthcoming, and always flocked together in big groups. I could never figure out how they were related to each other, or to me, for that matter; all I knew, was that they were my blood relatives. They were all Jewish (by their birth certificates and passports, not by religion)—my great-aunts' Yiddish accent would not let anyone forget that. I had no feeling of belonging there, save for my grandfather Solomon and his second wife Sofia whom I liked. (My paternal grandmother had passed away long before my birth). I could not remember anyone's name—and, to my shame, had no desire to. I preferred my mom's quiet friends, with their impeccably neat rooms (even when they lived in communal apartments), their polite kids, and their quiet intelligent conversations.

"You've grown so big," everyone was saying. "Such a smart and beautiful girl you have raised, Masha..."

"You look as if you may be ten years old already, not eight..."

If my relatives thought it was a compliment, they were dead wrong. I was tall, and, although slim for my height, I felt big. I was terrified of how I would go to the first grade on September 1, when everyone thought I looked like a fourth-grader.

* * *

Is this the right time to divert a bit from my story, and add a few words about my family members, who would later resurface in my life? Some were dead by the time I was born—but, like it or not, I had my roots from them—and, had those roots been different, I would have been different, too—or maybe I simply would not have been at all...

Mom's dad, Aleksandr Vasilyevich Staheyev, after having spent three years supervising reconstruction and operation of the war plants evacuated from the west of the country to the Ural Mountains, was called back to Leningrad as soon as the German-Finnish siege ended in 1944. By some great stroke of luck, the building where the family had an apartment before the war remained intact after the three years of heavy bombardment. (The whole building used to belong to the Staheyev family before the revolution—but that is completely besides the point.)

An apartment belonging to the family was obviously occupied by survivors of the siege, whose houses had been destroyed. While waiting for them to move out, Grandpa slept in the broken elevator of the building, working 16-hour days and happy to be alive and needed by his country. After a few months, one of the rooms of his former apartment finally became available, so he could move in. He eventually was able to arrange work visas for his wife and teenage daughter (i.e. my grandmother and mother) to return to the still-fighting city.

The Great Patriotic War ended for Russia in May of 1945. Survivors' tears of joy and pride mixed with overwhelming grief over friends and family who were gone forever. Then, slowly but surely, life started returning to normal.

By the end of the first post-war summer, my grandmother began pestering her husband that it was time to reclaim the entire apartment, which officially still belonged to the family. I suspect that my grandfather did not feel comfortable evicting strangers who, although illegally occupying the room, had survived the siege that had taken over a million lives. Stuck between his own feeling of social justice and his wife's temper, he (as most men would do), ended up surrendering to his own family demands. He reluctantly went to the housing authority office and requested that the occupants of his second room be given another place to live. The clerk in the office, a former soldier with a wooden prothesis instead of the right leg, probably half of my grandfather's age, nevertheless belittled him in a typical military-vs-civilian manner. After being called "a cowardly traitor," "a petty bourgeois," a "rotten intellectual" and the like, my grandfather in whose blood the strong moral values of his noble family had not been destroyed either by the revolution, or by surviving decades of Soviet power, must have felt pangs of conscience.

Had he decided to fight for his legal rights, he would have eventually won, and my family would probably still occupy its own spacious apartment in the very center of old Leningrad—but he couldn't bring himself to argue with the soldier-clerk. He thought of all his friends who had perished during the war, of his many countrymen who still lived without a proper roof over their heads—and without further ado signed the papers relinquishing his rights to the family apartment forever.

What my grandmother said to him upon his return home, remains a family secret. The fact is that from then on, my mother joined millions of young people living in so-called "communal apartments"—and, by the time I was born, she was so used to it that she took her situation for granted...

Running along a mile-long (at least from a toddler's perspective) semi-dark corridor, or playing ball there with the neighbors' children, became one of my very first early childhood memories. The large room with windows facing a busy street framed by a few old trees (war survivors, like the house) became my first home, which I shared with my young parents and my maternal grandmother.

Grandpa Staheyev died a few years after the war ended, from a heart attack that occurred a few hours after he had been discharged from the hospital. He was barely sixty years old—very young by our current standards, but in those times of post-war poverty and people still disappearing in Stalin's gulags, his age seemed almost acceptable for dying.

Luckily, my mom had already graduated from teacher's college and was working full-time at school, and my grandmother, although past the Russian retirement age of fifty-five, had not quit her job. So, life went on, although my strikingly beautiful mother was feeling increasing anxiety about the lack of suitable young men to marry: most guys her age had perished during the battles of the Great War.

My father, a Jew by birth who, as a proper Soviet young man knew absolutely nothing about Judaism (or any other religion, for that matter), was a son of one of Leningrad's most prominent criminal lawyers. Grandpa Solomon was lucky enough to have fully avoided Stalinist repressions, practiced law successfully until it was time to retire, and managed to secure handsome savings, so his widow could live comfortably for many years after he died from cancer at the respectable age of eighty. My grandmother, also a graduate of a law school, had started her career as an officer of NKVD (the organization that later became infamous as the KGB). However, like most women of that time, she quit her job after her first child (my father) was born, and spent the terrible years of Stalinist terror as a well-to-do housewife, completely removed from politics.

She died of (now completely curable) cancer sometime in her late-forties, when my father was a freshman at Leningrad University, with a brilliant future predicted for him by all professors, and my uncle a ten-year-old schoolboy with no obvious talents. By then my grandfather had quit practicing criminal law and switched to less stressful civil cases. Unfortunately, having been a brilliant criminal lawyer, he made quite a mediocre civil one. One of the cases that he shamefully lost was an eviction trial of a young Jewish widow. I could never understand exactly what my grandfather's mistake had been in the case, except that he corrected it gracefully: he married his client.

Sofia was eighteen years younger than her new husband—a small, very neat, and superficially friendly woman. Family was the center of her life, and as a devoted wife, she became a good mother to my pre-teen uncle. As for my father, it took him years to accept Sofia: his father remarried too soon after my grandmother's death.

I was never close to my stern grandfather, but I liked Sofia a lot. In my childish eyes, she was funny and cozy, and the Jewish food that she cooked was delicious. Besides, I adored my young uncle Victor, even though during that last preschool summer when I met him in Leningrad, he was a post-graduate student of some insignificant college working on a strange dissertation, something from the history of Russian theater, that no one (including my dad) thought much about.

One story that has always stuck with me, was the way my mom and dad had met. It was through Sofia, or rather through her cousin who was my mom's school coworker, and who had invited both my mother and Sofia's "difficult older stepson" to her birthday party. Knowing my father, I cannot imagine that, at the age of twenty-five, he would have agreed to waste his evening in the company of his stepmother's old relatives. However, the prospect of meeting a beautiful girl must have been a strong enough incentive for him to show up. Sofia's cousin turned out to be a good matchmaker: my parents got married less than a year after their first meeting. So, in some way, I am the child of an "arranged marriage"—and the fact that the marriage between young people of different national backgrounds was actively supported by Jewish parents, was not at all unusual...

Except that I never found out how my mother's mom felt about the match. From all I remember, she and my father didn't particularly like one another; both were "direct" people not used to hiding their feelings and emotions, or even choosing "polite ways" of expressing them. During grandma's annual visits to Akademgorodok, their verbal altercations used to be spontaneous and often heated, with elevated voices and not-always-printable words... Mom was devastated; I, on the other hand, was usually on my dad's side: although never as tender and caring as my mother, he was big, strong, and very handsome; most importantly, his weird but unique sense of humor made my tummy hurt with laughter. My grandmother, on the other hand—especially when angry, which happened all too often—reminded me of an old wicked witch from a fairy tale; she hated taking a shower, had no sense of fairness, and was quick to criticize everything and everyone, her own granddaughter included. I used to dread her prolonged visits.

She passed away quietly in her room in the Leningrad communal apartment when I was seventeen—so by the time I moved to my birth city as a college freshman, she was gone from the world—and from my life. The person I loved dearly instead of my grandmother, was her younger sister Galina, or simply *Grandma Galia*. During mom's and my summer visits to Leningrad, Grandma Galia used to take me and my second cousin Natasha to the dacha she rented year after year, and she took care of her two grandnieces with kind humor and tenderness; at the end of the day, she was the only "kind and loving grandmother" I ever knew.

6

As happens to everything in this world, my pre-school childhood, with its dreams, hopes, and anxieties, came to an end. The much dreaded and much anticipated September First came—and here I was, standing in a crowd of kids from all grades in front of the school building that was to be my second home for the next ten years. Dressed, like all other girls, in a brand-new brown uniform dress with snow-white collar and a starched white apron, with white bows in my long braids, holding a huge bouquet of fresh flowers to be presented to my first teacher...

Was that day a reason to skip the whole year of school? Mom was convinced it was, but I was not that sure: after all, the holiday repeats every year, for ten years, every September First just like any other one... The principal making a speech, especially welcoming first-graders, smiling teachers receiving flowers in such abundance that they have trouble carrying them, kids from the same classes flocking together...

A novice for school life, I had no idea who would be in my class, until I found myself in my very first classroom, seated with a boy I knew as my yard playmate. There were three rows of desks, each desk accommodating two students, all facing the front of the room with a blackboard and a teacher's table that today looked like a garden. The teacher was the one who determined who sits with whom; the arrangement was for the entire year (unless the teacher changed her mind later). Scanning the room for my classmates, who also would be my life-mates for the next ten years, I was overjoyed to see Anyuta. She sat in a different row, much closer to the front of the class, so she did not see me at first. Enviously, I studied the girl she was with: a miniature blond, with two long braids tied, like mine, with silk white ribbons. When she turned around to talk to a student seated behind her, I saw a pair of large bright blue eyes framed with the longest eyelashes I had ever seen. I wondered if Panna Andreyevna, our teacher, had deliberately placed the students together according to their physical beauty...

The break came—and Anyuta waved and flashed her amazing smile at me, but it was clear somehow that we were no longer *together*... She appeared much closer to her blonde desk mate, Tania (full name Tatiana, nicknames Tanechka or Tanyusha). She also seemed to know many more kids in the class than I did. I was hurt, but soon took rejection for granted. As for Anyuta and Tanyusha, the two girls shortly became so close that everyone at school started referring to them jointly, as Tania-Anya. (This, seemingly insignificant fact, will play a role later in my school life... My name was also Anna, which often nicknames as Anya—remember?)

During the first few days of school, I befriended my desk mate, Alex, and connected to a few boys from my yard (most of whom were in second or even third grades); we hung out during the breaks between classes, walked home from school together, and spent most of our free time chasing chipmunks and young squirrels in the woods. The fact that none of us caught anything did not matter: we were hunters, explorers, pirates looking for treasure, occasionally American Indians;

we built tipis from fallen brunches and covered them with grass and leaves that were quickly turning yellow and soon became readily available from the ground beneath our feet... On a couple of occasions, the boys told me that I was the only girl they knew worth playing with— and that was enough to raise my self-esteem to an acceptable level, at least for a while.

I had very little interest in homework, getting distracted during the class, more interested in looking out of the window, watching other kids, or drawing hunting scenes, and often missing assignments. And if I needed to say something to my desk mate, I would not wait for the lesson to end... It was not long until my mom began receiving calls from the teacher with complaints about my performance and behavior. Life at home became sour, with both of my parents scolding me for failures, each one in their own way, specific to their personalities—dad more concerned with my academics, mom upset over my behavior...

* * *

The first two years of school passed relatively uneventfully. Under my parents' pressure, my school performance gradually improved. Although I did not make any close friends among my classmates, I was invited to most birthday parties—and in those days that meant something. I still was by far the tallest student in all three third grades, and was often teased for my size, and not always kindly—but I learned to take it for granted and was no longer hurt. Or maybe just hurt a little bit... and then got over it in no time...

My real life was in reading. I read novels incessantly, constantly falling in love with one main character or another. To make my mental game more interesting, I would choose a boy from my class (sometimes from another class, but usually the same grade level) to "be" that character—and made up elaborate stories involving that boy and myself, always in love with one another, in some imaginable place that was a mixture of the novel setting and contemporary Russia. Of course, none of the "chosen" boys suspected about their roles in my life, and I had no close girl friends to share it with. At the end of the day, those imaginary literary masterpieces were lost to a larger audience, which may be just as well...

* * *

In the beginning of the third grade, my old friend Allochka (who was already a fifth-grader and insisted on being called her full name *Alla* rather than her baby nickname) handed me a book that I "had to read." The "had to" part coming from her sounded much more obliging than anything that my teachers requested; and in any case, there were very few people on this earth who dared to say "no" to Allochka... Sorry, to Alla. Oh, no—sorry again: as a way of protest, I started calling her *Alka*—pronounced "Al-ka." (The nickname took on, and by the end of school most of her friend were calling her *Alka*.) The book was thick, with rather small print and only a few pictures, so I started reading it with some trepidation. After a few chapters, however, the characters and the setting became familiar, and I sailed through the rest of the novel in no time. It was "the Three Musketeers" by Alexander Dumas, and it changed my life—at least for the next couple of years. I could discuss each episode with Alla, and that brought us closer together once again.

The next step was to join Alla and a boy in her class named Anton, in acting out the scenes from the novel. Alla, who was a natural leader of the game, was always playing the noble introvert Athos; Anton, known as "his class clown", agreed to be Porthos; and I was happy to accept the role of d'Artagnan, who had been my favorite character anyway. I was finally hanging out with the kids who were as big in size as I was—although having two fifth-graders as my closest playmates alienated me from the kids of my own class even more. But then the situation suddenly turned around...

We needed the fourth player in the game, the third musketeer, the most mysterious figure of all, Aramis. For a while, the role was assigned to Alla's little brother Ivan (*Vanyusha*), but he was too young to really understand what he was doing, even with his sister's continuous prompts. It was I who finally succeeded in recruiting the fourth player—and that fact not only lifted me in informal ranks of our little group, but seriously contributed to my self-esteem. The girl who agreed to play Aramis was as fit for the character as any third-grade girl could be. The best thing for me was that she happened to be my classmate; she was also a neighbor, her family living in the same apartment building as mine. The second tallest girl in our class, she was slim, quiet, wore glasses, and had her curly hair cut short. We often went to and from school together, and invited each other to our respective birthday parties, but it was usually me who did most of the talking.

Coincidentally, the girl's name was also Tatiana, like Anyuta's best friend: Tania-two. To distinguish her from Tania-Anya, at school she was called Tanika. It was not hard to sell Tanika the idea of our play. However, making her read the book appeared to be much harder: she was not used to long historical novels, so I had to literally lead her through each episode. At the end, however, she was almost as enthusiastic as the rest of us. Even outside the game we would call each other by our "novel" names: monsieur Athos, monsieur d'Artagnan... Tanika turned out to be an invaluable asset: she took our game onto a different level: she began writing poems depicting selected scenes from the novel. The rest of us immedeately joined in—but no one could rhyme as well as Tanika.

We all learned each other's verses by heart, anyway, and started each game by reciting the latest ones. My mom was finally happy about my pastime; I had friends I could feel close to without fear of being mocked for my height; at last, life began turning her brighter side to me.

Then, before I knew it, Alla and Anton moved a step up: they joined our famous fencing club *Victoria*. I said "our" and "famous" because both were true: a club like that one could only exist in Akademgorodok, with its non-conformist, adventurous, inquisitive, and international spirit. And, because it created a blend of unique opportunities for children and teenagers, it was frequently mentioned in various news reports all over the country, as a model of what a children's sport club should be.

In Victoria, students not only learned fencing; they had to be familiar with French history and culture and well versed in books about musketeers; they were strongly encouraged to take French lessons offered in the club for an additional symbolic fee. After a year of full participation in all activities, students had a unique opportunity to be initiated as Musketeers, an elite sub-club within the club. The requirements for becoming a musketeer were tough: a candidate had to come at least third in the city-wide fencing competition, plus pass an oral examination administered by Victoria coaches.

My first heartbreak came when I learned that the club would not accept students younger than fourth grade. Luckily, my father knew someone in Victoria, and it was my very own mom who went to the head coach and talked him into making an exception for me, since I was, by age, a fourth-grader. So, I was again reunited with Alla and Anton, although in a very different environment; this time it was Tanika who appeared to be left out.

I quickly noticed that there were a couple of other third-graders in the beginners' group, and started arguing that Tanika should be allowed to join. Since I was making quick progress in fencing and participated in all club activities, my request was heard, and the head coach himself promised to give Tanika a chance. I was overjoyed, but prematurely: even though Tanika seemed mildly interested, her mother was dead set against her joining the club. The reasons she cited were numerous and hard to refute: her daughter was too young for that crowd; she found the requirements too rigorous and therefore stressful for a young child; fencing—or any other fighting, for that matter—was not "a girls' sport;" most importantly, Tanika was already taking ballet lessons and piano lessons; there was simply no time in her day to take on another activity.

Still, I expected Tanika to fight her mother, and was gravely disappointed when, after bringing up the subject and losing only a couple of times, she gave up. She and I started spending less and less time with each other, but, contrary to all logic, it was I who envied Tanika, not the other way around: it turned out that our former Aramis practiced ballet in the same group as Tanyusha and Anyuta. A second Tania in the already established Tania-Anya pair; or the third member of the tight group of the most popular girls in the class: Tania-Anya trio...

A year and some months after first joining Victoria, in early spring of my fourth grade, I decided to try out for musketeer. I could say the few required phrases, such as "I challenge you to a duel," Musketeers never surrender," "All for one, one for all," in almost impeccable French. I could draw a map of seventeen-century Paris and talk about its historical landmarks; I knew the names and years of reign of all the French kings from the Middle Ages till Napoleon. Most importantly, I was winning in many club competitions. I just had to pass one last stage: come at least third in the city's fencing tournament for under-thirteens. My instructors were encouraging; Alla and Anton felt confident that I would do just fine.

I was scared stiff but there seemed to be no return. The night before the Big Competition I could not sleep. Deep wet snow that fell overnight slowed traffic to near-stillness; instead of the usual fifty minutes, it took the bus almost two hours to reach the city of Novosibirsk, and I was close to peeing in my pants. Since our group arrived so late, there was barely any time to change before we had to be on the fencing strip, in front of the judges, getting ready to fight and to be judged.

Both my opponent and I had long electrical cords attached to our heavy costumes, to register every touch received from the competitor's sword. Apparently, it was a rule for all formal competitions, but our club never used such elaborate technology. I should have been prepared for that, having watched other kids compete in the city tournaments—but I felt like a dog on a leash. Out of fifteen pre-teens taking part in the competitions, I came number eleven. I was so ashamed and humiliated that I could not even cry in the changing room; as a result, no one came to console me: my friends flocked around the crying girls, most of whom had scored better than me.

A week later, I attended Victoria's biannual initiation ceremony. Anton, who had come third in the boys' competition, was among the new musketeers. Our friend Alla, already a musketeer, welcomed Anton to the elite group with a big hug. I was just a spectator, applauding and trying to force a smile. "You'll make it next year," said my instructor. "There will be competitions in September, I will make sure you are well prepared... Just a few more months—what difference does it make?" Of course, being an adult, he had no idea that for an eleven-year-old a few months sounded the same as half-a-lifetime... As far as I was concerned, the game was over for me.

Out of pride, I stuck to my fencing lessons till the end of the school year, but, friendless again, I had very little enthusiasm. I did not return in the fall. To my surprise, Alla didn't either; she moved on to something else: she developed a passion for opera. Anton remained in Victoria and continued improving his fencing skills; he was now too old to hang out with girls, so he and Alla drifted apart. The latter didn't feel discouraged at all: she quickly found a new friend, Sasha, a girl a year older than she; just like Anika and me, Alla and Sasha were neighbors living in the same apartment building.

To Alla's credit, I must admit that she did try to involve me: a couple of times, I was invited to accompany her and Sasha to the Novosibirsk opera theater, to see some operas. The trip required taking two different buses, with a change in the middle of the big city, returning home well after dark. My mother wanted to hear nothing of me taking such a journey without adult supervision. My argument—that Alla's parents not only allowed her to go to the opera alone with Sasha, but often let her take her young brother—fell on deaf ears. "Yurivanych considers this world to be a safe place," was my mother's reply. "He is generally careless—and I don't believe it is appropriate for young girls to travel that far by themselves. Especially late at night. I won't even mention dragging a six-year-old with them..."

* * *

A few times I was invited to the Kotov's home to listen to operas on records. Thankfully, back then even Italian operas were sung in Russian—so, if you had a libretto in front of you and could follow the lines, you mostly understood what was going on. Eventually, my mother had pity on me, and took me to Novosibirsk opera theater, to see a few live operas. I began acquiring opera records of my own, mostly bought with my pocket money but occasionally given as gifts.

I still felt inferior to Alla, especially in the presence of Sasha, who, in addition to being two years my senior, was taking music lessons in a real music school—and could not only read notes but play a piano and a violin. She also had a nice singing voice, so she could sing most of the arias without mistakes. Before anyone knew it, Alla decided to open her own "home opera theater." Her parents neither supported nor discouraged her when she dug out old clothes and curtains to make theater costumes, and spent most of her pocket money to buy large sheets of paper to draw the scenery, turning the house into a perpetually messy workshop.

She and Sasha starred in major roles, Alla usually singing the guy's parts, while Sasha, with her almost-perfect soprano voice and gentle feminine looks, performed Violetta, Rosina, and Gilda. Little Vania, who had an extraordinary ear for music and an excellent memory, was assigned different smaller roles. Yurivanych soon grew fond of his daughter's hobby, and proudly invited his adult friends to watch her performances. All the while, the cast needed more actors, and I was invited for audition.

The judges (Sasha, Alla, and her dad Yurivanych) decided that my voice was Ok, even pleasant—and that I could sing both "low" female roles (contralto) and "high" male parts (tenor), such as Alfredo from Traviata or the duke in Rigoletto. Unfortunately, there was one problem that rendered me disqualified as an opera singer: I had a very weak ear for music, and beyond a few popular songs learned at school, could not carry a tune. Sasha argued that if I started taking professional music lessons, my musical ear would improve accordingly, so I was not beyond hope. My mom agreed to show me to a couple of music teachers she knew; after brief examinations, both pronounced me "lacking the necessary aptitude for playing musical instrument," and as far as my parents were concerned, the issue was closed. I cried, and begged, and even brought Yurivanych to support my case with my parents—but all in vain.

"No need to waste time and money on something she would never be good at," was their joint verdict. "I'd rather that you continue some sport," added my mom. "Notwithstanding the results, it is good for your health; you hardly ever got sick while you were doing your fencing..."

Still, I continued my participation in the theater for as long as it existed, for almost a year and a half. I only was trusted to perform drama actions, saying rather than singing the lines—but my acting was good, and I enjoyed the activity immensely. Other than the theater, however, I barely saw Alla: she spent all her time with Sasha, leaving me to suffer from jealousy.

The following year I decided to try figure skating; both Tanias and Anyuta were there, having outgrown their ballet lessons. They all were on a much higher level than me—but, surprisingly, that made little difference: we often had practice at the same time, shared the same coaches and frequently got together to watch our favorite skaters on TV. It was not the close friendship I yearned for, but still much better than nothing.

7

How can one's life change so completely, in just one day? It was a lovely spring Sunday at the end of the seventh grade. I was home alone, just finishing my homework for the weekend when the doorbell rang—and here they were, Anya-Tania, all three of them, asking me if I'd join them for a bike ride. That was not a mundane occurrence, and I accepted with poorly concealed enthusiasm.

I went to my room to change, while the girls were waiting in the living room, scanning my parents' book collection which was impressive even by Akademgorodok standards. One of them must have noticed a volume of poems by Anna Akhmatova, one of the greatest poets of 20th century Russia, but not the one whose poems you learn at school. For some time, Akhmatova was all but outlawed; the publication in our home library was rare—and the only reason we had it was because my mom worked in the book store.

When I returned to the living room, the blond Tanyusha was flipping through the book, apparently looking for some specific poem, with Tanika and Anyuta looking at her expectantly. She must have found what she was looking for, because she started reading with expression, then closed the book and continued by heart.

> How can you look at the Neva,
> How dare you climb its bridges? ..
> Do you know that I will forever
> Be sad after dreaming of you?..

One poem, then another. I had not yet read Akhmatova myself, but found the poems beautiful.

> Glory to you, desperate pain!
> Yesterday died our young gray-eyed king...

When Tanyusha forgot a line, Tanika helped her:

> "It happened at hunting,"
> My husband said calmly;
> The poor dear queen
> Turned gray in one night...

And then Anyuta continued:

> I'll wake up my daughter,
> I'll look in her gray eyes...
> Your king is no more,
> Whispers the wind...*

---

* *Anna Akhmatova*, translated by the author

Apparently, they both knew many poems by heart—but where could they have learned them, by an author who had barely been published?

"Typewritten copies," said the girls. "You are so lucky to own the actual book..."

At that moment, I would have given half of my life to be able to recite anything of Akhmatova. Akhmatova, Anna Andreyevna, my namesake—how could I have missed her book? Suddenly, a lucky thought struck me: I vaguely remembered that the poetess was married to Nikolay Gumilyov, whom I happened to admire and know by heart—precisely for the reason that he was really outlawed, with no prospect of being published in his home country in the foreseeable future...

> Listen: far, far away on the Lake of Chad
> Wanders a gentle giraffe.
> He is endowed with slender grace and bliss,
> And his hide adorned with a magical design...*

I joined in.

"Do you know more?"

I did:

> On the seas of the north and the south,
> Captains search for unknown lands,
> Between basaltic rocks and the pearl ones,
> Sails of ships rustle in the wind.**

The bike ride was forgotten. We sat there, in the darkening room, without turning on the light, and recited poetry to each other. Then we started talking about... What do fifteen-year-old girls talk about?.. It was personal, confidential—and I was fully included in that exclusive private circle. Naturally included. I was at home there—literally and figuratively...

When my mom came home, Tanyusha asked her permission to borrow a couple of poetry books. Then my mom sat with us, and talked about Akhmatova and Gumilyov, of their love, their lives, their poetry, of Gumilyov's tragic death by execution... It was rather late when the girls got up to leave.

---

* *Nikolai Gumilev*, translator unknown.
** *Nikolai Gumilev*, translated by the author.

"Be careful riding your bikes home in the dark," warned my mother. "Would you like me to call your parents to let them know you are on the way?"

From that day everything changed for me. Once again, I became a d'Artagnan, the fourth musketeer. We were now inseparable. Tania-Anya, times two.

* * *

Back at school in September, we were in the eighth grade: formal high-schoolers, allowed to come to high school dancing parties and participate in publishing of the high school newspaper. We had spent most of the summer together—biking, swimming, boating in the Ob Reservoir, discussing books that we had read together, drifting from the woods to the beach, from a movie theater to the ice cream café, from one house to another, and periodically letting other girls join our tight circle—but only when we felt like it.

But the most incredible change for me was not being the tallest student in the class any more: at least half of the guys had entered their growth spurt and were already taller than me. Tanika was as tall as I was, and several other girls just an inch shorter. And there were several girls in other eighth grade classes taller, and overall bigger, than me. My most impossible dreams suddenly started coming true.

"You are no longer yourself," my father would say, not trying to conceal his displeasure. "You used to be an individual. *Different*. Now you are becoming like every other girl... Short, like all of them—nothing to look at. And what kind of name is it, Tania-Anya?"

My father didn't understand a thing. I couldn't care less about *individuality*. In fact, I had always wanted to be *like everyone else*, and it looked as if the Almighty (or whoever was up there) had finally performed the miracle for me...

8

"Thank you, Scheichman, you covered the subject. You may sit down."
"Let him continue!"
"He is not finished!"

"You want to shut him up because you don't like what he is saying!"

"He is speaking on the subject—we want to listen to him!"

It was a lesson in Economic Geography in the 9th grade.

I would not have wanted to be in the teacher's place. The task was to compare the economic principles of socialism with those of capitalism. There was an article on the topic in our textbook, which clearly explained the advantages of the socialist system. The question seemed easy, so several students raised their hands. But the boy who was called up turned the lesson in a completely different direction: he was talking about the *economic advantages of capitalism.* He accompanied his presentation with so many facts and statistics, taken from Soviet sources but put together in an unusual way, even quoting our government leaders, that the teacher had nothing to say, except to try to stop him. After ten minutes, she offered him "five" (the equivalent of an American "A"), but the class demanded that the student continue.

And he continued—for another forty minutes, until the period was over.

He got his "five" and the class got complete moral satisfaction. The teacher, probably, got to take heart drops, but we did not see it—not that we would have cared anyway...

The boy's name was Igor.

He was my first love.

It was a very bitter love, never returned.

When had it all started?

Was it in 6th grade, when Igor came over to me at the end of classes, and asked to talk outside in private? We had never been friends, so I was puzzled—but also intrigued and probably nervous. The early childhood easiness with the opposite sex had vanished at least two years ago, and teenage dating had not started yet. A boy and a girl walking together after school would attract everyone's attention. In our class, only Anyuta had a boy from seventh grade who occasionally invited her to a movie—but she was the queen, everyone accepted that...

Igor and I walked out of school in an awkward silence.

"They asked me to make fun of you," he suddenly said. "I should invite you to a movie, and then not show up. You would be standing there and waiting, and they will see you and laugh... And... I decided I don't want to do that..."

I stared at him in bewilderment.

"Who are *they*?"

"I don't want to give names... The boys... You know... Well, a couple in our class... I don't want to do that, OK?"

While the meaning of his words slowly reached me, I felt hot, then cold, then hot again. "Why do people hate me like that?" flashed through my mind. "What if he had not warned me, and I were gullible enough to believe that a boy can indeed invite *me* to a movie, and wait for him outside the movie theater?.."

I was in a complete loss for works. The response came swiftly, without letting me think what I was saying:

"So, why don't we *really* go to that movie? Then we—you and I—will make fun of them?"

I was shocked with my own words probably more than Igor was, but there was no return.

"How do you know that I will actually be there? You'll trust me?" he asked hesitantly.

"Because you will pick me up at my home," I said. "And we will walk together."

Later at home I could not believe what I had said. How could I be so bold? The next day at school Igor and I avoided looking at each other. Sunday came, and from the moment I opened my eyes in the morning, the clock was barely moving. I spent hours doing homework that would usually take me one-third of that time. I felt feverish. I could not eat.

My mom grew suspicious and wanted to know what was going on—and for the first time ever I could not bring myself to tell her the truth. I just said that I might be going to a movie with some girls, if I finish my homework in time... Then I could not stop wondering how my parents would react when they see a boy coming to pick me up... Will they think I am beginning to date? Will they ask me questions?

There seemed to be no happy end to the story, no matter how you turn it...

Igor and I had agreed that he would pick me ap at 5:30, for a six o'clock movie. By 4:30 I could not understand a word from the text-book and decided that I was done with the homework for the week-end. I just sat there, staring at the clock. Then I changed what I was wearing; then changed again. I was about to change the third time but got worried that my mother could notice. Five-thirty came, then five-thirty-five... My whole being turned into hearing, waiting for the doorbell to ring... I kept rehearsing in my mind how I would open the door, how I would casually say "oh, hi, you are a little late!", how I would put my coat on...

About ten minutes to six, the phone rang. It was Igor.

"Anya... sorry... I don't think it would be a good idea... We are not going tonight, OK?"

"OK," I said, my throat dry and my eyes hurting. "Some other time then."

I felt slightly better after I hung up. "Why don't we really do that another time?" I kept thinking, while the world around me was gradually returning to normal....

It was such a great self-deception. Of course, we never went to a movie together. We barely talked at all. But now I was constantly aware of his presence in the class. And, almost every time I secretly looked at him, he was looking at Anyuta...

"He's been looking at her *like that* since the second grade," said Tanika. "Didn't you know? Where've you been? The entire world knows that he is in love with Anyuta!"

Of course, I should have known... How on earth I always managed to miss things that everybody else knew?

* * *

Should I fast-forward my memory?

Two years later. It is a gorgeous winter day, and we are on a two-day skiing trip. There are about twelve of us, all from the same class; for whatever reason, Anyuta could not come, but Tanika is here. Unlike me, Tanika is a very good skier, so she is way ahead of me.

Our goal is a log cabin deep in the forest, about twelve kilometers (8.5 miles) from Akademgorodok. Nobody has ever found out who built that cabin and for what purpose. Most likely it used to be a hunters' refuge, but, as many things in the Soviet Union, a house built on nobody's land has become everybody's house. Some of us have never been there, and only one or two people know the way well enough to lead the group.

56

Ski trails are the only roads that exist in these woods in winter. They are easily distinguishable in the white snow and easy to glide on, since it has not been snowing for over a week, and many skiers passed before us. Tree branches, covered with sparkling snow, form a lace roof over our heads. The sky is hidden behind a thin layer of clouds, a luxurious garment that the Snow Queen dropped from her shoulders over her magic blue quilt. White, almost crystal, birches give way to emerald green pine trees, their trunks creating an endless gallery that leads to a mystical kingdom....

I used to think of myself as a rather athletic girl, but my cross-country skiing technique clearly sucks. I have overestimated my ability to ski non-stop for almost eight miles... I am nearly out of breath. And there is nothing—absolutely nothing—that I can do about it. I cannot turn back, even if I knew the way home (which I do not). We are supposed to spend the night in the mysterious log cabin, and we are at least half way there. I try to keep my pace even and not fall behind; still, I am afraid that I am slowing the others down. There is just one boy who is skiing behind me, even though he himself is a fine skier. He wants to make sure that I am ok and don't get lost....

This boy is Igor.

We are in the eighth grade, both of is fifteen.

That's when my first love really started...

We spent the night in the log cabin.

It was built to sleep, probably, four or five people, and there were twelve of us, so nobody slept. We had a fire going all night in a little brick stove, and tea made from melted snow.

The tea smelled of smoke and firewood, and the sandwiches that we all shared kept the coldness of the outdoors. The moon was full, mysteriously lighting the white lawn in front of the house, our skis stuck vertically in snow like a makeshift fence, and trees at the edge of the surrounding forest.

The boys took turns playing guitar and almost everybody sang along. The only light available in the cabin came from a candle and from sparks of the fire in the stove. Igor and I did not talk directly to each other. Neither was he sitting next to me, but I wished that the night would never end. I could sense his presence even when I was not looking at him. It was much stronger than any feeling I had had before.

Stronger even than my childhood infatuation with Anyuta... Or anything else I had experienced so far...

* * *

I got used to it later. It continued for two-and-a-half years, until the day that I had been dreading as the worst disaster in my life: the day of our graduation from high school that would forever end life the way I knew it.

I used to know whether Igor was in the classroom during the break even without seeing him. I could sense it when he was walking behind me, without looking back or even hearing his voice, when a large group of us was returning from a party. I probably knew his grades better than he did himself. Before every party, I imagined him inviting me to dance, then the two of us standing closer and closer together, my breath on his neck, him looking straight down at me... Then asking to walk me home...

Even in my dreams, it did not go farther than that. Dancing parties came one after another, during holidays, birthdays, on any occasion and without occasion. If Igor was there, he would usually dance one dance with me—as he did with all other available girls. But even then, he would look above my head...

That was the first dream in my life that never came true. There were others later, but none ever seemed as unjust or was as painful.

The only thing that consoled me was my close friendship with his unrequited love, Anyuta... She was so deserving of his love—or anyone's love, for that matter... And she had no interest in Igor.

* * *

The one and only time Igor and I walked together from a party alone, we got into a fierce argument. It happened in tenth grade, a couple of months before our graduation.

It was a warm spring night, the half-moon in the sky lighting the dark park, the air smelling of tree buds ready to open and bloom into young leaves. We finally sat on a bench in a grove of still-bare trees.

"I hate these tales about anti-Semitism. There is no evidence of it, just talks by some angry individuals who want to justify..."

"What do you mean, *no evidence*?!" I was so shocked that I interrupted him. "What about people who cannot get jobs, only because their last names..."

"How do you know it's because of their last names? That's what they are saying, right? Nice way to justify the fact that you did not get the job!"

"But, listen, the employers often do not even hide the reason. As soon as they hear a suspicious last name, they won't even invite you for an interview!"

"Really?" He grew sarcastic. "So, is your father unemployed? Or my father? My name is typically Jewish, everyone knows that my father is a Jew. He is a well-respected person in his institute. So is your father, as far as I know..."

"And has your father ever been abroad? My father has not..."

"Oh! Are all Russians going abroad?! More than half of my father's department have classical Russian names—do you know how many of them ever go abroad? I know two people, and one of them is the boss..."

I was getting frustrated. I knew he was wrong, knew as well as you know things that you have been hearing from your parents—no, from every person who has ever come to your house—from the day you learned how to talk. But argumentation? The hardest things to prove are the ones you have been taking for granted.

"Ok," I said, "how about students who apply to colleges? A more timely topic for us than a job. What about them?"

"What about them?" He was getting angry. "Do you know a single Jew without higher education? Just one? My cousin has just graduated from MFTI—and that is probably the most prestigious technical school in the entire country. How, I wonder, do they all get higher education if they are not admitted to colleges?"

"That's not *they*, that's *us*..."

"Oh, don't mix me in there! I do not identify myself with losers who can only vent their anger by slandering their own country!"

"Well, maybe I am a loser who slanders my own country..." I was thinking more about my failed love than prospective colleges.

"And what have you lost, if I may ask? You are an attractive girl whose father has an excellent job. Your mom does not even have to work! You are about to graduate from one of the best schools in the country. Or maybe you have been persecuted at school for being Jewish? No one even knows you are Jewish! I would not know, if you had not told me!"

"That's exactly the point, nobody knows..."

"Don't twist it all around! Everyone knows I am Jewish, and there has been no difference. At least a quarter of our class has last names that can be interpreted as Jewish! Besides, everyone's nationality is in the class registry. Mine says "Jewish", not that I care..."

"Great! So, there is a nationality in the class registry—why? You just said, you don't care. No one cares. Not that Jewish kids go to a synagogue or do something else special. We're all atheists and so are our parents. So why is a nationality there at all? Someone needs it, or otherwise..."

"Maybe someone does need it. I don't know for what purpose. We are a multinational state—that's the whole point. Maybe it's an atavism, left over from the old days. You know, I do not pretend that I know the answer to every question, as you do..."

I was hurt. In the heat of the argument I forgot for a few minutes that I loved him—and that he did not love me. I wanted to stop, to talk about something personal, something that could suddenly bring us closer. There were still two months left. So much could happen in two months....

"There are some colleges that don't accept Jewish kids," I said, trying to compromise. "And some do, but with limits. And some, probably, have no limits.... That's why sooner or later everybody gets higher education..."

But Igor did not have any desire to compromise:

"And then postgraduate education, and then PhD's? I bet one-third of our scientists are Jewish, at least by the last names!"

"Well, maybe Jews are more talented, or more hard-working."

"Oh, don't give me that racist crap! I used to respect you, you know..."

The conversation was turning in a dangerous direction.

"Where are you going to apply?" I asked, as softly as I could.

"I don't know yet. Maybe to our university."

"Physics?"

"I am not sure yet. Maybe physics. Of maybe geology. I would like to work with my dad when I graduate."

"But you were going to study in Moscow, weren't you?"

Something hurt me there, but I could not yet figure out what it was.

"I'm not sure. Our university has a stronger geology department than Moscow University. Anyway, it depends..."

He paused.

I already knew whom he was thinking about. Anyuta. He was still in love with my friend...

I knew Anyuta was not planning to apply to Novosibirsk university, although she was going to study in the city and continue living with her grandparents in Akademgorodok. But Anyuta had a boyfriend of two years. Sergei. Tania-Ania, Sergey-Andrey. Two friends, the most popular boys in the tenth grade, were boyfriends of the two most popular girls in the tenth grade, Anyuta and Tanyusha. The first two girls in our class who started dating, and the two with the most consistent relationships... Tanika also had a boyfriend, but he was relatively new, and not from our class. I was the only idiot without one. Surprise-surprise... How would I get a date, if I do not see other boys except Igor? Look at everyone else as if I am a stuck-up snob. Preparing to remain an old maid, just to be faithful to the knight of my dreams...

With all the time I spent together with Anyuta, I did not really know how deep her feeling for Sergey was. Some of her affection for him could be caused by habit, or vanity... Who knows, if they remain a couple after they both graduate high school and stop seeing each other every day?.. Igor is persistent... And how, how on earth could Anyuta reject him for anyone else?

And how could I ever compete with Anyuta in a boy's affection? In anyone's affection?

But so far... No evidence that she had any interest in him. At least for now, I could have my moral satisfaction: his love was also unreturned.

But the hopes that had made me happy just a few minutes ago were dying.

He probably guessed what I was thinking about.

Did he know how strongly I felt about him? He may have suspected something. I did not know.

"I wanted to study in Moscow," he said firmly. "I am still thinking about it. But I do not want to go that far away from home, either. It will be very hard on my mom."

"Novosibirsk University is the one with a zero quota for Jewish students," I said. "My father used to teach there until they laid him off, together with the other Jewish professors. They are simply Jews-free. You won't get in."

"It's midnight, Anna," said Igor sharply. "We've talked enough. Let me see you home."

9

Igor failed the admission exams to the Novosibirsk University.

Or, rather, *they failed him*. He got "three" (the equivalent to American "C") in oral Physics—his strongest subject—while the "4" was a required minimum. I've never learned what exactly happened at that particular exam, but I heard stories from several other students who had thrown themselves into a stressful and tedious process of applying to the largest and the most prestigious university in Siberia.

Per my request (or, better say, per my plea), Igor and I had spent the night after the prom together and mostly alone. It was nothing much, just walking along the dark and silent beach... I was dreaming of a kiss, but it never happened. That is when I finally told him about my feelings—there was no more hope anyway, and nothing to lose... At least he would remember me, I thought. And that was the last time I saw him that summer.

From the bits and pieces that I heard later (mostly coming from Igor's mom who shared information with my mom), Igor had been subjected to a "standard procedure" by one professor Larin, famous for "thorough testing" of the applicants whom the university didn't want. After a student answered his initial questions, the professor would ask him another one, and another one, and so on, each question more difficult than the previous one, until—sometimes several hours later—an exhausted and discouraged applicant would fail to answer correctly.

Igor, completely unprepared for that turn of events but intelligent enough to understand what it meant, had a nervous breakdown that required hospitalization. He left for Moscow almost immediately after his discharge from the hospital. I did not have a chance to see him, or even to say good-bye. He was clearly avoiding everybody, not just me.

Before I get off the college admission topic, I would like to share a similar story, related personally by another boy from our class, Alex Parm, who treated the whole affair with good humor. Alex, a typical representative of the united international family of the Soviet Union, was a child of a Russian mother and a Lithuanian father. Born and raised in Russia, he naturally had chosen "Russian" to be listed as "the nationality" in his passport. The boy was subjected to a testing procedure similar to the one Igor had gone through, received his "three" ("C")—and subsequently was denied admission. His father, who could not believe that his son had been discriminated against as a Lithuanian, is reported to have gone directly to the head of the Admission Committee, and thrown his own passport at the man's face:

"Don't you see that I am *not* a Jew, but a Lithuanian? Can't you read?"

The head of the Admission Committee seemed embarrassed. He pulled out the boy's file; his nationality there was stated as "Russian." The professor was upset.

"You should have registered him as a Lithuanian," he said apologetically. "Because your son's last name is clearly not Russian, the professor who administered the exam thought that he must be Jewish. If we had known that he was a Lithuanian, we certainly would not have flunked him. It is too late for this academic year, but I assure you that if your son decides to apply again next summer, there will be no mistake..."

Knowing Alex for ten years, no one thought he would have invented the story; his father later confirmed it, and it sounded plausible in any case. Waiting to be accepted in college for another year was too risky: upon turning eighteen in the fall, Alex would have been subjected to the spring military draft. He had little choice but to apply to a college whose exams started later in summer; he was admitted to a good technical school in the city of Novosibirsk with flying colors. I am not sure whether he had told them in advance that his last name was Lithuanian, or if that particular college had no restrictions on Jewish students...

* * *

A few days after graduation, the four of us were sitting on the porch of Anyuta's grandparents' cottage, the way we had done hundreds of times before. Except that all of us knew that it would never be the same again. We could no longer be *the Tania-Anya from the tenth grade*; each of us had her own road to travel on—and we just had to hope that the road would be smooth and straight, and wouldn't take us too far apart from each other...

Tomorrow, I would leave for Leningrad with my mom. Anyuta and Tanyusha would study in Novosibirsk, but in different colleges. They would both still live in Akademgorodok and might continue seeing each other. It would never be the same as at school, but... Tanika and I envied them.

Tanika would go to Moscow, to receive her higher education in the country's best university.

"If I get accepted," she said with a grin.

"Of course, you will!" the three of us answered in unison.

Tanika was probably the brightest girl in our class. Not that anyone in our school was dumb—but Tanika was brilliant. Especially in math. True daughter to her father, one of the country's most prominent mathematicians—and one of the youngest *academicians (*please, don't confuse with *academic!),* which means a full member of the Academy of Science of the USSR, the highest scientific rank anyone could achieve.

Tanika shook her head:

"My dad is not going to call anyone. Not this time."

We all knew what Tanika was referring to: an incident that could have ruined her life, as bright and talented as she was. If it were not for her famous father...

We had all grown up without religion, and so had our parents. Christianity was something belonging to textbooks—or to very backward old people from some god-forsaken villages. By the time we reached high school age, however, many young people started viewing religion as a secret way of defying the government; doing small "Christian things" (such as dying eggs or decorating tree branches for Easter) became a game—a little dangerous, but therefore more exciting. Some girls dared to wear crosses—but only in summer, when they could be seen under an open blouse.

We were all members of *Komsomol*[1] (the abbreviation stands for All-Union Leninist Young Communist League, a youth organization

---

[1] See notes at the end of the book.

controlled by the Communist Party of the Soviet Union). Membership in the organization was considered to be honorary; in reality, it was a prerequisite for college admission—so all college-bound kids became members at the age of fourteen. As in any organization, it had its IDs; and IDs needed to be updated periodically, which required a new photo.

Tanika was by far not the only teenage girl who wore a tiny golden cross with her non-uniform clothes; but she was absent-minded enough to forget to take it off while having her picture taken for a new Komsomol ID. The photographer did not pay any attention; Tanika had no idea about the mistake she had made, until it was too late: the photo was noticed by an officer of the Komsomol Regional Bureau. The scandal was enormous: Tanika was accused of "betraying the ideals of Communism," of "cheating on her Komsomol comrades" and the like—not fun accusations to have. The school principal summoned all the high school students to the conference hall and delivered a thunderous speech, using words like *"we must not tolerate in our ranks traitors to our ideas..."*

The next step for the poor girl was an unconditional expulsion from the Komsomol, which meant in those days no college. Ever. The fact that she was one of the school's brightest students did not make any difference. That was the one and only time when her father, Academician Somov, who was known to have never used his high rank or his famous name for any personal benefits, picked up the phone and called the President of the Siberian Department of the Academy of Science. The latter, in turn, called the local Party boss... The case was closed as suddenly as it had emerged. And wearing crosses in our school became even more fashionable.

Anyuta's grandmother had brought us a bottle of red wine. Not that we had never drunk alcohol before, but none of us was accustomed to it; or maybe we were all unusually fragile at the time—but the little bit that we did drink, put us in an even more somber mood. The wine bottle was sitting, half-empty, in the middle of the porch table, among the four cups with almost cold tea that none of us could drink. Tanyusha had just finished telling us all about her painful breakup with Andrey, her boyfriend of two years. It was the first time she told the entire story to all of us, instead of isolated bits and pieces we knew or had guessed... By the end, we were all close to crying.

Then I told them about Igor. My three friends stared at me in disbelief.

"You loved him all these years—and never told us?.."

"How could I tell you, when everyone knew he was in love with Anyuta?!"

"Because... I would have done something"—cried Anyuta. "If I had only known that you loved him!.. Do you consider me such a bitch?..."

"What would you have done? Promise him to kiss him in exchange for dating me?"

Anyuta bended over the table, holding her head with both hands. She looked so distressed, I almost felt sorry for her.

"That evening... when he told me he loved me... I could have said to him..."

"He *told* you he loved you?"

I didn't know he had told her... Not that it mattered any more... Sharp pain stabbed me once again, then gradually started to subside, replaced by some dull feeling I could not define.

"It would not have been a fair competition," I said quietly.

"What?"

"Anyuta, you know, I could never be your rival." I looked in her unsmiling eyes that now seemed even larger than usual... "Not with boys... Not with friends. Not in anything, be it figure skating or... whatever... Since we were little girls... Since we first met as seven-year-olds, and I fell in love with you—almost as bad as..."

That is when I started crying. A minute later we were all weeping. Sitting there, with a half-drunk bottle of red wine that didn't taste particularly good, not saying anything, just crying together. And that was the best: one for all, all for one. Still, the four of us inseparable in that big wild world... no matter where our lives would take us...

Intermission
JEWS IN A MULTI-NATIONAL STATE

IN AMERICA, I AM OFTEN ASKED by my Jewish friends: *What did it mean to be a Jew in the Soviet Union?*

They do not realize how difficult the question is. The concept of "nationality," the way it was understood by the Soviet authorities, is unknown to most Americans. And most Russian citizens had never heard about Judaism as a religion. They associated the word "Jew" with one line in a person's passport, with the last name of his ancestors, with some mythical ties with that evil and mysterious land called Israel. And many Jews would have given everything in the world to erase that one line from their passport, birth certificate, job application. They had no desire to be different—they would have gladly forgotten their ancestry and fully assimilated into Russian culture.

My grandfather Solomon (who would have never been able to pass for a Russian, both because of his name and his appearance) belonged to the "first generation" of Soviet Jews who had actually benefited from the Socialist Revolution. Since Jews had been discriminated against under the tsar's regime (in "colonies" such as Ukraine and Byelorussia, currently called Belarus, even more so than in Russia itself), the newly formed Soviet government treated them like "proletarians," i.e. made them a privileged class who were assumed to welcome and support the new regime. There is no way that my grandfather, one of fourteen children of a Jewish barber in a small provincial town in Byelorussia, bright as he was, could have ever made it through law school without the Revolution and the Soviet government supporting him. As I said earlier, he was both smart and lucky to keep not only his freedom, but his lucrative job, throughout the terrible years of Stalin's terror. What he really thought about the regime remained his own secret; he never shared his thought with his sons, even less so with extended family members. The first time he set foot in the synagogue (there was one synagogue in Leningrad, and one in Moscow, both strictly controlled by the government) was after he had fully retired; even then, it did not go farther than buying matzah for Passover.

Solomon's older son, my father, who from early years displayed remarkable mathematical talent, received his doctorate from Leningrad University, his original alma mater, which meant as fine an education as anyone could get in the Soviet Union. His second son, my uncle Victor, unremarkable as a child, later became even more successful than my father—although in a completely different field.

Times changed, and greatly increased government liberalism (compared to the 1930s and 1940s) coincided with its dissatisfaction with the policies of the newly created State of Israel, which in turn caused suspicion, and later discrimination against "Soviet citizens of Jewish nationality." Not that it was ever acknowledged—officially we were a multinational and equal-national society, with "the friendship of all peoples" remaining the cornerstone of official ideology. But, unlike my grandfather, both my father's and my uncle's lives and careers were eventually touched by government anti-Semitic policies, subtle and secret as they were.

The invitation for my father to work in Akademgorodok came personally from the president of Leningrad University, Professor Alexandrov (in exchange to agreeing to move to Siberia, the latter received the title of academician, i. e. was promoted to the highest ranks of the Soviet science). It was flattering, presented new professional opportunities, and promised numerous social and economic benefits for the family. In spite of all these advantages, my young parents hesitated a lot. Having all their roots in Leningrad, they could not imagine their lives without that city. They finally decided to accept the offer, but only temporarily, so my father signed a three-year contract.

If they had known back then that they would live in Siberia for the next thirty-six years, I wonder if they would have agreed to go at all...

But I am very happy that they did not know it back then.

✳ ✳ ✳

The day my father was laid off from Novosibirsk University, where he had been teaching part-time as an associate professor for over ten years, did not come unexpectedly. There had been other Jewish faculty laid off before him, and a few years earlier the university had started reducing the number of Jewish freshman students, so the tendency was clear. My father took it with humor, rather than bitterness, and financially it was not a catastrophe, as he still had a very secure full-time job in the Institute of Mathematics. But a few months later the money became tight. It was clear that with one salary in the family we wouldn't be able to afford going on vacations, and even our traditional once-a-year trips to Leningrad would become a problem. There was a brief discussion about my mother going back to work (the book store where she had worked as the head of acquisitions for a few years would have gladly hired her back), but my parents decided against it. It was agreed that my father should look for another teaching position.

He had no doubt that, with his experience and well-established name in the scientific world, he would find something sooner or later: Novosibirsk had dozens of colleges, and Mathematics and Physics were taught everywhere. The problem was that he had gotten spoiled by having worked within a fifteen minutes walk from home for many years. All the other colleges except Novosibirsk University were in the city of Novosibirsk itself, an hour bus ride away from Akademgorodok. But there did not seem to be any choice.

First responses to my father's resume were good. He went to the first interview but not get the job. He did not think that there were other applicants for the position, so he was a little discouraged (and, almost certainly, very angry about the wasted day). The next time he received a phone call, he said directly that he was interested in coming for an interview, but he would like to warn that he was a Jew. The person on the other end of the line thanked him for having saved everyone's time—and hung up. That scenario repeated itself several times. Month after month went by. My mother started saying that maybe she would have to go back to work after all. And then my dad got an offer.

It was a small school, but with a good reputation. My father worked there for many years and became one of their most respected professors. He hated the commute though, and constantly threatened to quit (my mother and I both knew that he would not).

In one respect Igor was right: anti-Semitism in Russia was inconsistent, and very hard to prove...

* * *

There was one situation however, where being Jewish (or, more exactly, having the word "Jew" in your passport, regardless of who you really were) made all the difference in the world. By some, it was viewed as a unique opportunity, an advantage completely undeserved by those who had the courage to use it. That happened when an individual—or more often a family—applied for emigration to Israel. Not because Israel was so desirable—but because going there meant leaving the Soviet Union; once you were outside and free, you owned the world.

The would-be immigrants had to go through a lengthy process of obtaining an invitation from a "relative" living in Israel. Then they had to get permission from family members staying behind: old parents (even if a parent had had no contact with the émigré for years, or had never raised him), adult children, ex-spouses. Members of the Komsomol (abbreviation for the League of Young Communists, which included pretty much everyone between the ages of fourteen and twenty-seven), and especially the Communist Party, had to resign—or were expelled with disgrace.

With all the documents in hand, you could apply to the local visa department, called OVIR, and then wait for many months for permission to leave the country. The permission, if granted, allowed you "to reunite with your relatives in Israel." The reality was, that most Jews did not have such relatives—and had no desire to live in Israel anyway. "Israel" served as almost a code word for an exit visa—after which you would fly to Australia, New Zealand, or most likely to Italy. The American consulate in Rome reviewed applications for granting Soviet emigrants the status of political refugee to the United States; for decades the process was a mere formality: over ninety percent of applicants were granted the status. America wanted Soviet intellectuals.

I do not want to speculate about the game that the three governments played with human lives and dignity, but they worked in surprising unison. The Israeli government issued false affidavits from fake "relatives," the Soviet government pretended those "relatives" were real—and kept requiring the affidavits, instead of just letting people go; the American government granted the status of "Political Refuge" to Soviet citizens most of whom had never been persecuted or had their lives in any way endangered. The last fact in particular made many people angry—not just in Russia but all over the Soviet Union: there were plenty of non-Jews who would have liked to leave the country, and they could not forgive Jews for having that "privilege".

"That is fair: Jews do have limitations in getting jobs and being accepted to colleges, so they have reasons to feel oppressed and should be able to leave if they want," argued some.

"But if Jews were not leaving, there would be no necessity to restrict them," refuted others. "They are getting free higher education in our colleges and universities, and then using their skills to make money in the United States. Why should the Russian people pay for that? Jews learn the secrets of our newest technology, and then sell their knowledge to American and Israeli governments. Of course, we need to protect our country by keeping them put!"

This was an endless dialogue, like the argument about the chicken and egg. *Are Jews emigrating because they are being oppressed here, or are they being oppressed because they might emigrate?*

It is possible that each explanation had some truth to it, but more likely that they were both wrong. There were plenty of citizens labeled "Jews" in their passports who did not want to leave because they considered Russia *their* country and loved it too dearly to be able to imagine their lives without it. And there were many ethnic Russians who went out of their way to emigrate, by marrying Jews (sometimes fictitiously) or somehow obtaining Israeli affidavits, even though they had not had any Jewish relatives for a hundred generations. Those who succeeded were often grateful to Jews for "creating the opportunity" for others, but the ones who failed felt patricularly bitter that Jews "had it easy".

As for lay people, most of the country's population hated and despised emigrants; to them, those people were traitors of the motherland with no morals and no gratitude. "Our country gave them everything, and what are they leaving it for? For more material goods?"—they would say. Popular opinion split in two. Many believed that the emigrants deserved the most severe punishment, because trading your country for mere money was a despicable thing to do. Others said that you must throw rotten vegetables out of the basket: the traitors should be let go, the sooner the better—just make sure that they never come back.

Therefore, these potential emigrants were, indeed, courageous people. They were ready to give up established lives, subsidized apartments, and for some, nice private dachas, free and well-organized medical care, one of the world's best school systems, and secure jobs, to start everything all over again from point zero, in unknown societies based on different—and totally alien—rules and values. They were ready to face the contempt and hatred of their co-workers, neighbors and often yesterday's friends. But their worst risk was *a refusal* of the authorities to let them go. They could either be denied permission to leave the country on the basis (often false) of their former job's security classification, or just not given any answer for months and years, without any explanation at all. Those people became outcasts. They were forced to leave their jobs; their adult kids were expelled from colleges; younger kids faced harassment at schools. The applicants who were refused emigration had to continue their lives, nobody knew for how long, amidst the hatred and contempt of others and without any steady income.

In short, they became *refuseniks*.

* * *

There had been talks of emigration in my family for as long as I could remember. Israel was never mentioned even as a theoretical option. My parents spoke only about America. They said that they would go there if... There were always very respectable reasons why they could not do it *now*. Later, when the number of permissions issued by authorities began to dwindle, and the number of long-term refusniks grew dramatically, it became clear that it was just the wrong moment. We had to wait until the politics changed. Few people had doubts that it would change sooner or later; the only question was *when*.

There were moments in my childhood when I hated my life to the point that I wished we would all emigrate, and I could start all anew. Those thoughts would disappear as soon as my personal girl's life turned brighter. They were totally gone during the last three years of school, when my friendship with Tania-Anya crystalized and I became one of the four—"all for one, one for all…" Overall, in my childish dreams, I always saw my adult self in Russia, married to a guy who had the same political beliefs as my parents and their friends, living in a house full of interesting books and interesting people, having great jobs, great kids, and, of course, traveling abroad when and where we wanted (in the Soviet reality in those days, the least realistic dream of all). But I could not picture my life outside Russia.

Even in later years, when thoughts about possible emigration returned, they never went past the mere *process of leaving*. After that they turned blank.

There was a social paradox with the *applicants* (i.e. people who applied for emigration): while some of their acquaintances expressed hatred and contempt, many others considered it almost prestigious to be associated with people who wanted to leave the country. Every applicant automatically moved into a category of "interesting people" and therefore immediately acquired new friends. My father befriended every refusnik in Akademgorodok, and my parents seemed to feel almost honored when one of them stopped by for a cup of tea. And my parents were in no way an exception.

Notwithstanding their difficulties, in my eyes refuseniks were people who could never be lonely. The closed groups they formed with each other functioned almost like extended families; "respectable citizens" such as my parents, were proud to name anyone who openly proclaimed their non-acceptance of the Soviet reality, as their new friend. It appeared the same in Akademgorodok as in Leningrad, Moscow, or any place throughout the country—wherever the concept of emigration existed.

Later, in some low moments of my adult life, I envied refuseniks. During lonely weekends and endless winter evenings, I often wished I were one of *them*, those strange people who never seemed to be alone. But I was rarely envious of those who had actually received *the permission*…

You become half-dead. Your former life is still here, with all its disappointments, suffering, frustration, failed and fulfilled dreams, happiness, connections with those who love you and those who hate you. Your friends are still gathering around the same tables drinking tea from the same cups, talking about the same books, scolding the government, gossiping about each other, falling in love, having affairs, breaking up, getting married, having children. But you are already out of this life that was yours only yesterday—out forever, even though physically you are still present. The people you love have to start arranging their lives *without you*, the same as when you die.

* * *

There were years and years when nobody was leaving, and the status of *refusenik* seemed permanent, like the nationality in your passport, or your profession. And there were years when so many people were leaving that the ones who stayed behind could not keep up with reading the letters, sent from the "other side" of the planet. The empty spaces left from people I knew were so enormous that I gave up hope of ever filling them.

There were farewell parties, each one heartbreaking, and all of them alike, with the same speeches, the same wishes and the same promises to write. And then their hosts were gone, and the empty space that was left behind gradually got filled with something or someone else.

Then, often many months later, the letters started coming. They were addressed to the closest friends but were read by everyone who used to know the émigrés, and then by those who knew someone who knew them, and then just by those who were curious about how it is "out there".

There were crying letters (*What have we done? It is not at all the way we had thought. It's cold and lonely here, and we are working much harder than we could have ever imagined, and still have no place to call home...*). There were also boasting letters (*We've just bought a two-story house with a huge garden, and the kids study in Harvard, and we have just been to Hawaii—it was nice, but the flight too long, next time we'll go to the Caribbean instead...*)—but then, if their new life there was so great, why did they keep writing?

And there was the envy of those who could not leave but wished they could. And there was hope, and sadness, and hatred, too. There were long lines in OVIRs, formed by those who wanted to apply. There were even longer lines for the airplane tickets, lines formed by the lucky ones for whom the tedious and often dangerous process was over. And there were airplanes flying several times a week, the planes that carried passengers with one-way tickets.

But then they were free.

Free from trying to figure out how to avoid writing "Jewish" in their job applications. Free from having to acquire permissions from ten different organizations every time they wanted to go abroad. Free from typing books on typewriters at nights and being afraid that someone whom they considered a friend might report them. Free from reminding their kids daily never to repeat at school what they heard at home. Free from having to register their address with the police. Free from life-time relationships. Free from the homes where they had grown up, from the books that they had read as teenagers and that their parents had been collecting for them since the day they were born. Free from all obligations to people whom they loved, and to those whom they hated. Free from having to respond to a government official whom they despised. Free from having a childhood friend living around the corner.

For many, many years I tried to imagine the feeling that one must have on *that* airplane. The airplane that, like a spaceship, is to take you to a different galaxy, where you own nothing and owe nothing, about which you know nothing except that only the fittest survive there and all you can do is to hope that you are the fittest.

Many times on domestic flights, traveling for work or leisure, flying away for vacation, visiting my parents, leaving whatever was then my home or returning back—I would fancy that it was *that plane,* the one that was taking me out of my country forever. The images got vivid, and I concentrated hard on my feelings: now a stewardess is locking the door, now the "fasten seat belts" sign comes on, now the plane starts moving, first very slowly. I can still clearly see the airport buildings I had seen so many times that I long ago stopped noticing them, which I know I will never see again; then even they disappear from view. The plane pauses for a moment, only to roar with all its engines and start accelerating, accelerating to enormous speed. The airdrome is flying back past the round window, and for a second, I can still see the ground that has been *mine* all my life, that I have taken for granted. I can still see houses, trees, tiny people back there on the ground, and I know that I am leaving it all forever, *forever*. And I feel the excitement, and chill, a wonderful sense of liberation, and incredible pain.

And then I remember that it was all just a dream. I realize over and over again, that I will probably never have to fly on *that* airplane—and that even if it happens in some remote future, I have no idea what I will really feel. And I would open my book or my unfinished letter, and tell myself to shut up, stop wondering, stop dreaming... because no matter how many *letters* I read, I would never really know...

Chapter Two

LENINGRAD

1

CHILDHOOD WAS OVER.

It ended abruptly, and although I had known for a while that it was coming to an end, I still found myself entirely unprepared for it.

I could have made the transition smoother, by staying at home and studying in one of the colleges of Novosibirsk, but for a variety of reasons it had been decided that I should return to Leningrad, the city where I had been born eighteen years earlier.

I thought I knew this city, and even loved it. This was the city where both of my parents had been born and grown up (save the years of the Great War and the Siege); the city my mom and I had been visiting almost every year, where relatives were always excited to see us. The city in whose art museums I had spent countless hours. The city I had dreamed about, learned poems about. The city where I had always imagined myself being loved, popular, successful... And here I was— lost in the maze of its endless streets, scared, profoundly lonely, suffocating among its granite buildings, longing for trees, space, fresh air, clean grass, clean snow, desperately missing the streets where I could walk with my eyes closed. But, most of all, I missed the warm home where hot meals were always ready, and my mama was waiting for me.

Worst of all, I was at the Library school—something I had never thought of. Not that I had any interest in becoming a librarian: I had always had a profound contempt for people who had to go to a library, as if they did not have books at home, or, at the very minimum, friends who had books at home. I wanted to study foreign languages, history, art. Maybe become a journalist, or an interpreter; unfortunately, such studies were all but closed to a girl with a Jewish last name—never mind my mom's heritage going to old Russian nobility... Technical schools were easier to get into, but I did not want to have to study any more mathematics, or physics, or any hard science—I had been fed up with them as a child.

By the 9th grade I had started thinking that I could possibly become an actress—or at least study to be an actress—it would be higher education all the same, and almost certainly the most fun college of all. In my case, it was not a completely impossible dream—at least the first part: my uncle Victor, whom no one had taken seriously as a young man, had become a well-known theater critic and a respected professor of the Leningrad Theater Institute. That may have been the only college in the country where my last name would have served an enormous advantage. The niece of professor Chernetsky—who would turn me down? I entertained the idea for a while and got moderately excited at the prospect of having a fun five years, notwithstanding what might happen after graduation; but my father wanted to hear nothing of me becoming an actress, and refused point-blank to ask his brother for assistance. At the same time, Grandpa Solomon remembered that one of his cousins was pretty high up in the administration of the Institute of Culture, and that there was no reason why I couldn't study library science. My parents liked the idea; I tried to argue but could not come up with a viable alternative plan, except that I probably did not need family connections to get accepted to the library science program. The college did not appear to have any anti-Jews policy, and my grades were good enough.

"Why take chances?"—asked my mom. "Do you want to waste another year?"

I did not. So I applied to the library science program, and successfully passed all entrance exams. Then I had four more years to be miserable and regret my choice—not that there had been much of a choice, if you come to think of it...

For better or for worse, came the end of September, the time to harvest summer crops. College students habitually got sent out to the countryside, to help employees from understaffed villages, or *kolkhozes*. Most city folks continued receiving their regular salaries, which frequently were several times higher than the salaries of *kolkhoz* farmers, plus they received bonus vacation time for longer hours and weekends.

At the same time, they had no incentive to do their job well. Economically such assistance was a disaster, even according to Soviet economists. But economy is, well, just an economy; understaffed kolkhozes counted on the cities to help during the time of intensive harvesting, so the government continued to provide such help—like it or not.

College students were the most popular labor force—not only because they were younger and presumably could work harder, but mostly because they were free. *Kolkhozes* were required to provide meals, working clothes, transport to and from the fields, and accommodations. Those were usually less than modest: trailers or barracks, with dozens of bunk beds in one room, well heated at the end of September, but with no other conveniences whatsoever. There were unheated outhouses within walking distance, and cold water for washing hands, at best protected from rain by a shed. Spending two to three weeks in such conditions could be a hard thing for city kids spoiled by modern comfort, but the ones who complained were treated with contempt by their own peers. For seventeen to twenty-year-olds there was a certain romance in that semi-camping life. The atmosphere of comradeship— where friends were made easily, love affairs started daily, and singing to the guitar could be heard every evening well past midnight—compensated for the lack of urban conveniences.

Much as I dreaded having to live without a hot shower and share the room with thirty other girls, I needed a change so badly that I was almost happy when it was our turn to go to *kolkhoz*. I found working in the field, with all its dirt, rain and wind, far less depressing than confinement inside the stone jungle of a huge city. Besides, like most of my new classmates, I was counting on finding a boyfriend. There was a sufficient number of male students in the music and drama departments of our college, but we (future librarians) did not have any classes together. Living for three weeks next to each other and working side by side in the fields would provide an excellent opportunity to meet them, not to mention a chance to get to know my girl classmates better.

We were lucky with the weather. It hardly ever rained. Mornings were cool and crystal bright, with golden tree branches looking almost unreal against a silver-grayish sky. The fields spread wide and free, almost to the horizon. The air smelled of healthy rich soil, clean rain, and fallen leaves, its quietness interrupted only by the twittering of birds and the voices and laughs of the girls. Professors worked along-side their students, dressed similarly, in black heavily lined jackets and tall rubber boots.

The students formed teams of three or four; I found myself working with two other girls. The first one, Irina, was slim and miniature, with one of those faces you will remember for a long time. Her sparkling green eyes, almost unnaturally long eyelashes, and long dark curly hair reminded me of Anyuta, and caused painful nostalgic feeling, but also a belief that we would be friends. The second girl was called Natasha, like my favorite second cousin. She was tall and plain, but friendly—and I tried to persuade myself that I liked her: not everyone had to be beautiful...

We were pulling carrots, cutting their grass tops with big knifes and sorting them into wooden boxes. It was not hard work, but it got boring after a while, so all the girls were chatting with their teammates and occasionally singing. I can't remember now what the three of us were talking about, until Natasha said something that seemed totally out of the blue:

"All these problems come from Jews. They penetrate everywhere; some even take Russian last names to disguise themselves. They learn our state secrets, just to sell them to the West. That's why our country must spend so much money on defense and intelligence—and then we don't have enough for social programs. We would have higher living standards than America, if our government did not have to spend so much on watching over all these Jews. And they leave our country as soon as they have learned enough of our secrets to make them rich abroad..."

I looked at Irina. She could not possibly be Jewish, with that face of hers, so I wondered how she was reacting. Irina was clearly uncomfortable but said nothing.

Natasha interpreted the lack of objections on our part as consent, and continued on the same topic with even more enthusiasm. Irina and I remained silent, not knowing what to say. I remember clearly that I did not feel for a second that Natasha was insulting me personally. I did not feel the slightest bit hurt, just appalled, the same way I would have been appalled if someone had been saying that kind of garbage about the Tatars, or the Germans, or blacks. I wanted to respond with something very strong, to make her shut up—but could not think of anything that would be good enough: that seventeen-year-old seemed so convinced of the truthfulness of her opinion that there was no reasoning with her. Suddenly, someone outside me said with my voice very calmly, almost lazily:

"Natasha, you know, everything you are saying is very interesting. I agree completely that you know what you are talking about. I have only one objection: I am *a Jew*, so I would rather not listen to it."

She stopped in the middle of her sentence as if she had choked. Her face became so gray and stern that I almost pitied her. The three of us continued picking up carrots for a few more minutes in absolute silence, until Natasha came up with some excuse to leave. Then Irina said:

"I am glad you shut her up. How wittily you did it! I was struggling to think of something to say but could not come up with anything. My goodness, remember her face! She nearly choked. She must have believed you!"

I thought for a while about whether I myself believed in what I had said, or had just wanted to silence Natasha, and found no answer. Then Irina asked me the same question:

"It is not true what you said, is it?"

I looked in her eyes. There were sparkles of laughter and almost childish curiosity, and I suddenly felt very comfortable.

"Fifty percent," I said honestly. "It is fifty percent true. Why, do you care?"

"No," she answered. "I just liked your response, in either case."

It took me years to realize that it was a turning point in my life: the first face-to-face encounter with what was called *common antisemitism,* and my gut reaction to it. It was also the beginning of my friendship with Irina; it never became as close and intimate as with Tania-Anya, but it lasted long after our college graduation, and it certainly brightened my life.

2

A few years have passed.

The city is now warm and alive for me. Its streets, its parks and gardens, its subway stations are talking to me in a secret language that only the two of us can understand. Leningrad is full of memories, some sweet, some bitter, some very painful, but it is never indifferent to me anymore.

Here is the Summer Garden, where I used to go with Marik, my second cousin on my dad's side. In the white summer nights when it never gets dark, we used to climb over the fence after the garden was officially closed and its gates locked, and kiss each other until it was time to run and catch the last subway train. Marik and I stopped dating years ago, but we are still second cousins, and will always be part of each other's lives, even if we only see each other several times a year.

At this subway station I used to meet Valery. He was always standing next to the last car, reading a magazine. This is the street that leads to his friends' house. We bought pastry for their party in that bakery around the corner; I never went there again; the memories are too painful. It was my fault that we broke up. My mother insisted that he was not right for me (what did she know?!) and I obeyed her as if I were still a little girl. Why, why did I do that? I tried to take it back later on, but it was too late. Valery could not forgive my unexplained withdrawal. He was hurt, and now I have to live with all these memories, in the town where streets and gardens and subway trains speak out his name: "Va-le-ra..."

This is a café where we girls used to go for ice cream after classes. And there's the one we went to when we wanted to skip a lecture; we always had the closest, most intimate conversations while standing in line for coffee.

If I go only two stops on this bus, I will arrive at Nina's house. Nina, the best girlfriend I have ever had. Closer to me than Tania-Anya; closer than a sister, if I had ever had one. Her building is at the corner, the second entrance from the right, fifth floor. I always run up the stairs, too impatient to wait for the elevator. We sit in Nina's room until late at night, discussing everything in the world, from politics and human rights to love, clothes fashion, and gossip.

The city is alive because of the people I love. Every part of it is associated with somebody who lives here—or used to live here—or used to meet me here. Each evening is lit up by the windows of people whom I can visit any time. They are scattered all over the city, so in no part of it do I feel lonely any more.

I even have a place I can call "home"—although sometimes I hate it. I live alone (rare luxury in an overcrowded city!) in two conjoining rooms, sharing the apartment with two other families. When my grandmother was still alive, she received the place from the government when the house she lived in (that coincidentally had belonged to my grandfather's family before the revolution) was taken over by some offices. Everyone says she was very lucky: the building is still in the city center, and the rooms are spacious. The place is not without faults, of course. In order to enter the building, one has to cross the inner yard that people call "a well". The sun never comes into the well-yard; there are no trees or even grass, just lifeless cement. It is spooky to walk through the yard after dark, although so far nothing bad has happened there to me or to anybody I know. Luckily, all my windows face the street, so I get all the sunshine that there is in Leningrad (in summer it sometimes becomes almost unbearably hot, but in winter you value every timid ray of sun). I also get plenty of noise from street cars that stop right below my windows, and a view of a typical residential section of downtown Leningrad, with its small dark grocery stores, littered gardens, and busy beer stands—things that tourists usually don't see.

Before the Revolution, it was clearly a house for the wealthy. The rooms are huge, with parquet floors, large windows and double doors. The ceiling is decorated with stucco moldings and is so high that, even with a long hanging chandelier, one needs a ladder to change a light bulb. Our building, like many others, has been turned into a multitude of so-called "communal" apartments, where a few families share the common areas. The only window in our kitchen faces the well-yard, and the bathroom has no shower. Like many other residents of downtown Leningrad, I go to public *banya* once or twice a week. And sometimes it is even fun.

Banyas (or public bathhouses) are numerous here in the old city. They provide plenty of showers with unlimited hot water and are often equipped with steam rooms; and the price is symbolic. Some luxurious and more expensive banyas may have hot saunas and even swimming pools. Old peasant women sit in the foyer, selling dried birch bunches that have been used in Russian steam rooms for centuries. "*Banya* meetings" have been one of the most beloved entertainments in my little circle of friends for years. Of course, social activities tend to happen in the most expensive places. We jump from an unbearably hot sauna into an ice-cold tub, then swim naked in a warm pool. We slap each other's backs with hot-wet birch brunches in the steam room—a wonderful and refreshing massage, if you know the right way of doing it. We drink hot tea with honey from the thermoses. Intimate conversations flow easily when we are all naked, admiring each other's beautiful young bodies and maybe showing off (but just a little), while older—or just heavier—women around us cast envious looks...

* * *

The biggest problem in my apartment, therefore, is not a lack of shower or bath, but the communal kitchen. Both my neighbors are middle-aged blue-collar working women, and our daily close encounter in the small kitchen becomes a burden for all three of us.

One of the women, Klava, is married to a man who served eight years in jail for having stabbed her with a kitchen knife, presumably out of jealousy. He has recently returned home after serving his term. When he is sober, he is the nicest guy on earth, always ready to go out of his way to help everyone with whatever chores might require a skilled man's hands. If only he were always sober...

Klava has two sons, the older one, Tolik, only a couple of years older than me, a tall and handsome high school dropout. Like his mother, he works at a shoe factory called *Skorochod* (which literally means "magic fast-running shoes"—a romantic name for a grim building with long conveyer lines run by unskilled workers). Like the overwhelming majority of young men of his social class, Tolik frequently gets drunk. He recently joined the Communist Party, naively hoping that it might help him with a job promotion; so far, however, his Party membership has not gotten him anywhere. I try to be friends with this young man for the sake of maintaining a good relationship with his mother, but conversations with him are boring and our late-night encounters in the kitchen provoke anxiety. I know all too well that if Tolik decides to become too friendly, no one in the apartment would do anything to protect me.

Klava is a weary woman, almost an old lady in her mid-forties, with a face deformed since girlhood by a bomb shell that hit her house during the Great War and left her lying under rubble for two days. She is an assembly line worker, and her legs are always swollen with enlarged veins, from standing on her feet most of the day. Unless Klava works an evening shift, she rarely comes home without being loaded with several heavy grocery bags. I've never understood how on earth a family of four could consume that much food, but apparently Klava's three men have a different opinion on the subject. Klava's major pride in life, in addition to having two healthy sons, is her ability to make enough money to provide abundant food and decent clothes for her family. She does not seem to want anything for herself.

Klava talks loudly and uses profane language every time something interferes with her household plans, such as me doing my laundry in the kitchen sink when she has been planning to cook dinner. When Klava is in a bad mood, I am much more afraid of her than of her son or even her alcoholic husband—and Klava's bad moods are frequent and unpredictable. Two or three times a year she has periods of binge drinking. Then she stops cooking, stops buying groceries, and does not even go to her factory, but just lies on the couch in the one big room allocated to her family by the government, and moans. I have no empathy for this problem of hers, and no respect. If I felt so miserable that I wanted to send everyone to hell, I would be lying all day in bed reading books. Klava seems to become bored with any book within ten minutes—but whose fault is that?

To be fair, I must add that occasionally Klava becomes the kindest and warmest person in the world. She would run to a pharmacy for me at midnight if I am sick, or bring a hot supper over to my room if I come home late and forget to do my shopping. Or she would cry on my shoulder about her wasted life and call me her best friend. Nevertheless, I wish I did not have to live with her in the same apartment; in fact, I would rather not know her or her family at all—they don't fit my image of the way "people should be," and that is distressing.

* * *

My second neighbor, Praskovya, is a small, quiet, and very clean woman without any age at all. She has been working as a manicurist in a nearby public *banya* since she was young (provided she was once young, which I have a hard time imagining). She has never been married, but has a thirty-year-old son, who, by rumors, has also served a jail term; the mother never talks about it. In fact, she barely talks to us at all; the only time one can hear her is when she is on the phone with one of her numerous girlfriends; she can spend hours tying up the only phone in the apartment, creating huge inconvenience for everyone. Her son officially lives with his wife but spends most of the time in his mom's room—and in our communal kitchen.

Like Klava's family, Praskovya and her son occupy only one room in the apartment. Unlike Klava, Praskovya never uses profane language, or raises her voice, but she never acts close and intimate, either. In some way, I distrust her quietness and neatness, and prefer the volatile Klava, whose temperament is closer to mine and with whom I can empathize more easily.

I will confirm my intuition later, when I will be moving to what my neighbors consider a better place, while they stay behind. Praskovya, with no more reasons to be polite, will turn out to have hated me quietly and consistently. The main reasons for her hatred are not my occasional blow-ups in the kitchen, or my educated friends who, in her opinion, stay overnight too often and never get drunk. She does not hate me for anything that I might have done or said—but for something entirely beyond my control: for belonging to a different social class, never (at least on appearance) having to work hard to make a living, being able to sleep until eight in the morning, wearing clothes that my neighbors could never afford, going on vacation to places that they have barely heard about, having parents who live in their "own" apartment in the fairy-tale Akademgorodok... In short, it is a typical *class hatred*, described by Karl Marx a century earlier—a form of hatred responsible for more bloodshed than any other, except maybe an ethnic one. In Soviet society that formally denies social classes, this hatred inevitably takes perverted forms.

Klava hates me for exactly the same things—but Klava's hatred is spontaneous, violent and short-term; it comes and then completely goes away, suddenly and unpredictably like capricious Leningrad weather. It is thanks to Klava, however, that I have encountered a *common* anti-Semitism closely and personally. Unlike the episode in the kolkhoz, Klava's anger was directed at me, rather than at some abstract Jews.

"You are just a f-ng Jew. There is nothing Russian about you!" she says sometimes during her especially bad outbursts of anger in the kitchen.

Those remarks, to Klava's disappointment, have not been hitting the target as much as she wants them to. I usually answer something like "How many Jews have you met in your life to know them so well?" Or, if I want to be vicious too, I come up with a stronger statement. "If being a Russian means getting drunk, having a messy room, and swearing like a truck driver, I am quite happy not to be one." I feel half guilty saying that, not because I have any remorse for hurting Klava's feelings, but because, considering myself much more Russian than Jewish, I do not like putting down the Russians... The ones I know, respect and love are not at all like Klava or Praskovya. I feel that my neighbors, just by being who they are, are discrediting the Russian people; and I do not know how to convey it to them without causing another outbreak of hostility.

* * *

There was one instance, however, when a remark of Klava's did hurt me badly.

During one of our usual kitchen arguments about who needs the sink more urgently, Klava, beside herself, screamed:

"You damn, f-ng Jew! Too bad Hitler did not slaughter enough of you!"

Until then, I've never had problems responding to Klava's insults, but that time I just turned around and left the kitchen. For that night, Klava won her battle. She got full possession of the sink and I went to a friend's house to eat. I could not bear the thought of ever seeing Klava again, not to mention being polite to her. I tried to remind myself that Klava was a very unhappy woman whose life had no joy in it and, worst of all, no hope. She had nothing to feel good about, nothing to *like herself* for. Her anti-Semitism, as any nationalism in general, was a sign of incredible weakness, a desperate attempt to mask her own inferiority complex. I had known all of that before, and I had no difficulties forgiving her for her previous remarks. That time, however, I thought that Klava had gone too far: every Russian, including Klava, was proud of having won the war against Hitler. Klava's father died at the German front fighting fascism, while Klava's face had been permanently disfigured by a bomb from Hitler's airplanes. She undoubtedly hated

German Nazis no less than any Jewish person. But her hatred for her own life must have been even stronger if she turned everything upside down like this.

That evening changed something in me; something very subtle, hard to pin down with words—a feeling, a thought, an understanding of myself—that began one crystal bright September morning in kolkhoz when I had just turned eighteen... There will be many more years before the new, unknown part of my soul starts demanding an identity, asking burning questions and urging me to learn about the history, the land, and the faith of my father's ancestors. But after that kitchen incident, whenever I asked myself what nationality I considered *mine*, I realized that I did not know the answer any more...

3

Will my readers forgive me if I return a few years back?

As you have undoubtedly understood already, my first few months in college were very lonely.

Irina, my new friend from the kolkhoz, Irina with dark curly hair and sparkling green eyes, who, at least by the way she looked and carried herself, reminded me of Anyuta, had no idea that she was supposed to become my close friend. Even though in college we were always together, as soon as classes were finished, she departed to her own cozy world: an apartment that she shared with her parents and two siblings, a neighborhood where her former classmates and boyfriend lived. She had a complete *life* awaiting her just a few subway stops away from college—while my *life* remained three thousand miles away—and, considering how many people had left and how much had changed, may not have existed at all...

To be fair, I have to say that I tried to reach out—but with little success. My mom's relatives and friends, although always welcoming me in their homes, did not have children my age. A couple of times I ran into my uncle Victor while visiting Sofia and Grandpa Solomon. Victor was always extremely friendly and appeared sympathetic.

"Why on earth did you make her go to that godforsaken college?" he reproached my grandfather. "There is nothing there to do for such an original, bright, creative, and non-conformist girl as my niece. She should have gone to the Theater Institute. Her father was opposed to it? I would have talked to my brother myself—if only I had known... The girl has talent—I heard her reciting poetry... And such an unusual face, a rare beauty ...Not the face you forget, you know... She could have possibly become a well-known actress... And even if not—she would be having much more fun now... I would have helped her to get in, at least!"

"Victor promises much more than he actually does," whispered Sofia; unfortunately, it was not helpful at all. I was pulling my hair thinking of all the exciting opportunities I had missed in my life.

The fact that my uncle offered me theater tickets that were unavailable in the box offices for regular mortals, was a weak consolation: I had no one to go with. Irina appeared mildly interested, but she was always busy. Once I went with my mother's childhood friend. The next time I invited my second cousin Natasha, who had recently graduated from college, was enjoying her first job and engaged to get married; seeing a play together was fun, but my weak attempts to share my loneliness bumped into sincere non-understanding: Natasha dwelled in a completely different world. The third time, I decided to offer a ticket to someone from my college group; since Irina was unavailable, my choice was rather random. I asked a plain, quiet and friendly girl named Nina. She and I had engaged in small talk several times, and she had a pleasant smile. Other than that, Nina didn't seem like anyone who had much of a "life." I decided that I won't be upset or discouraged if Nina refuses; I will just ask someone else. I was not sure whether I was relieved or disappointed when Nina accepted my invitation with gratitude and even enthusiasm. She did not look like any of my high school friends, so I had no interest in getting to know her better. Later, glancing at her in the semi-darkness of the theater, I admitted to myself that some people could consider her pretty, even beautiful. She was of a medium height and very slim, her pale complexion brightened by large eyes and the long red hair that she wore in a tight knot at the back of her head—somewhat old-fashioned but elegant nevertheless.

I didn't have much to say to her during our evening out; Nina appeared to be a low-key person, comfortable to be with—and that would have been just fine, if only... From Nina's few casual comments I understood that she had already seen most of the shows in that super prestigious, no-way-to-get-tickets-to drama theater. Matter-of-factly, she analyzed the production, the acting, and to my shame, remembered actors' names and where else they had appeared, be that a play or a movie. I suddenly felt inferior and unexpectedly powerless: how could I ever catch up to know all that stuff? Of course, having professor Victor Chernetsky for an uncle, I could see all the plays I wanted; and movie tickets were available without any strings to pull. But going out alone was not fun; moreover, it felt humiliating—as if everyone would look at me and think that this poor girl has no friends... Which was, in my case, very close to the truth.

It felt awkward to invite Nina again; we had nothing to talk about, and I didn't want her to think that I wanted anything from her. We did sit together at some classes and occasionally kept each other company standing in line in the student cafeteria, to grab a sandwich and a cup of hot tea during a short break between classes. Still, I much preferred to spend time with Irina. I soon discovered that if Nina and I had anything in common, it was our ability to laugh heartily, to the tears in our eyes, to Irina's jokes. Other than the times the three of us happened to be together, neither Nina or I ever laughed; a small smile was the most we were capable of. And, save for occasional late-night phone consultations before tests or exams, I barely had any contact outside classes with either girl.

* * *

Grandpa Solomon finally remembered that a grandson of his late sister was my age, a medical student who conveniently lived in the same area of Leningrad. I had vague memories of that boy from brief childhood visits of the large and loud *mishpuha* of my father's relatives, but did not think any of my second cousins could have interest in me. Luckily, my grandfather had no idea of my distrust of the Jewish part of my family; he spoke to the boy's mom, his niece, and the two agreed to re-introduce us. My second cousin Marik turned out to be very social, spent minimal time doing his homework, and loved having fun. He didn't mind bringing me to parties—and he had many to go to. We both loved to dance—and both were good at it. I soon felt at ease with most of his friends, and finally met my other third and fourth cousins:

Marik appeared to be close with everyone. Another great thing about Marik was that he loved movies and theater, and never turned down an opportunity to watch a play or a film. He became my first "date" and my first kiss—although not a pure kiss of the first love I had been dreaming about. It just had to happen: I was eighteen, and I needed the experience in order not to feel infantile, unattractive, and a future old maid.

Part of me despised myself for giving in so easily; another part felt proud that I had finally grown up to become a girl who could be desirable: Marik was a rather handsome and charismatic boy. The time I spent with him was mostly a happy one—except that it made me realize how much I missed out by not growing up close to my extended family, turned off by their "Jewishness." No matter how much I wanted to become one of them now, it seemed to be too late: they all appeared to share childhood memories that I was a stranger to.

When the novelty of my relationship with Marik began to wear out, I started getting bored more and more often. Occasionally we began fighting over nothing—and, in retrospect, I am pretty sure that I was the one responsible for most of those fights. The long summer vacation served as a natural interruption in our romance; the breakup of my first romantic relationship was initially painful, but gradually turned into a low-key cousin-to-cousin friendship. Unfortunately, I continued missing his merry group of friends for a long time. But the saddest thing was that Marik remained the only one of my paternal second cousins I ever got to know well. The rest of them continued living active, close, and somewhat disorganized but very communal social life; no matter how much I wished to be a part of that group, without Marik it was not possible, and I forever remained an outsider to my large extended family.

4

Sometime in the fall of my second college year, Uncle Victor introduced me to his girlfriend, a young woman in her last year of the theater institute. Marina, very intelligent, witty, spontaneous, but not particularly beautiful, was planning to become a theater administrator and, with luck, a critic and writer like my uncle. The fact that she was not a future actress made her more accessible; she and I never ran out of topics to talk about. Marina (I suspect per Victor's request) invited me to a couple of student plays of the theater institute, and even to some parties. Whatever her motives may have been, they were not important; a brief and rather superficial friendship with my uncle's young mistress nearly changed my life.

It was at Marina's birthday party that I met Valery, her high school friend and a student of the most prestigious technical college in Leningrad. I was nineteen, he was twenty-one. Valery was tall, handsome, highly intelligent, with a subtle and slightly ironic sense of humor, skeptical of the "Communist propaganda," well-versed in underground literature. It didn't take long for us to start dating—and before I knew it, I was in love heads over heels. That second love of mine promised to turn much more serious than the fruitless teenage infatuation with Igor: both Valery and I were at what was considered to be "marriageable age" in 1970s Russia; most importantly, Valery appeared to be as involved as I was. There was not a single topic, from politics to art, from how-to-make-the-world-a-better-place to books, that we could not discuss; not a single movie or play that we disagreed about. We would hug and kiss for hours, our breath taken away, our bodies aching for more closeness which none of us dared to name aloud.

All in all, it could very well have been the last love of my life. Had things been allowed to take their natural turn, Valery and I would have probably gotten married and lived happily ever after. In which case, I would have ended this book right here—with a boring happy end. But God, or Fate—or whoever is out there watching over us—must have had a different plan for me.

My mother showed up in Leningrad—as usual on a very short notice—a few days after Valery and I had spent the New Year night dancing till morning and holding hands, in a very merry company of his friends. Everyone looked at us as an engaged couple—and although none of us pronounced the final critical words, we were both at the point when words seemed unnecessary.

Whatever crazy ideas my mom could have regarding Valery (whom she had never met), will forever remain her secret. I am almost sure that Sofia, who still had a mindset of the 1940s, had alerted her that "things were moving too fast between me and my new boyfriend". My mom had always been paranoid that I could lose my virginity without getting married—and she was certain that Valery would try to sleep with me, and suspected that I would be too weak to say "no." And, not unusual for someone of her generation, she was convinced that no man would marry a girl with whom he had already slept—love or no love. That belief of my mother's—who still had a very strong influence on me—has played a tragic role in my life more than once.

During the next few weeks, I acted as if under a strong hypnosis. I felt like in a fog, observing myself from a distance as a separate creature who spoke my mother's words and had little to do with real me—if at all... Valery must have been puzzled by my frequent and unexplained changes of mind, not showing up for dates, and then crying and asking his forgiveness (the latter was outside my mother's scheme but contributed to Valery's alienation nevertheless). After Valery was shaken enough (and almost certainly had heard his own mother's advice to leave that capricious and hysterical girl before it was too late), he accepted my request "to stop our relationship and remain friends" without arguing. I had rehearsed these words for many days—but each time in my imagination Valery would ask "why?"—and then I would cry and tell him that it was all my mother's doing, that I loved him and always would, and that things would get back to normal as soon as my mom left. Instead, he said nothing. His face was pale and tense, but the only words he uttered were "as you wish."

I woke up the next morning convinced that I had had a bad dream. I called Valery from a pay phone at the street corner, but he was not home, and his mother's voice sounded icy. When I finally reached him after a few days of trying, and attempted to sound matter-of-factly, he replied that he was very busy with his final school project and hung up. That is when I realized that my heart was broken—this time almost certainly forever. Understanding that the fault was mine alone, made it thousand times worse...

My mom, having successfully saved me from disgrace, finally went home.

* * *

If you have ever blamed yourself for something awful you have done, you'll understand how I felt that spring. Attempting to hate my mom was no help: it just added a new burden to my soul. Until then, my mom was my refuge, my best friend, my savior—someone I could trust unconditionally. That was now lost: I could no longer trust my mother to always be on my side; she turned into someone to fear as much as to love.

During the long empty hours I now had in infinite supply, I thought once again how much I hated my college. I had no interest in becoming a librarian—and by the end of the second academic year I had no illusions that, with the education it provided, I could hardly hope of becoming anything else. I still had no close friends. Marina, apparently upset by my breakup with Valery, threw a special party for me, where we were supposed to reconnect and make up; but Valery never came. I got so distressed waiting for him in vain that I eventually got drunk— for the first time in my life. Unable to go home, I spent the night on Marina's couch throwing up and cursing the day I was born. After that night, I hardly saw Marina again. She had done what she could for me— and now had to look after herself. Writing final graduation papers kept her busy, and her affair with my uncle whom she loved deeply and sincerely, took a painful turn that she had no desire to discuss. I knew more about it than I ever wanted to know—but was in no position to offer Marina any consolations, even less advice. That was just another devastation in my life: uncle Victor was determined to leave the Soviet Union—no matter what it took...

Natasha, my favorite second cousin who shared my memories of early childhood summers at Grandma Galia's dacha, was now married and expecting a baby. I had no one to be friends with, and nothing to live for. That was the first time in my life when I began contemplating suicide.

* * *

Had it still been winter, with its endless nights and six hours of shy daylight, I almost certainly would not be here today, to write this memoir. But with each day longer than the previous one, with nights being eaten away by returning sunlight, birds even in the city center chirping as if they were in the forest, something resembling hope began moving through the air, and ... I can't say that I completely abandoned my thoughts, but I decided to give it some time. Just to see one more spring—and then... After all, the option of dying would always be there, no matter which way I would choose to end my life.

Spring in Leningrad was nothing like spring in Akademgorodok—no smell of awakening earth, no watching woods becoming faintly greenish with swelling tree buds, no crystal brooks carrying makeshift boats with sails made of lined notebook pages, with happy six-year-old captains running behind them. Dirty snow looked even dirtier melting on sidewalks. Still, spring meant the end of darkness and the promise of light. In my mind, Valery was often with me, waiting behind every corner I turned, standing outside my college entrance at the end of every school day; I spoke with him, confessed to him, cried on his shoulder. It was not the first time I was living in my dreams, letting real life just slide by—but it was the first time those dreams became so tangible that for some brief moments I felt almost happy.

5

The Institute of Culture, located on the bank of the Neva River almost across from the Peter Paul Fortress, boasted one of the most spectacular views in Leningrad, the famous Summer Garden serving as its own backyard. During warm weather, the garden was an escape place for students who wanted to skip a class; after dark, when its gates got locked, it gave shelter to young couples looking for romantic privacy. During the long summer days, it was one of the main tourist destinations of the city. Twice a year, in late autumn and mid-spring, students of our college were sent out with rakes, to clear fallen leaves from the ground. Free labor that the exploited students never objected to, regardless of what they studied. And who would?...

It was a regular day in April, gray and peaceful, when, instead of sitting in a stuffy lecture hall, our entire group of students was sent to work outside. Unlike in the kolkhoz, everyone worked individually, no groups were required. There were no quotas, no minimum to be done—so everyone moved at a leisurely pace, enjoying the outdoors. Somehow, I ended up working next to Nina. Was it a coincidence, or did she make an effort to be near me? Whatever the reason, it appeared that Someone Out There decided to remind me that life was still worth living...

"Sorry, would you mind if I ask..." Nina did not bother with a small talk. "You look like... something very bad happened in your life... I could not stop looking at you... and I kept wanting to come over and ask... But you seemed so..."

"Unapproachable,"—I said, forcing a half-smile. "Correct. I did not want anyone to be nosey... it would have been no help. Do you think anyone else noticed?"

"Anya... I have been watching you all these months... In fact, long before you invited me to the theater... You are so-oo different from everybody else here! From everybody I know... I was feeling... Ok, it does not matter. I just want to know if there is anything that happened to you, that I could help you with..."

I stopped, leaning on my rake. The smell of spring air suddenly intensified; I could no longer hear voices of other girls—just the wind gently playing with the branches of still-bare trees above our heads, birds telling each other their little secrets ... as if I were in Akademgorodok again. Suddenly, it became incredibly easy to tell Nina everything. My first happy love, my mother's unexpected and unwanted arrival, my ridiculous obedience to her command to break the relationship, as if I was hypnotized. And the empty world I was facing now, without Valery in it.

Nina said very little, but the way she listened... If anyone could help by listening, Nina did. I found it so hard to stop talking... And so I did what I would have done with Tania-Anya, in my former—and much happier—life: I cited a poem, the first one that came to my mind:

> Loss knocked me off
> like a thunderbolt
> Left me deaf
> With a bleeding heart*

I could not imagine that plain, quiet Nina would recognize the verses, even less know the author who, a once famous and successful actor, poet, and playwright, was now all but outlawed. But she just continued the verse from where I had stopped:

> Don't give me back my grief
> As a small change,

---

* *Aleksandr Galich*, translated into English by the author

like and old
Worn-out dime.
Crying for the dead
Is more than I can bear-
Since I know not who is dead
and who is not...*

How could she possibly know Alexander Galich? The god of underground, a singer songwriter whose plays were forbidden, whose poems had never been published, and whose songs were officially performed only once—in the House of Scientists in Akademgorodok, and even that years ago... After that one performance, his songs were available only through *magnitizdat*, tapes recorded in private concerts given in people's homes, or worse even—after he had been exiled from the Soviet Union in 1974—broadcast by foreign radio stations, illegal as all (true or false) information they provided, and jammed by Soviet authorities. (The word *magnitizdat* had been created to describe underground songs on tapes—as opposed to *samizdat*, that denoted unpublished—and often outlawed—books printed on paper.)

There was no need to say anything else. We had just exchanged the password. We discovered that we belonged to the same secret group, a group that included millions of people throughout the country. Totally informal, without a charter, registration or membership fees, this group was the one that our government feared probably more than external enemies. The bravest from us became dissidents, who gradually contributed to the collapse of the Soviet socialist empire. Others lay low, serving as the base for the pyramid, providing moral support—occasionally betraying the ones who dared to speak out, but secretly admiring them and giving blood to the movement...

By the end of the class we had told each other things that would have been enough to expel both of us from college and cause our parents to lose their jobs. However, neither of us had any uncomfortable feelings. Somehow, we both knew that we were safe with each other. I could not believe that for two years I had been considering her plain...

---

* *Aleksandr Galich*, translated into English by the author

* * *

We did not talk much about politics later in our friendship. We both *knew* that we shared common feelings and opinions about vitally important issues, and that was enough. Our relationship was very personal. Within a few weeks we told each other all about our lives—our childhoods, our friends, our happy and unhappy romances. It turned out that we lived only a few blocks away from each other, so we often rode home on the same street car. Nina's mother, a professor at our own college, was a friendly and very talkative woman with a PhD in Arabic studies. Hers turned out to be a bad career choice for a woman with a heavy Jewish heritage, so she ended up teaching German in an insignificant college, the Leningrad Institute of Culture. But, had Nina's mother been more successful pursuing her professional ambitions, she would have never landed in our god-forsaken institute, and her only daughter would have never become a student there. I would have never met Nina—and then who knows how my future life would have developed? Unknowingly, Nina became a catalyst that started a chemical chain of events that eventually turned tragic. Which was in no way Nina's fault, even less her intention...

* * *

According to the Halakha, the Jewish religious law, Nina was a "real Jew:" her mother, Rahel Naumovna Bagarat, a granddaughter of a Rabbi, had both of her parents "Jewish" as far as the nationality in their passports was recorded. Ironically, Soviet civil laws had it just the opposite: to authorities, Nina was far more "Russian" than I: her father was a pure-blood Russian, with almost a stereotypical last name Petrov. Moreover, being older than my parents, he had fought in the Great War, received many medals for bravery, and could enjoy veteran's benefits.

In our college, Rahel Naumovna was known as Raisa Nikolayevna (patronymic derived from the name Nikolay, which was as Russian a name as they get). "Easier for the students to pronounce," she used to say—but we all knew that there was more to it... Her last name, per her marriage, was Petrova. Profesor Raisa Nilolayevna Petrova, Russian as her name may sound, was nevertheless obliged to write

"Jewish" in every questioneer, to match her passport. Therefore, it may not be surprising that Nina, who had never experienced anti-semitism personally, was well aware of it. (The knowledge not to be taken for granted; remember Igor?) But how and where she had read all samizdat books and knew by heart such unpopular-with-the-government singer songwriters as Alexandr Galich and Vladimir Vysotsky, continued puzzling me for a long time—until I began to know Nina's friends.

Unlike me, Nina had lived in Leningrad all her life. Having never left her parents' home, she had not experienced the shock of being lost in a new city or the loneliness of having to come home to an empty dark room. She never went through the pain of separating from her child-hood friends. At the time she and I became close, Nina was dating a boy from her high school. She was still hopelessly in love with an earlier boyfriend of hers—but she knew *that* was over. She told me she was going to marry Leonid, a smart and hardworking Jewish guy, quiet as he was; she had decided to get married by the end of college—regard-less...

During that spring, I became a welcome guest in Nina's home, part of her extended family, with Nina closer to me than a sister. Even our birthdays were only a few days apart, except that Nina was a year younger: in spite of her perpetually poor health, she had never missed a school year.

I was no longer alone in Leningrad. Moreover, I was no longer alone in my life.

* * *

"Her last name is Kogan... Lena Kogan... You still think she needs the questioneer?"

Our interviewer nodded understandably. "All right, girls. You'll hear back from us shortly." He did not hand us the questioneer for our classmate, who was sick and therefore could not come to the interview. Nina and I looked at each other. There was no need to say anything.

Before we left, Nina made a subtle gesture pointing to the portrait gallery of the company's leading specialists. One of them had a promi-nent Jewish face; it should have served as a good sign, indicating that the company that was interested in hiring us after graduation, did not have strict anti-Jewish policy. The interviewer's reaction to the last name "Kogan" was discouraging.

A few months before college graduation, students began to think seriously about employment. According to the Soviet labor laws, colleges had to find jobs for their graduates—and our college was no different. Where they would place us, was a separate question: no one could guarantee that we would like the job, and students were strongly encouraged to arrange "invitations" from places they wanted to work. At the same time, many employers were out looking for young people to hire.

The place where Nina and I had an interview that day, was known as a "PO Box"—a name given to companies who would not publish their physical address and required security clearance for all employees. Working in a "box" meant greater job security, higher salary—and never leaving the country. Nina was very uncomfortable with "never leaving the country" requirement, but I convinced her that it did not matter: who travels abroad nowadays, anyway? We may just as well enjoy an interesting work and a higher salary; plus, we would be working together. The company had three positions for junior information specialists, and our adviser professor Shlomov, who taught a course with a bizarre name *informatica*, recommended his three best students: Nina, myself, and Lena Kogan.

Later I wondered if Lena deliberately got "sick" on the day of the interview, knowing that it was pointless. Nina and I decided to go. My last name Chernetsky was ambiguous, and I had "Russian" as my nationality in my passport. Anna Andreyevna Chernetsky could be considered a Russian, if one chose to look at it that way.

The interview went well. The two guys who questioned us repeated several times that my specialization was exactly what they were looking for—what a stroke of luck for their company! Nina was met with neutrality. A week later, however, it was Nina who received a letter with a formal job offer. I never heard from the company, either way.

There were no questions to ask, and Nina threw the letter in the garbage can. "I won't work for them," she said; "not for all the money in the world." I admired Nina. I was not sure how I would have reacted had the job been offered to me.

6

After graduation, I lucked out with my first job. A research assistant in the Saltykov-Shedrin Public Library (known among Russian intellectuals under an affectionate nickname "Saltykovka"), I was the only librarian among engineers and computer programmers—and by far the youngest employee. Indispensable professor Shlomov had arranged my internship in the brand new and experimental *department of library automation*—and I suddenly "fit in," to the point of being offered a position in the largest scientific library in Leningrad. No one else from my graduation class had received such an honor... Our goal was ambitious: developing a strategic plan for automation of the entire library, which, if successful, could serve as a model for other libraries in the country. I almost stopped regretting that I had spent four years at the Library School.

Without realizing it, I was probably living the happiest part of my life. I had made quite a few life-time friends in Leningrad—in addition to numerous buddies to hang out with, without much commitment from either side. My two rooms were a popular party venue for the merry company of recent college graduates, and I remained as close to my former classmates from Akademgorodok (two Tanias and Anyuta, in particular) as the distance allowed. The only upsetting part of my life was the recent emigration of Uncle Victor, my beloved uncle and my father's only sibling.

In spite of what Sofia had said about him, professor Victor Chernetsky once again proved himself to be the man who never abandons his own dreams. By the late 1970s, leaving the country was all but impossible: old-time refuseniks, who had long ago lost their professional positions, began settling in, finding jobs as street cleaners or boiler rooms operators, to avoid accusations of *idleness* (a criminal offence under the Soviet law). Uncle Victor, a senior professor of the Theater Institute Victor Chernetsky, did not want to take any chances, so he pursued the one and only way that was still open: he married an Englishwoman. She had been a doctorate student of Russian language and culture in Leningrad, met my uncle at some social function, and, charmed by his irresistible charisma, fell in love with him. My grandfather embraced her warmly as his daughter-in-law; my father was proud of Victor and happy for him, apparently having no concern that having a brother living in a capitalist country could affect his own job and career. Uncle Victor, however, did not hide from the family that he was still in love with Marina, and that no other woman would ever take her place in his heart, or in his life. It took him a year after the marriage was officiated, to receive permission from authorities to join his wife in London.

I could only guess how Marina was feeling all that time, but she refused to see me. I briefly met her at the airport where the family got together to see my uncle off: marriage or no marriage, his could very well be a one-way ticket. Marina, her eyes full of angry tears, saw no one except her lover. As for my uncle, he was clinging to her and barely said goodbye to his father and Sofia—there was no time or place for me... The pain of losing him, combined with the shock of rejection, was nearly intolerable—so the best I could do was try to forget that I ever used to be close to my uncle... Or had a fantasy that I was close to him...

It took some effort, but I thought I succeeded. Then I married someone I did not love (just like Uncle Victor—although I doubt that I was thinking of him at the time).

Accepting the marriage proposal from Nikolay (Nicknamed Kolya), had been a tough decision. My friends and relatives were encouraging me: libraries in Russia were not known for having young men working there—and the prospect of meeting a guy to marry would become slimmer and slimmer with every passing year. I was already "the last of the Mohicans:" by the time I graduated from college, all my girlfriends were married or about to become so. Mine was the choice of remaining the only unmarried girl among my female friends or marrying whoever was available; with a heavy heart, I chose the latter. My mom, upset by my apparent mismatch with my husband, tried to talk me out—but this time I refused to listen to anything she said.

And so, I got married the weekend before my college graduation. If I was not in love with my husband, I compensated for it by having my dream wedding—with a plush ceremony for a hundred people, two receptions, spectacular dress, two professional photographers, etc., etc. On my first day as a married woman, I defended my diploma, and three days later received my *higher education* certificate.

I had met my husband the previous summer, during the two-months' work at the job corps. Well, that is why girls go to job corps, isn't it?

Making some money while still in college was a good thing in itself—but foregoing vacation at my parents' home, surrounded by childhood friends, was not. However, notwithstanding hard physical work and poor living conditions, job corps all over the country were famous for being the most romantic way for college students to spend the summer—and giving them opportunities to find love mates; so that is why Irina and I went there. (Nina could not join us—she suffered from poor health, which at our young age we had trouble understanding.) And that is what I got—Kolya Tynenko (Russian mother, Ukrainian father—all was well, except subtle antisemitism on his father's side of the family—but I could easily ignore it). Irina ended up marrying her high school sweetheart, even though at the job corps she had dated someone else.

At twenty-six, Kolya was still a year before graduating college. Some of that delay could be explained by his past service in the army—but then, of course, he must have wasted a few years working, instead of going straight to school—something that I was embarrassed to tell my friends. In our Institute of Culture, he studied music: he played the piano and clarinet—and, in my opinion, was especially good at the latter. Like me, he liked classical music; unfortunately, he knew very little about operas, which were my favorites genre in both music and theater. We enjoyed some movies together (although I had to be selective about what I could watch with him; frequently, I would go to a movie with Nina or another girlfriend of mine). Kolya never loved to read and was amazingly ignorant of many things that my friends had known since childhood; his grades in college were mediocre, to say the least. In group conversations, he would often get lost or say something out of the blue that made others embarrassed. He was a terrible dancer, and an awkward lover. With all those faults, he never ran out of energy to make jealousy scenes—even though I did not think I was giving him sufficient reasons. As for the rest of his character traits, I had all the time in the world to find out...

7

My immediate supervisor in Saltykovka, Stanislav Rozov, was a computer programmer. Like everyone in that brand-new department, he had been hired only recently. A man in his mid-forties, Rozov held a *candidate of science* degree (the Russian equivalent of an American Ph.D.) and had extensive experience in writing all kinds of proposals. One could only wonder why a person with such credentials would take a relatively low-paying job in the library. Rozov's explanation sounded plausible: he came to our department to write his *doctorate dissertation*. (Please do not confuse this with the dissertation for a *candidate*; the degree of *doctor of science* is the closest Russian equivalent to an American *post-doc*, with a candidate status, or Ph.D., being a prerequisite.) Our department boss, Mr. Kharetov, however, whispered in everyone's ear a slightly different story: some years ago, Stanislav Rozov had had serious problems with the authorities for criticizing the government, resulting in suspension from research work for nearly two decades.

I always suspected that there was more to the story, so Rozov, despite his receding hairline, small boyish body, and double-lenses eyeglasses, intrigued me. A few years later, when Rozov and I became friends, I had a chance to confirm my intuition. In his company's Communist Party meeting, Rozov had spoken up against Nikita Khrushchev, then the chairman of the Communist Party of the USSR and therefore the head of the Soviet Government. The consequence was six years of imprisonment in a top-security labor camp, where Stanislav served four full years before being released on parole for excellent work and good behavior. (Please, don't confuse Khrushchev's era with the preceding Stalin's times!)

Upon his release from prison, Rozov managed to defend his candidate dissertation, although I am sure it was not easy; in any case, his professional career was seriously compromised. In this situation, the position of a senior consultant in one of the country's leading libraries was a promotion rather than a setback. It had taken Mr. Kharetov lots of effort and a fair amount of personal courage and charisma, to persuade the library leadership to hire a former political prisoner.

The work in the department was mostly unstructured, with creativity and initiative being the main requirements. Working with Rozov was both stimulating and fun. Before I knew it, I began to trust him completely—although I would have never been able to explain, why. Stanislav sounded moderately skeptical about the prospects of our success but knew his part of the job well and was willing to learn things from me that he did not know. Most of the time he related to me more as to a friend than a subordinate, which made me feel flattered. During our frequent tea breaks (oh, those tea breaks in Russian offices!.. how much I miss them!) our conversations often slid from work to various unrelated matters, including subtle (and very mild—it was a workplace, after all) criticism of the Soviet economic and political system. Still, we were nowhere close to having an affair: our relationship, although increasingly pleasant, was of a purely intellectual kind.

When Stanislav spoke about his wife or his friends, his stories were always amusing and entertaining. The person he mentioned most frequently, was his best friend and colleague from Moscow, with a rare name, Lev. (Lev means "lion" in Russian; the name would sound familiar to American readers because of the famous writer Lev Tolstoy—if only, contrary to all phonetic logistics, he would not be called *Leo* by English speakers...)

The more stories I heard about Lev Fedorov (a lucky guy with a purely "Russian" last name), the more he sounded like a fictional character, rather than a real person. Lev shared Stanislav's passion for motorboat travels and camping in the wilderness. (Presumably, he shared his political views as well—but that went without saying.) He had worked as an engineer in various corporate organizations for many years, until he suddenly and unexpectedly for his colleagues abandoned what appeared to have been a very successful career and switched to the just-emerging field of office automation. He explained it by his intention to write a *candidate's dissertation* (read: PhD)—and not for salary increase or to gain a higher position in the company, but for the most unusual reason. Fedorov's goal in life, according to Rozov, was to resign from an official job, leave the city forever, move to a little house in a village, and become a peasant. He had already purchased a small lot of land some hundred kilometers from Moscow and was building a little cabin there. I did not fully understand why one needs a Ph.D. to live in a village, but Rozov explained that the authorities were much more likely to leave you alone for not having an official job, if you had a Ph.D.

Was Fedorov a real person or a product of Stanislav's rich imagination, I didn't know. Someone by that name must have existed, however: the whole department, and Mr. Kharetov most of all, were talking about Fedorov's dissertation. In his Moscow company, abbreviated as INION, Fedorov had apparently achieved what we in Saltykovka were just beginning to plan: a computerized process of managing books, periodicals, and other printed materials. His dissertation was brilliant, and as mystical as its author himself; Rozov became indispensable by the mere fact of knowing that remarkable person...

* * *

It was a fine April morning—when even the city stones were awakening to welcome spring, gray sparrows crazily chirping in still-bare trees, and the very air filled with love, hope, and yearning for change—when Rozov casually asked me if I was interested in a brief business trip to Moscow to take a look at Fedorov's automation project. My subsequent report would help the specialists in our department learn about the INION system and, hopefully, find parts of it that could be adopted for the Saltykovka.

I barely caught my breath. For a junior research assistant with less than a year of work experience, it was a challenging job assignment. More importantly, a trip to Moscow would mean a break from Kolya's never-ending jealousy scenes. (There would inevitably be more when I returned—but I was still at the age when taking one-day-at-a-time was the prevailing attitude.) I would be able to visit Tanika and meet her new husband—not to mention our common classmates from Akademgorodok... I might even see Igor... Igor had recently gotten married, to a girl he met in college (I was dying to see his wife, who managed to compete—and win—with Anyuta)—and that was exactly what would make our meeting safe. And, of course, I would get to meet that mysterious, that legendary man, of whom I had heard so much, but whom I could never imagine as a real person...

* * *

When Lev and I met for the first time in the INION foyer, my immediate feeling was intense disappointment. Fedorov did not look like a Superman, or any kind of romantic hero. He was a man in his mid-forties (Rozov's age, which met the description), of a medium height, dressed very formally in a suit and tie, his slender figure with erect posture made you think of a retired military officer. He was not especially handsome, save for the dark-brown hair, thick and wavy; it was only the next day that I noticed that his brown eyes had a sparkle of humor and laughter, even when he appeared the most serious.

Fedorov greeted me formally and asked to follow him to his office upstairs. Considering myself a friend of his friend, I had been hoping for some informality (much more appropriate in Russian offices than in American ones) and found Fedorov almost rude. During the five days I spent working in Fedorov's office under his direct supervision, however, my feelings changed gradually but drastically. It was a strange, almost physical sensation that I had never experienced before. Trying to analyze it left me confused. Sometimes I thought that I could follow Fedorov anywhere, without ever asking where we were going, and just be happy that he was aware of my presence.

Not daring to fall in love with Lev Fedorov, I fell in love with his city instead. Not that I had not been in Moscow before—but that spring it appeared particularly beautiful, bursting with life, full of sunshine, with wide boulevards, modern buildings, and joy resonating through the spring air—so unlike always cloudy and grim Leningrad. Thoughts of my dark communal apartment with its often-drunk neighbors and always-jealous Kolya, in comparison with Tanika's cozy place where I stayed, intensified my wish that the week would never end... But of course, it did.

On my last day at INION, Lev gave me a chocolate bar as a farewell present, and said something I was completely unprepared for: "Too bad I am so old. I would woo you a little if I were twenty years younger..." He smiled for the first time in a week—not a mocking smile, but a rather sad one. I was about to blur out: "Oh, you are not old at all! I live with a young man, and he is boring and annoying as hell. I would much rather spend time with you, but I am leaving tomorrow. Where have you been all this time?"

Of course, I could not say that. Not even in Russia, which (at least compared to the US) was very, very liberal when it came to office relationships. Still, my answer was rather bold: I asked Fedorov if he could show me a little bit of Moscow on my last evening there. (Not that I really thought I needed a tour guide—but imaging walking next to Lev in the darkening city, breathing the wet evening air, made my heart skip a beat...).

"No, right now I can't." Fedorov did not seem at all surprised, even less embarrassed. "I am working on my dissertation, as you probably know. I have a deadline next month, and the only time I can work on it is at home in the evenings. There is no time in the office, as you might have figured out. But I *will* show you Tallinn."

"Tallinn???"

"There will be a conference on office automation in May, in the Estonian capital. I suppose you should attend: there will be specialists from all over the country, and some of them will have interesting presentations. You can learn a lot there—certainly more than you will ever learn sitting in Saltykovka... Rozov is a smart man and a fine specialist, but he is only one person... And I like Tallinn far better than Moscow. Moscow is crazy. It's too big, too polluted. Tallinn has much more character. I'll show you places that tourists usually miss..."

I was sure that he was just politely brushing me off. Who on earth would send me to the national conference? Even my boss had not been invited. I was almost hurt, thinking that Lev was simply mocking me.

But he was not mocking.

* * *

Two weeks later in the office, when I had returned to my everyday routine and the week in Moscow was beginning to seem like a beautiful dream, I received a phone call inviting me to stop by the office of the library director. That most unusual invitation almost scared me, especially when I caught a strange look from our boss Kharetov, who must have been already informed of the matter. When I shyly walked into the huge reception hall and told the secretary my name, she simply handed me a telegram. The telegram from the Conference Scheduling Committee in Tallinn, addressed to the Director of the Saltykov-Shedrin Public Library, contained a formal invitation for the junior research assistant Anna Andreyevna Chernetsky to attend the all-union conference in Tallinn; the room reservation in one of the city's most luxurious hotels was confirmed. I had to read the telegram several times, to fully understand its meaning. I wished the secretary were not staring at me like that, studying every change in my expression. My face must have changed color several times. If Lev Fedorov had sent me a love letter asking for my hand in marriage, I could not have been more startled. What connections he must have had all over the country to persuade the organizer of the conference in Estonia to send a telegram like that!

The secretary was clearly waiting for an explanation. No one else from our library had been invited to that very prestigious conference, not even the director himself. I mumbled something about having to talk to my boss, and left.

Mr. Kharetov, the head of the Automation Department, was easier to deal with than I had feared. Obviously, he had already seen the telegram and even discussed it with the library director.

"I can see you haven't wasted your time in Moscow," he stated bluntly, "which is good, because we need an *informal* relationship with INION. Unfortunately, there are no funds in the library to finance your trip. However, if you are willing to pay your own expenses, we will let you go, and consider that you are working. You will bring us the Conference handouts, write a report and... well, make more informal connections."

I felt as in a dream, afraid to wake up. I decided that if I can't come up with the necessary sum of money, my parents would certainly help me out.

"I'll go," I said.

8

The week in Tallinn was a fairy tale: it simply could not have been real. The first unrealistic thing was the old city itself, with its gothic architecture and dark narrow streets, preserved almost untouched from the Middle Ages. The luxury hotel where the conference took place on a large square overlooking the walls of the old city; the bright blue sky, quite unusual in the Baltic even in May; friendly Estonian women selling freshly cut roses from dawn to dark; ubiquitous European-style cafés and tiny shops, then completely unknown in Russia; and the conference itself, organized with taste and generosity by hospitable Estonians—all were part of a fairy tale in which I, by the whim of some mysterious wizard, was suddenly supposed to play a role.

Lev was one of the organizers of the conference that had representatives from most of the fifteen republics of the Union. His presentation (of which I understood almost nothing, most likely because I could not take my eyes—or my mind—off the presenter himself) appeared to be the most interesting one; every participant wanted to get a copy. He was the soul of every little group, witty and competent, and everybody wanted his attention. But he preferred to spend most of his time with me, apparently oblivious to the gossip that would undoubtedly start circulating among his colleagues.

He called my hotel room every morning, inviting me to meet him downstairs for breakfast. He sat with me during official lunches. And, as soon as the business part was over, he and I ran away from the conference crowd, walking for hours through the streets of the medieval city, stopping for meals or coffee in small cozy restaurants and talking, talking as if we had known each other forever.

Lev told me about his father, who had spent fifteen years in Stalin's gulag as an "enemy of the people"—and survived due to his extraordinary will for life and belief in ultimate justice. He described his mother, who raised four children alone, constantly fearing arrest, and therefore having to move all the time from place to place. She finally found herself safe as a chief agronomist in a small Siberian kolkhoz, where the family lived through the Great War. Lev was too young to have consistent memories of that period, but he had heard numerous family stories that helped him recreate forgotten details. His criticism of the government was much steeper than what Rozov had ever allowed himself. Lev said more than enough to end his career forever, had I chosen to report him. But he obviously trusted me fully.

He had been married and divorced, with two teenage children, the older one already in college. He had nearly married the second time— but realized that the lady "was not the one for him" and broke the engagement. That failed affair increased his desire to leave the pollution and noise of the city forever and settle somewhere in a quiet village, among woods and fields. Being a man of action, he started working on realization of that dream—and now it was close to coming true. The little log cabin had already been built; all he needed, was to defend the almost-ready dissertation, and then quit the job. He would slowly expand the house, making it bigger to welcome his children who—he was convinced—would happily live with him when not at school.

In turn, I told him about my rushed marriage to Nikolay.

"Just get a divorce before it is too late," he pleaded with me as if asking for a personal favor. "Do not make the mistake I've made; don't have children with someone you don't love! I married my wife because I was afraid of hurting her, and that marriage turned into a disaster not only for her and me, but for the children as well. You are so young, so intelligent... and so beautiful. You don't even understand how precious you are... how happy you could make a man... Do not stay with this guy out of pity!"

It was not exactly out of pity that I had married Nikolay—but I did not say that to Lev. In fact, during those moments I was not thinking of my past fears of remaining an old maid. I wanted to believe every word Lev was saying. Perhaps for the first time in my life, I felt good about myself. Life suddenly grew so big, happiness so reachable—just stretch a hand, and...

Every day during our walks in the old city, Lev bought me a rose—one at a time, so I could replace it the next day with a fresh one. Together we explored old churches and monasteries, climbed spiral staircases to the tops of medieval towers. Lev knew the old Tallinn amazingly well; there seemed to be a legend associated with every street and every building. He paid for my breakfasts, lunches and dinners. And he never crossed the fragile barrier that separates intimate friendship from something closer. He did not even touch my hand.

But I could not forget for a minute that as soon as the conference ended, I would wake up to my old everyday life, which now appeared dull and meaningless. I would almost certainly never see Lev again. Even going to Moscow (provided I could find a reason for that) would not help, for in a few months he would be gone to his village... That week was very, very long. It seemed like half of my life, but it was finally coming to an end.

The closing night of the conference ended with a farewell banquet in a luxurious countryside dacha belonging to some republic's Party official, a personal friend of the conference organizer. And after that—after that there were darkness and emptiness that I did not even dare to think about.

Under any other circumstances I would have been excited to attend a party like that, but when Lev suggested that he and I spend the evening together alone, I could not refuse. We walked the streets of the old town until it started to get dark, and then sat down in a small but expensive restaurant. There were hardly any other guests, the semi-dark room lit with fragrant candles, quiet music playing at the background. A waitress in Estonian national dress brought us champagne and the menu. We drank a little. Lev was talking gently and quietly, but suddenly I stopped understanding what he was saying. The dim light in the restaurant started to fade even more. I felt dizzy and thought that I was about to lose consciousness. In my almost twenty-three years, I had never experienced anything like that, but I managed to understand what it all meant. The man I had been waiting for all my life was not Igor, or Valera. He was right here, sitting across the table from me. I could touch his hand if I dared. In less than twenty-four hours two fast trains would be rushing us away from each other, and everything would be over. Forever.

And then I said—and it was probably the boldest thing I had ever done in my entire life—I said: "I'm not hungry. Can we go to the hotel? Yes, right now. Please, Lev Alexandrovich, please..."

He touched my hand for the first time and looked straight in my eyes:

"Are you sure? I am so old. I am tired. What can I give you?"

"Just tonight," I said. "Just give me tonight. I will never ask for more."

He asked me to marry him the next morning.

I almost laughed internally: he must have been kidding. There was nothing else in the world that I could possibly want more, but it was simply too good to be true. Even at twenty-three, I was not too naive to know that forty-five-year-old department heads do not marry girls who jump into their beds after having known them for just a few days...

* * *

I was awake most of the night on the train, lying on the top bunk bed in a second-class compartment, thinking about everything that had happened during the last twenty-four hours. I was beginning to believe that Lev might have been serious in his marriage proposal. He spoke about practical aspects of our life together as if it was a done deal. He told me I needed to move to Moscow, find a job, and write a dissertation. He understood that I was too young to live permanently in a small village, but most important, the children (our children!) would need to go to a good school. We would spend our summers in the village, in a much bigger house he would build for the family. In winters he would continue his work at INION, at least while I worked on my dissertation.

The most persuasive thing, however, was what Lev had *done,* even more than what he had *said.* His train to Moscow was supposed to leave a few hours earlier than mine to Leningrad. We stayed in the hotel room all morning, talking; Lev knew that he was missing his train, but did not seem to care. Before checking out of the hotel, he called the organizer and chairman of the conference at home and asked him to *find one ticket* for an evening train to Moscow. The chairman was astonished: he was sure that he had taken care of everybody's tickets far in advance.

"Yes, Anatoly," said Lev. "You certainly took care of everything. That was one of the best-organized conferences I had ever attended. But... I did not leave with my train. Why? Well... I wanted to spend a few extra hours with a certain lady... Now, could you please *make* me a ticket for tonight?"

Of course, all the trains to Moscow were sold out for the entire weekend, and poor Anatoly had to literally *make* the ticket, by spending a good two hours of his personal time on the phone, calling different city officials for a reserved ticket...

Lev and I spent our last day in Tallinn wandering around the town, holding hands, and hardly talking at all. One of the few things that Lev said, however, kept sounding in my ears all night:

"If you return to your husband now, after *everything that happened between you and me,* then you will be just an ordinary whore, not the girl I think you are."

He did not need to tell me that. I knew that I would never go back to Kolya. Not even for one more day. Even if I were certain that I would never see Lev again. That chapter of my life was over.

9

Aunt Olia. Olga Petrovna. She was not really a relative of ours, but we called each other relatives to define the closeness of our relationship. She and my father became friends when they, both in their twenties (Olga being a few years younger), were working in the Leningrad Institute of Mathematics after having graduated from Leningrad University. They were members of the same group of friends, young mathematicians who spent time together outside work. (Most of them stayed in touch for the rest of their lives; some ended up in Academgorodok, where Olga was a frequent visitor.)

My father, Andrey Solomonovich Chernetsky, had, as many very talented people, quite a difficult personality. Social and easy-going on a superficial level, he was a loner deep inside, and his people skills were all but absent. My only explanation of his life-time closeness with Olga (without a trace of romance!) is that the latter, a mathematical genius herself, was even more unusual person than my father.

Very outgoing but extremely opinionated, Olga was not the type that attracts Russian men. It must have been a surprise for many of her acquaintances when, already in her late-twenties, she suddenly got married. Her husband Arkady (nickname Arkasha), a talented physicist, had a character even more difficult than Olga herself. The two loved each other dearly and parented two sons—which did not prevent them from fighting and arguing more days than not...

By pure coincidence, it came to pass that Arkady's brother was married to my father's second cousin. When my father and Olga discovered that, they happily announced to the world that they were now relatives—and continued treating each other as such for the rest of their lives. As a true family member, Olga soon became close to my mother, and then—strangely—to me. By the time I graduated from college, Aunt Olia (as I used to call her) was more my girlfriend than my aunt. If nothing else, both of us liked people who don't fit in. With passing years, when the age difference became less significant, Olga and I got even closer.

I learned, for example, that Aunt Olia had never met her biological father, and knew nothing about him. Judging by her patronymic, his name could have been Peter; or maybe it was just the first name that came to her mother's mind when she needed to register her baby daughter. The war separated Olga from her mother, and she ended up being raised by her mother's sister. As an adult, Olga tenderly cared for her aged aunt, but had a very strained relationship with her mother. She never fully explained the reason, but, from bits and pieces, I eventually constructed the picture: Olga's mother, a very strong and probably despotic woman, did not want to accept her daughter the way she was, and tried to change her according to her own ideas. Olga could never forgive that. She made sure that her mother had everything, including money—but that was it.

* * *

It didn't take long for me to realize that the only realistic way to break up with Nikolay was to leave home. My husband tried to hold on to me, alternating pleas, guilt trips, and threats. Aunt Olia, who pronounced him emotionally unstable, became concerned for my physical safety and offered me time-unlimited refuge in her house. Arkady did not even try to conceal his annoyance, but Olga was not a woman who allowed anyone to tell her what to do—not even her beloved husband. So, I spent the following few weeks as Olga's guest, moving from her city apartment to her dacha, and back.

In Aunt Olia's house I found the familiar atmosphere of my parents' home: walls lined with bookshelves; hours-long suppers with different people casually dropping in for an evening tea; conversations that would begin as a small talk, but within a few minutes turn into either somebody's very personal confession or a political discussion, sometimes quite heated.

Aunt Olia was my only "pro-Soviet" friend. She believed sincerely that the socialist system, although it had its obvious faults, was much more humane, kind, and just than the capitalist one. Her husband, as a typical Soviet Jewish intellectual, had quite the opposite opinion. As a result, there was a standard set of "underground literature" in circulation in their house, and their guests felt perfectly safe and at ease scolding the Soviet political and economic system, while the lady of the house never stopped arguing with them.

Despite Aunt Olia's political beliefs (or possibly because of them), she was one of a very few people I met who *openly* spoke against the Soviet system. I knew many who wrote, typed at night on home typewriters, and even distributed (the biggest crime!) so-called "anti-Soviet" literature. It was always dangerous, so people did it secretly. Aunt Olia, who believed in socialism and in its ultimate justice, and had a psychological inability to do anything behind somebody's back, be that a person or a government, spoke out publicly. Her protest was not as drastic as that of Lev Rozov; she did not end up in prison—she simply lost her job and ruined her scientific career.

That is how it happened.

By the time she turned thirty years old, Olga was already a full-time professor of the Leningrad University, and teaching was her life. Her works were cited by the world's leading scientists. She regularly received invitations to international conferences from various foreign countries—and she did travel abroad at the times when very few Soviet citizens did. (She had wisely kept her maiden last name, and that way avoided antisemitic discriminations; her husband Arkady was never allowed abroad—but he was never jealous of his wife: he was proud of her.)

At the age of thirty-five, Olga had her *doctoral dissertation* (read: "post-doc") ready to defend; she was well on the way to more fame and higher positions in the scientific world. And she herself ruined everything in one day, all the while perfectly understanding what she was doing.

One of her students (not a special or a favorite one; just **a** student) applied for emigration to Israel. According to the unwritten rules of the Soviet regime, such a person was supposed to be expelled from the *Komsomol* and then from the university itself (remember Tanika's story?). All classmates of the *applicant* and faculty of his department were expected to publicly condemn "the traitor." It was merely a formal procedure, and often the prosecutors went for a drink together with the condemned after such a meeting. Olga's student, whose strongest desire was to join his older brother in Israel, needed membership in Komsomol, as Arkady phrased it, "as much as a fish needs an umbrella". Olga undoubtedly understood that as well as her husband. The problem was that she disagreed with the very idea of ostracizing a person as a form of punishment; nor did she believe that anyone should be punished for the desire to leave the country. She considered it her moral duty to explain that to her students, no matter what's the cost...

When it was Olga's turn to speak at the meeting of the Komsomol Bureau, instead of repeating the words of condemnation and contempt for the "traitor of our motherland," she said something totally different. She said what she *believed* in, not what she was *expected* to say. She said that she was profoundly sorry for her student, because there was no greater tragedy than leaving one's motherland. She confirmed that the student had suffered many hardships after his older brother emigrated to Israel; her student was not strong enough to keep fighting and successfully continue studying at the university at the same time. The society acted as if it was punishing him for having the "wrong" brother, which was outright unfair. Olga's point was that the young man should be pitied, not punished.

It doesn't seem like a big deal, does it? In the 1930s, having said something like that, a person would have ended up in prison camps for twenty years, and her entire family disappear. In 1970s, Olia merely lost her job. And her career. And she was not at all naïve—she knew it would happen. She came home that night, announcing to her husband:

"It's over, Arkasha. I am not going to Germany. No, not just next month. Probably never. I've just told them what I think about them..."

But she never blamed the system. She blamed individual people.

For a year Olga was without a job. As in the case with my father, the disaster was not financial (Arcady made enough money to support the family)—but moral and emotional. Olga continued working at home, reading mathematical journals and writing articles that no Soviet journal dared to publish. When the weather allowed it, she would work passionately in her dacha, taking care of plants as she used to take care of students. In winter, she would knit dresses for all her female friends. She spent hours each week making humiliating phone calls and pulling whatever few strings she had left, but no college dared to hire her.

At last (per the personal request of some VIP), Olga was offered a half-time position as a senior research assistant in the university's Department of Economics. It was better than nothing: some extra money for the family and, most importantly, an official status that allowed Olga to continue working on her dissertation. But she seemed to be banned from teaching forever—and without teaching she could never feel a complete person...

The role that my friend Olga, my Aunt Olia, played in my life cannot be overestimated. But it is not the main reason I've spent so much time writing about her. To me, her life represents one of the many faces of my country—and the most beautiful one. Olga's life is even more inseparable from the history of the Soviet Union because she did not outlive it... But that is another story.

The year is 1981—and we are all alive, stubborn, hopeful, boldly swimming against the current—by the mercy of God unaware of what the future shall bring us...

Chapter Three
Imprisoned

1

THERE WAS NO TELEPHONE IN Aunt Olga's house, so until it was safe for me to return home, my daily phone calls with Lev had to happen in the office. Trying to compensate for the lack of privacy, I never called him by his name. Rozov, of course, heard most of my conversations, but said nothing—at least for now; understanding that he must have figured out who my daily caller was, I nevertheless hoped that he would keep his guesses to himself. I had no desire to discuss my love with anyone; even Nina was not privy to that part of my life.

In early June, I took a weekend trip to Moscow, this time staying in Lev's apartment (*my* future apartment, as he kept stressing), and had a chance to meet his elderly aunt who lived with him. That old lady, whom both he and I called Aunt Katia, will play such an important role in this story that I should say a few words about her.

Aunt Katia was a childless widow of a high-ranking party functionary. Naturally, she had never heard any songs of Galich or Vysotsky, never read any underground literature, and was convinced that Solzhenitsyn should have been imprisoned for life rather than merely kicked out of the country; in short, she was an adamant supporter of everything Soviet, one of the pillars of the system. Aunt Katia was only in her early seventies, but already suffering from severe diabetes that she had no desire to control. Lev had moved in with her after his divorce, even though she apparently had a very strained relationship with his mother, her only sister. Needless to say, when I first met Aunt Katia, I was almost as much in love with her as with her nephew; I had no doubt that she and I would become good friends. That was one of many dreams that was to crash mercilessly. It was not long until I started seeing Lev's aunt as the most self-centered person I had ever met.

That weekend in early June was a continuation of the fairy tale that started in Tallinn, and I could not fathom that the future could bring us anything but overwhelming, breathtaking happiness. Two weeks later, Lev came to Leningrad for my birthday, and we were desperately searching through the city for a restaurant that could be compared with the one in Tallinn—with little luck. We finally settled on a very formal (and a very expensive) place inside the Peter Paul Fortress. Since I had been born not far from it, there was a symbolism in having a birthday dinner there—and celebrating it with my future husband.

* * *

The first blow came unexpectedly. It was a bright sunny day at the end of June, one of the first days of the short Leningrad summer when everyone wishes to escape a stuffy office and be outside, makes plans for the coming weekend, looks at the clock, talks of upcoming vacations—in short, a day when no work gets done. I don't remember how Rozov pulled me into the conversation about Lev Fedorov. It almost certainly started innocently, and I hoped Stanislav had not figured out my true relationship with his friend. Naïve wish: Rozov was certain that something was going on, and must have decided to put me to a test.

He could consider his experiment a complete success when my face turned gray at his matter-of-fact phrase:

"By the way, Fedorov's third wife..."

"What, was he married more than once?" I asked, my lips barely moving. I was so shocked that I heard almost nothing of Rozov's story about some scandalous affair that Lev had had with his coworker, followed by an even more scandalous divorce only a few months ago. I found an excuse to leave the office, and walked around the city like a zombie, trying to understand what I was to do now.

Lev had told me about only one marriage, the one he had entered as a young boy just demobilized from the army, where he was trapped for nearly two decades, out of fear to hurt his children. In Tallinn, he briefly mentioned an affair that had almost led to another marriage, but that he recognized just in time as a mistake. But three wives? Was it possible that Rozov lied, or invented the story to see how I would react? That would be the best of all explanations; yes, I would lose

Rozov as a trusted friend—but what was that loss in comparison with losing Lev?...

Unfortunately, some subconscious intuition, some sixth feeling, was telling me that Rozov had not lied... But why did he say that? To see my reaction and confirm his suspicion regarding my affair with his friend? Or maybe... maybe to warn me to be careful, to stay away from that man, before it was too late?..

I wandered the city streets until late evening—so late that the sun had almost set. I needed to create a new image of Lev Fedorov, the man I could still love and trust. And during all those hours one painful memory haunted me: Lev and I in the Church of the Dome in Tallinn, on our last day there, visiting what was believed to be the grave of the legendary Don Giovanni, and Lev's eyes shining when he told me about all the women Don Giovanni had seduced. Was he Lev's hero? Maybe Lev had not been sincere with me at all, but was just enjoying the affair, almost believing, as a good actor, in the role he had chosen to play?

I came home, exhausted more morally than physically, desperately wanting to call Lev in Moscow, while realizing that a long-distance phone conversation would be of no help.

And suddenly I understood something very important. It did not matter anymore what kind of person Lev Fedorov was: I simply could not stop loving him. No matter what else he might have done. Regardless of what may have happened in his life, he was infinitely better than any man I had ever met. I knew I would forgive him anything... As long as... as long as he was sincere in his words of love to me. The most unbearable thought was that Lev might have not really been in love. There was no proof of that so far, but what if he was just playing, like Don Giovanni?

I walked around the room like a wild animal in a cage. A lioness trapped in a floating zoo, from which there was no escape. No friend would have been able to help me. I was alone in the entire universe—just me and my pain. And then, the words of a poem started coming into my head. First one verse, then another... It felt as if someone outside me was crying out my pain. Finally, I sat down at the desk and wrote something like this:

Don Giovanni

Many hearts have been broken by you,
Many virgins and wives you seduced
Don Giovanni, my lord,
My beloved, my Only One.
Now my turn has finally come,
But it's harder for me than for them:
My anguish is greater: I know
What awaits me: nothing but shame.

You will leave me as you left them all
As a man shakes an old glove off his hand.
Tell me, why are you lying to me?
Don't you have enough sins on your soul?
I know all that comes at the end,
And I love you in spite of that,
Don Giovanni, my lord,
My beloved, my Only one...

Let me be your concubine, your slave,
Be your servant all days and all nights,
Follow you to the edge of the earth...
But you need me not, that's the worst,
I'm a shadow in your radiant life...

Your best friend will recall with a grin
All the women who died for you,
Laughing as my face's turning gray.
But I love you even more this way,
So why lie to me?—it's another sin
I've sinned too—so we better pray,
Don Giovanni, my lord,
My beloved, my Only one...

I know all that awaits me soon:
Endless nights of despair and tears,
Endless hours of praying in vain.

But I care no more: I am yours.
I am ready to take all the pain.
That's my body, and here's my soul,
Don Giovanni, my lord,
My beloved, my Only one...

My brother won't forgive me my fall,
My mother will forget my name,
God will hear no prayers at all:
I will go directly to Hell,
Where eternal darkness is filled
With cries of unbearable pain.
And that's where we'll meet again,
Don Giovanni, my lord,
My beloved, my Only one...

I wrote the last verse and put the pen down. A short June night was over. The sky over distant roofs was turning bluish-pink. It was absolutely quiet, almost unreal—no street cars, no voices, no sounds of steps on sidewalks. And I finally felt that I might be able to fall asleep...

2

It was an unusually hot summer in Leningrad: my two sunny rooms at the top floor turned into an oven; at night the thick stone walls of the hundred-year-old building radiated the heat they had stored during the day. The air in the rooms was warm and thick, filled with industrial exhaust of the big city and sweltering vapors from the Baltic Sea. My bed sheets felt like they had been warmed with a hot water bottle, and became covered with my sweat even before I lay down. Sleeping was impossible. And my vacation was still two weeks away.

Kharetov finally took pity on me and allowed me to work at Aunt Olia's dacha. I escaped to the coolness of a small wooden cottage protected from the merciless sun by tall trees and, indeed, worked there for two or three days (or, rather, attempted to work, without much success). Then I moved to another dacha: a log cabin in a tiny village in the woods, some sixty miles from Moscow.

It was a fascinating place, at least in summer. Branches of birch trees formed a canopy over the roofs of the two dozen village houses, their green lace providing soothing coolness. The big lawn, covered with bright green grass mixed with colorful wild flowers, served as the village main square; snow-white goats slowly walked around it, thoughtfully chewing grass and meditating under the blue sky.

Our cabin stood at the very edge of the village, backed by woods and facing a picturesque round pond. The pond's water was warm as fresh hot milk, and white lilies slowly floated on its surface. In the evenings, merry frogs filled the air with their bizarre symphony.

The woods surrounding the village were as beautiful as summer woods in mid-Russia could possibly be. Above sunny green lawns full of flowers, buzzing of bees and grasshoppers filled the air. In the dark shady groves of pine trees and lighter groves of slender birch trees, birds sang their endless love songs. Mud roads that were impassable only a couple of months ago turned into a green carpet, inviting you to walk on them forever and ever, as far as the woods stretched...

It was the real, native Russia, the country I had instinctively loved and known from nineteenth-century paintings and poems. It was a place in the middle of nowhere, the next closest village being an hour's walk away. In the opposite direction, you could reach the main road where several times a day a bus passed on its way to the district town.

In the small cabin between the woods and the pond, Lev and I worked on our respective projects: Lev polishing his dissertation, me presumably writing a section of the Technical Proposal for the automation of the Saltykov-Shedrin Public Library. My work was done before the first week was over—and it certainly was a far better proposal than I could have ever written on my own. As for Lev's dissertation, he did not worry too much about it: he had a full three months to finish it, and by his estimate, only a few weeks' worth of work.

Lev had no problem explaining his two other marriages to me. Some details sounded different from the way Rozov had presented them, but that did not surprise me. Lev was upset that I had heard it from someone else: he would have told me himself as soon as he had a chance. And after all, he did not think that it was such a big deal anyway. Nevertheless, he loved the *Don Giovanni* poem, and kept asking me to read it again and again. And I was happy as I had never been before...

We went for long walks in the woods. The scenery was different every time, depending on the direction Lev chose. Once we hiked to a marsh, all covered with tall cane grass. Another time we traveled through endless fields, picking up huge bunches of daisies. A couple of times we visited the nearby village to buy freshly baked bread in its only grocery store. Peasant women, our neighbors, sold us goat milk and vegetables from their gardens. Lev cooked simple but delicious meals on a small electric stove and fetched ice-cold water from the well. He gave me a tour of his garden, explaining what and where he would plant next summer. There were lots of raspberry bushes and a couple of patches with radishes and scallions, but most of the garden, covered with tall grass, would still require lots of hard work.

We swam in the pond several times a day. In late evenings, when darkness covered the village, we jumped in the water with no swim suits, scaring away frogs who in that late hour considered themselves the sole owners of their small kingdom, and not worrying at all about a late neighbor who might see us naked. Sometimes we made a camp fire in our back yard, looking at the stars above us and talking about our love and happiness. My magic dream that had started in Tallinn was beginning to shape into reality.

We decided that we would get married in the fall, and that I should move to Moscow as soon as Lev found a job for me (we were both confident that it would not take him very long). We would try to have our first child as early as next spring. I could start working on my dissertation as soon as my maternity leave was over (at the baby's age of eighteen months).

Having laid out our plans, we suddenly realized that it was early July. We looked at the calendar, laughed together, and threw away our contraceptives...

3

A break—or rather a pose—in that fairy tale existence came all too soon. None of us wanted it, or was prepared for it—and the fault was all mine. Although, at that point there was little I could have done about it. Lev, nevertheless, did not conceal how upset he was. The problem was that life, indeed, moved too fast. Three months ago, I barely knew of Lev's existence; now I was happily preparing to become the mother of his child.

Still, obligations from my previous life lingered. This time it was an exciting two-week Tania-Anya vacation, the first time when the four of us had agreed to spend it together—as it used to be in high school. Tanyusha's husband, a graduate of a prestigious technical school in Novosibirsk, had arranged for the four of us to spend two weeks in his (i.e. his school's) very exclusive summer camp in the Altai. The highlight of the retreat was an eight-day backpacking trip through the mountains.

Lots of planning and organization had been put into those two weeks. It was supposed to be for us, girls—and for us only: the husbands would stay behind. Anyuta, the only one of us with a one-year-old child, took great pains to persuade her mother to babysit for two weeks. By early June, everything was arranged: the camp and the hike paid for, the train tickets bought, and we, girls, were super-excited to dive back into our childhood—no husbands, no babies... Somehow each of us understood that it would probably be our last careless summer, combined with an intimate reunion that might never happen again. ...

For some brief moment, I thought of inventing a story and backing out, so that I could stay with Lev instead—but somehow that did not feel right. Moreover, Aunt Olia strongly advised me against doing that. "If Lev were a guy your age, spending two months together could be OK," she said, "but older men do not respect women who hang on to them. Your Lev will get bored and annoyed with you as soon as he realizes that you have no other life except being with him. No matter what he says now, you *must* go away, even if only for a couple of weeks. The less he sees of you, the more he will want you." Could I doubt my Aunt's wisdom? Besides—even though I would not admit it to myself—I was becoming slightly home-sick: I wanted to see my mother.

* * *

My reunion with the girls was full of joy and laughter. The camp site, located at the bottom of the mountains, with a clear-water brook flowing across it, was as perfect as any tented camp could be. We arrived in the evening, just in time for the campfire, with potatoes backed in the coal, plenty of beer, and guys taking turns playing guitar, and everyone singing along. The following days, there were plenty of things to do, from short walks in the mountains (to prepare us for a longer hike) to dancing to the foreign music (often outlawed at formal discos) in the evenings.

Despite that, it was not long before I started feeling surprisingly distant from my girlfriends; unlike them, I had no desire to make new acquaintances. I slept soundly in a sleeping bag placed on the floor of the tent I shared with my three friends, but I always woke up before everyone else, and the spectacular sunrise over the mountains did not inspire its usual awe in me. Was that the beginning of depression? It was too early to tell—and who knew about depression in those days, anyway?

Lev was the only person in the world with whom I wanted to be, and Lev was over two thousand miles away. There was no way of calling him or reaching him. My heart ached almost as if I had lost him forever, and I was already blaming myself for having made the wrong decision. Nevertheless, there were two weeks of camping and backpacking ahead, and another week in Akademgorodok with my parents. Somehow, I needed to survive...

Being close to several big industrial cities, the Altai Mountains themselves are (or at least were back then) surprisingly uninhabited. One could hike there for days and weeks without meeting another human being. The most likely encounter was with a lonely shepherd tending his flock of sheep, or a herd of wide horses of unimaginable beauty.

Things got better for me when the actual hike started. It is possible that I had less time for ruminating over my own feelings—or that rigorous movement and hard work by itself turned out to be therapeutic. Even in my subdued state, I could not help admiring the fascinating beauty of the mountains. The slopes were covered with fast running brooks that invited you to lower your face into crystal clear water and drink, drink until your teeth ached from the cold. Flowers of amazing colors, many of which do not grow anywhere else in the world, were tall and sometimes so numerous that one could barely see the grass.

Our hiking group consisted of nine people, five girls and four guys. The girls were: the two Tanias and Anyuta, then me, and a young woman only a couple of years older than us, who was the instructor and the guide (and who quickly became everyone's friend). Out of the four boys, two were recent graduates and two others entering their last year of studies. Two boys and the instructor brought along guitars, and at night everyone sang around the campfire. We were lucky with the weather: it hardly rained at all. In the afternoons when the sun was the hottest, we bathed in swift rivers, cold as white snow from the mountain summits that had given birth to them. I walked along with everybody, carrying my heavy backpack and feeling surprised and annoyed at getting tired too soon. I attributed my physical weakness to a possible pregnancy, and later found out that my perception was correct.

I hardly spoke to my comrades and tried to be alone at every opportunity. My biggest joy was taking pictures of the breathtaking scenery. At almost every rest stop, I got out a small notebook and wrote a short poem. The verses flowed so freely that I barely had time to put them on paper. I produced nothing as dramatic as Don Giovanni, just some light love songs about a lonely traveler in endless mountains thinking about his lost love:

> *Your name on my dry lips*
> *Feels like drops of cold water...*

The girls found most of my verses quite good, although they had no idea who had inspired them. Was it Kolya, my husband I was in the process of divorcing? No, that was unlikely... Was I involved with someone new? or just dreaming of a perfect love? In spite of our years-long friendship, I could not bring myself to tell the girls about Lev who was, indeed, beginning to seem a beautiful dream rather than a real person of flesh and blood...

* * *

He became more real when I returned to Akademgorodok and my mother told me about several long-distance calls from a man who had not given his name. "It must have been Lev," I thought, fearing that my mother might hear the pounding of my heart. And, indeed, it had been Lev. He called again the very night of my return, reiterating how much he was missing me and how impatient he was about my coming back. Then I gathered my courage and told my mother that I was about to marry a man twenty-two years older than I was. She accepted the news better than I had feared, but was terrified when she realized that Lev and I had spent two weeks together alone in the log cabin. "He will not marry you after that," she said, her face turning pale and her lips tightening. "Why on earth couldn't you have waited?"

I was scared out of my mind that she might ask me if I could be already pregnant. If she had, it would have been very hard for me to lie. Fortunately, she did not bring up that subject.

4

Never in my life had I been on an airplane that flew so slowly. I did not even have my usual anxiety about a possible crash: I feared only that Lev might somehow not be at the airport when I arrived.

But Lev was there. He looked a little stern and even slightly sad, rather than excited—but the change was very subtle. I could not explain what exactly was different about him, except that his right arm was in a cast. Of course, I immediately asked what had happened. He smiled and said that he had helped the police to arrest a criminal. I laughed and did not insist. That was my mistake. Lev rightfully suspected that I did not fully believe him. And he was not someone who forgave anybody that kind of thing.

We came home from the airport. I was thinking of how to tell Lev about my pregnancy and must have acted slightly distant. I knew that he wanted the baby, probably as much as I, but at that moment I was alone with my secret knowledge. A woman is always alone when she first learns that she is pregnant, regardless of her relationship with the baby's father.

Several times during that day I opened my mouth to tell him, but always ended up saying something else. The day was coming to its end, with no special events. We had lunch with Aunt Katia, as before; we made love in the afternoon, as before; we talked about nothing. And then Lev asked the question himself.

"Isn't this what you have wanted?" I asked instead of replying, feeling my face hot and my mouth dry. (Why, why on earth did it have to be that difficult?..)

Lev said nothing. He kissed me gently on the forehead, and we went to bed without making love.

*　*　*

The next morning Lev had some prior social engagement. He had invited me to accompany him—but I thought I would feel awkward being introduced to strange people as his mistress, and preferred to stay home with Aunt Katia.

We hardly spent a few minutes engaged in a small talk, before Aunt Katia blurted, completely out of the blue: "Did Lev tell you how he had broken his arm?" There was a strange expression on her face that I was unable to discern.

I had a vague feeling of an animal being cornered and had no option but repeat the story that Lev had told me at the airport. He went for a swim in the Moscow River in the Kolomenskoye city park. (I knew the place very well. It was one of the best swimming areas in Moscow, close to Lev's house, and we had spent several afternoons there escaping from exhausting city heat.) The part of the park around the beach was almost empty, as it often is on weekday afternoons. Suddenly Lev saw a group of three people: they were fighting, and one of them wore a police uniform. Lev quickly realized that two criminals had attacked the policeman to get his gun. Since possession of guns in Russia was strictly forbidden, the criminals had a strong incentive to succeed, and an even stronger one not to be caught. The few passers-by who could have witnessed the scene hurried to disappear. Lev, however, was not a person who runs away: he came to the policeman's rescue. He attacked the criminals, thus saving the young officer from likely death. Moreover, the two of them managed to detain one of the criminals, while the other one escaped.

As I was repeating the story exactly the way Lev had told me, the horrible feeling that it could not possibly be true, a feeling that I had been suppressing until then, grew stronger and stronger.

"Oh, that's what he told you?" asked the aunt in a mocking tone. "And you believed your hero, of course? Poor silly girl! Oh, well..."

It is hard to describe the pain I felt. Lev was gone—it seemed that he would not come back for years. And I could not figure out why—WHY did he lie to me? Was it to look like a hero so that I would love him more? As if he did not know that I already loved him more than any words could tell... How could I continue to trust him, or even be with him, if he was capable of such lying?

I spent the next few hours in agony.

The most amazing thing that I learned only much later was that out of all tall tales and lies that Lev Fedorov told me during our almost ten-year-long relationship, that story was probably the only true one. Aunt Katia, unlike me, knew her nephew's love for making things up, and reacted logically—except that, had she had a little bit of a heart, she would have kept her distrust to herself.

As for me, I appeared to be correct in my perception that Lev was, indeed, a liar. But I made an unforgivable mistake of letting him see that I doubted his words...

* * *

Lev returned in a few hours, with a very expensive French perfume. I remember feeling awkward—I always felt awkward receiving expensive gifts—but he laughed and said:

"Don't worry, I'll never buy anything that expensive for you again!"

"Why?" I asked, feeling slightly hurt.

"Men only make presents like this to mistresses. Nobody gives them to wives. And you are going to be my wife very soon..."

I felt warm, happy, secure. He simply must have been joking about the story with the policeman and the criminals, and stupid old Aunt Katia could not understand that! I asked about his broken arm again, as casually as I could. Lev frowned a little, and repeated the same story, word for word.

"No, what really happened?" I was getting desperate again. I did no longer care about how he had broken his arm. All I wanted was for him to laugh and say that he had just been joking... I could not, not, not make myself think that he had been lying!

And then I saw Lev getting furious—saw it for the first time. His face changed completely, so that I did not recognize the man I loved in him. That face could scare anyone who looked at it, even if it were the face of a stranger. And then he started saying the most terrible things, words that exceeded my worst possible nightmares.

He said that he had been mistaken about me. I had nothing in common with the girl he had dreamed about, and it was a good thing that he found it out in time. He did not want to repeat his previous family situation of staying at work late at night, just to avoid coming home. Our romance was over: I could go to Leningrad, back to Novosibirsk, or wherever I damn well pleased. He would recognize my child and help me raise him. Provided, of course, that it was indeed *his* child—but how could he be sure? I had been so anxious to get away from him—to the Altai Mountains (did I have a guy waiting for me there?), or possibly it had been a different place, and my mother just covered up for me... In any case, he did not want me in his life, and the sooner I leave the better...

The most logical thing, as I see it now, would have been for me to turn around and leave, get onto the next train to Leningrad, and go directly to Aunt Olia, stay at her dacha for a few days to calm down—and then get on with my life. After all, I could always tell everyone that the baby was Kolya's, and thus save face.

My mother's words, however, kept sounding in my ears: "So, you are already husband and wife? He won't marry you after that... Why, why on earth you couldn't have waited?"

I had already lost the love of my life, Valera, and never completely got over it. I could not afford to go through anything like that again... After what had happened, I was convinced that Lev was my *last* love— how could there ever be anyone else?

I cried. I begged him to forgive me. Of course, I believed every word he had said—but why, why had Aunt Katia played that cruel joke on me?!

I have very little recollection of what happened next, except that, before nightfall, we were again in each other's arms, which was the only thing that mattered.

The next morning, we went back to our village. For the last few days, before my inevitable return to Leningrad.

* * *

We got married in Leningrad in early December. It could have happened sooner if the lady in a district ZAGS (the boring abbreviation of the office that registers marriages, divorces, births, deaths, and so forth) had not required us to wait for three months, "to think well about what we were doing". She referred to our age difference: the standard waiting period required by law was only thirty days. We could have appealed her decision, by just presenting a note from my doctor: pregnant brides were exempt from the rule. But Lev did not show any impatience, and I suddenly decided to be proud. We accepted the three-month wait without arguing.

Those months between our last few days in the village at the end of August, and the December marriage ceremony, were hardly any happier than the day Lev first disowned me in Moscow. I had none of the excitement, even less happiness, expected of a young woman getting married; I just moved from despair to hope, then back to despair, with short breaks of emotional numbness in between. Lev called almost daily—but appeared to "change his mind" with every phone call. If today I was his beloved, he worried about my health and could hardly wait till I finally move in with him, then tomorrow he would tell me that he had been mistaken and asking to call off the wedding and "set him free."

Whatever Lev had been saying, did no longer matter when he suddenly showed up in Leningrad the day before the wedding, acting like a proper bridegroom. I almost forgot that only twenty-four hours before his arrival he announced that he was sick and therefore unable to come.

Rozov was the best man, and Nina my maid of honor. Her husband Leonid, an experienced and skillful amateur photographer, took our pictures. He later said that the one and only time his entire film did not come out, was at our wedding. I am sure it was true (Leonid never lied)—but back then I refused to see a bad omen in that incident.

The ceremony taking place on Saturday morning, I had only one more guest, my long-term friend Lida. She was a medical student, very serious in her studies and a straight "A" (u-ups, sorry, straight "fives")—but it had not occurred to anyone that Lida might prefer to stay in classes (because Russian college students had full day of classes on Saturdays, Sunday being their only day off) and skip my more than modest wedding. Her only regret was a super-short notice, which did not allow her to prepare a proper dress.

It might be unnecessary to mention it—but none of my guests received the wedding invitation until the night before the ceremony. In spite of that, neither Lev not I had any doubt that everyone would be there—classes or no classes.

Many years later in America, I cried bitterly before my wedding to Walter, when people whom I considered my *friends* turned down my invitation because I had given them *only three weeks notice*! (Nobody in Russia had ever invited people to any event earlier than two weeks in advance, one week being the most common.) Little did they know about the concept of true friendship, and what real friends mean to each other...

Even less did I know on the day of what I considered to be my escape from Russia, how much I was losing and how impossible it would be to ever replace the relationships that all my life I had been taking for granted...

5

My baby girl was born in Moscow on April Fool's Day, two weeks prematurely.

The day before her birth, I was hospitalized for extremely high blood pressure, from which I had suffered during most of my pregnancy. The fact that the doctor expected breech birth, did not seem to bother anyone.

Tanika gave me the list of maternity hospitals with the best patient ratings in Moscow, but none of them was in our administrative area, so admission there required pulling some strings. I could hardly believe that Lev, who seemed to know everybody and everywhere, had not made a single phone call attempting to arrange a better hospital for his pregnant wife. He insisted that "all hospitals in Moscow are equally good"—something that I didn't think he believed himself, and that made Tanika outraged.

By then I had lost my will to fight, so I obediently got into the ambulance that picked me up at the ob-gyn office during a routine visit. I used the telephone at the doctor's office to call Lev—and asked him to bring me a change of underwear, some books, and my knitting.

I got the requested book in the evening; knitting was not allowed in the maternity ward, because the medical staff were paranoid about infections. As for underwear, I never had a chance to use it, since that very night, terrified by the atmosphere in the hospital, I went into prolonged labor.

From a dark quiet room full of sleeping women, I was moved to a brightly lit ward, where twice as many women were trashing in their beds, screaming, begging for a drink, or throwing up. Nurses in white robes were walking among them, occasionally taking blood pressure and cleaning up the vomit. They were the ones who decided when a woman was close to giving birth and should be taken away—to the next room with a doctor—and the screams I heard through the thin walls would have made my hair stand on end, if I had been in the position to care about anything besides my own pain.

According to the clock on the wall, many hours had passed, with no one taking interest in me. The night had ended long ago, the sun was high in the sky, many women had been moved to the next room, new ones arrived; the night shift nurses went home, replaced by others— just as stern and indifferent as the early morning ones.

Many years later, I was told that, in my condition (breech pregnancy combined with a high blood pressure), I should have had no labor at all, the baby being delivered by prescheduled C-section. But at that moment all that existed for me was the excruciating pain, enormously heavy head, and unbearable nausea—with some vague hope that soon- er or later it would all be over somehow—either through the birth of the baby or through my death—and the latter appeared an easier and faster option.

Like in a fog, I saw the approaching nurse and felt blood pressure cuff squeezing my arm—and then the nurse stated screaming. Her scream was louder than the collective moaning of a dozen women in the ward—high-pitched and panicked. I did not have the time to understand what was happening, before a few more women in white encircled me and dragged to that very room next door where I had expected to find the Ninth Circle of Hell—if one consider that until then I had been at a lower level.

To my great surprise (if surprise is appropriate here), I heard the women in white calling me "darling", "sweetheart," "good girl," asking me to "please, breath", "please don't die..." I have no idea what they did to my body—except that it was not a C-section (probably too late for that, anyway.) They did do something, however, their clever hands moving fast and in unison with each other—and suddenly the pain subsided. Someone held a baby in front of me—a tiny pale creature, all smothered with blood.

"Who is it?" I heard someone asking.

It was my baby, I had to tell myself. It is the baby I had just given birth to. My baby boy that Lev and I had been waiting for all these months ... But the baby did not have a penis, only a tiny folding between her legs. I was looking at the little body that I knew was my child—and could not find my voice.

"Is it a boy or a girl?" someone repeated with annoyance.

Not a trace of the "darling" or "sweetheart" that sounded so natural only a few minutes ago. Once again, I felt guilty, although I could not define what for—for my pain, for creating so much work for the doctors, for occupying someone else's space, for having taken so long to produce that pale, bloody, and strangely quiet baby.

"A girl", I finally whispered with a great effort—and lost conscious. I did not hear my daughter utter her first cry.

6

Five days later my daughter and I were allowed to go home. We were both pronounced healthy, and there was no reason to continue staying in the hospital. I had shared the room with seven other young mothers but had no one to talk to. Another episode of "not fitting"—the role I had long started taking for granted. Not that it mattered very much: Lev was visiting daily, looking happy, strong, and caring—once again the man I fell in love a year ago. My mother's childhood friend Ella (one of those ladies who called me their "niece," even though we were related not by blood, but by friendship that ran several generations back—a much more sacred tie) arrived from the city of Kalinin (that later regained its ancient name of Tver), three hours of train ride away, just to stand outside my window...

Visitors were never allowed inside maternity wards—for the same ever-present fear of spreading infection; all they could do was to bring small gifts of food to the young moms, and wait for the latter to waive through the window. Nurses and custodians, however, did not mind carrying handwritten notes back and forth—lovely predecessors of cell phones... To this day, I remember the joy I felt seeing Aunt Ella's lovely face down below, after completing a hard task of dragging myself to the window; holding fast onto the windowsill, I waved to her...I could see her lips moving, but could not discern individual words—not that I had any doubt of what she was saying... I don't know who else in my ward had visitors from that far away.

* * *

Lev and I agreed to name the girl Nadia, which is a nickname for *Nadezhda* that in Russian means "hope." I don't think my husband understood the special significance of the name, but for me it meant an awful lot. My daughter's life had to be better than her birth; and I had a big job ahead of me—to earn her forgiveness for having wanted her to be a boy... The poor thing already had the disadvantage of being born to a mother who, at twenty-three, was completely clueless about how to care for babies, the father who was too busy to care—and no grandmother nearby to help...

Tanika, who was pregnant herself, shared all the knowledge she had acquired from reading numerous baby books—but Tanika lived in another part of the city and, in her condition, did not venture far from home, so our interaction occurred exclusively by phone. In addition, Tanika had a young and very caring husband, and even more caring mother-in-law, right there. She helped me with baby clothes, but other than that, understood very little of what I was going through... As for my own mother, in addition to being over two thousand miles away, she understood even less than Tanika.

The local pediatrician's home visits were the highlights of my days; she was a friendly woman, always willing to sit down and chat—but her mildly expressed concern about the baby being yellowish from jaundice did not alert us that something was dangerously wrong. On the eleventh night of Nadia's life, she developed a fever and tremors, so I insisted on calling emergency medical services. The doctor on call who arrived fifteen minutes later, dismissed the fever but pointed out that the jaundice should have been cleared by the end of the first week. He ordered immediate hospitalization, called an ambulance, and left.

It was already after midnight when, holding the bundle of a heavy winter blanket with the sleeping baby inside (the mid-April weather was unusually cold, with northern winds adding chill that made night temperatures fall below freezing), I climbed into the ambulance. I was too anxious about my baby's condition to feel upset that my husband had chosen to stay home and go to bed, as if nothing had happened.

A half an hour later, the ambulance dropped me near the entrance to the Central Children's Hospital—or, more precisely, to the entrance of the park surrounding the hospital. Hundred-year-old trees were still bare, their dark wet branches moving in the wind and stretching far and wide, as if looking for prey to grab; patches of white snow on the ground seemed to provide more light than electric lanterns above our heads.

When the nurse who was showing me the way, ran in front of me so fast that I soon became breathless and almost dropped the baby, I suddenly felt hurt that my husband was not with me. My pain and loneliness grew even stronger when I found myself the only single mom in the emergency room: all other babies were accompanied by both parents. I thought that their fathers had to be at work in the morning just like Lev—but that did not stop them from coming.

It must have taken at least two hours for Nadia to be seen by a doctor and all the paperwork filled. The nurse took the totally awakened and crying baby away from me, and they both disappeared into the part of the hospital where parents were not allowed at night. I was told to come back at nine o'clock in the morning, and the hospital's doors closed behind me.

By the time I found my way through the dark park to the street, it was after three in the morning. I stood in a reasonably well-lit but completely empty street, in an unfamiliar area of the city, hoping for some crazy taxi to come by and thinking that my parents would be terrified if they could see me right now. I had no real fear, only a feeling of dull surprise that my husband could leave me alone in the middle of the night, when finding a taxi in the city was far less likely than running into a bad man. I was thinking about it, however, as if it concerned someone else, feeling almost no cold, hunger, or fatigue. Much worse was the feeling that my daughter's sudden illness might have been my punishment for not appreciating her enough when she was born, and I prayed to God (in whom I did not believe) to forgive me, forgive my husband, forgive the baby—and not to take her away so soon after her birth...

* * *

Nadia spent almost two months in the hospital. The conditions were good: newly renovated rooms for two babies and two mothers, with private bathrooms and hot meals served for the moms three times a day. There was a strict rule that the mothers could (and were expected to) stay with the babies from nine to six daily—but leave exactly at six, without extra reminder. As for the fathers or other family members, they were never allowed inside the baby's' department, under no circumstances—to minimize the chance of infection, I suppose. And no one knew what care the babies received at nights, when moms were gone...

I remember different doctors coming into the room, examining my daughter, talking quietly to each other and avoiding looking in my eyes, as one remembers a nightmare. For the first three weeks, despite all the treatment, Nadia's condition was getting worse. She was on IV fluids twenty-four hours a day and received several blood transfusions, but for a while nothing seemed to work; her bilirubin had reached dangerous levels; her tiny liver appeared to be powerless to fight it.

At the beginning of the fourth week Nadia's leading doctor looked in my eyes for the first time and smiled: "It dropped," she said happily. "Her bilirubin has dropped. Finally. It's a miracle. Maybe, she will somehow pull out of it."

That evening, instead of diving into the subway and going straight home, I stopped in a nearby department store for the first time after Nadia's birth. I needed to do something special, to buy toys and baby clothes, to call somebody, to rush home and tell my husband that our daughter was getting better. But it was Friday, and Lev had gone to the village as usual, till Sunday night. As for Aunt Katia, at best she did not care; at worst (and I strongly suspected the latter) she would not have minded if our baby had died, I go back to Leningrad, and she remained alone with Lev in their large modern apartment.

Once again, I thought how incredibly lonely I was, being married to a man I adored who occupied his proper place in the society, having an interesting job waiting for me in Leningrad, a comfortable place to live, having a baby—being as much "all right" as any young woman could dream of... Except that, at least three nights a week, I had to come home to an empty house, cook special meals for capricious Aunt Katia who took my services for granted—and then sleep in an empty bed, swallowing tears...

But that day there was something different in the air: spring was finally there, with small sticky green leaves making trees look like they were covered with thin green veil, sky deep blue, passers-by dressed nicer than usual, with faces full of hope and friendliness... So, in the department store, I bought two identical rubber toys, funny-looking piglets who squeaked when pressed—one for my daughter Nadia, another one for Nina's one-year-old daughter, Anya, my namesake. I did not know when and how I would go to Leningrad, but it was important to make Nina remain part of my life, and my joy.

When I came home, despite Aunt Katia's protest about wasting money, I dialed Nina's number in Leningrad. Nina was about to leave for a theater, so our conversation was rushed; I managed to notice, however, that her voice was not happy—although that unhappiness was very subtle, and she refused to talk about herself. At the end of the brief chat, we both felt frustrated; there clearly was much more to say than we could squeeze in a few minutes. Nina could not believe that Lev would leave me alone on weekends, while I had to stay in the hospital with the baby; she was particularly astonished when I told her that the baby could have died—she had no idea things were that bad...

7

"You should call your aunt in Kalinin," said Lev. "What's her name, again? Ella? She can come over and help you take care of the baby, if you are so sick... although, I am sure you'll be OK—just take some aspirin and wear a protective mask...

"In any case, I can't sit under your skirt all my life, can I? Now, when the Lady Bug (the affectionate name he had given our daughter) is home, you need to learn how to manage mother's responsibilities. I am managing the man's stuff, you know..."

He started softly, but anger in his voice increased while he was speaking; the last phrase sounded almost like a threat, with a barely concealed fury. Being accustomed to his mood swings and not quite ready to give up, I thought of ways to reason with him—especially regarding having Aunt Ella come all the way from Kalinin (three hours on the train—and that is only one-way, and only if tickets are available—never mind the cost...) And, after all, Aunt Ella, much as she loved me, had a family of her own, plus the garden to care for. But before I had time to come up with anything that could sound even remotely persuasive, I heard the front door slam: Lev left the house for the long weekend, leaving me alone with the baby... no, sorry, with Aunt Katia as well—but the latter only made things worse...

Two weeks ago, Nadia and I had been finally discharged from the hospital. The doctors, especially the pediatric neurologist who did not like the way she moved her eyes and her unusually light sleep, wanted to keep her longer—but I felt that I had had it. Nadia's bilirubin continued falling speedily, so there was no direct danger to her life. As for various psychiatric medications, I could as well give them to her at home. Except, to obtain all that had been prescribed, we had to turn for help to Lev's sister, who worked in the central pharmaceutical dispencary of Moscow: most of the drugs, prescribed or not, were not available to regular mortals...

* * *

That Thursday morning, I had woken up with a high fever and cramps all over my body. I dragged myself out of bed to take care of the baby, feeling dizzy and afraid to faint before my husband returns from work. I knew that he would come home earlier than usual: he always left for the village on Thursday afternoons—and he did not like arriving there after dark. I was sure that he would delay or maybe even cancel his trip when he learned that I was sick.

I appeared to have been totally wrong: Lev did not even try to conceal his annoyance at my ignorance regarding vegetable gardens—not to mention my profound selfishness. The work in the village was urgent. I obviously understood nothing about agriculture: missing one day when planting the harvest may be equal to missing a year. I could very well sleep when the baby was sleeping, there was not that much to do. Of course, I should wear a cotton mask while feeding and changing the baby, to protect her from my germs, but with elementary precautions my illness should not be a problem. Needless to say, there was no such mask in the house, and the bottle of aspirin I found in Aunt Katia's infinite supply of medicines, had expired a year ago.

That night I cried bitterly, not from physical pain caused by the fever—and not even from the fear of falling even sicker and being unable to care for my daughter. Despite all my love for Lev, I could not justify his leaving me alone with the baby for three days, when I was so obviously sick. I knew all too well that planting vegetables in the village was nothing but a hobby. Moscow stores in the early 1980s were full of every imaginable food all year round (it may not have been true in the rest of the country, but we lived in Moscow after all), and Lev was making more than enough money to afford any food our family would ever need.

And he had guts to call me "selfish..."

* * *

Only a few weeks ago I was dreaming of bringing my baby home, having her sleep on the balcony facing the green inner yard, instead of a stuffy hospital room, or strolling the carriage outside, along with other neighborhood moms. Now I hated that summer even more than I had hated my two-month confinement in the hospital. I saw my husband as infrequently as before—and when he was home, he was in the bad mood more often than not. Besides, now Aunt Katia, who was weakening day by day, was also my responsibility—and the latter was never satisfied by the care I provided and had no reservations about complaining to Lev about my "insensitivity to her needs," which made him furious. With the implicit "help" of my own mother (who stayed on top of the things through the long-distance phone calls), Lev nearly succeeded in persuading me that I had no needs of my own—except to always be there for my husband and baby.

142

I might have accepted that as I accepted everything else coming from my husband, if it were not for the motorcycle. Lev had bought it in the fall, claiming, as usual, that it was needed "for the family". The motorcycle, of a beautiful maroon color, had a side carriage that could accommodate one adult passenger (or an adult passenger with a baby in her arms)—or a couple of large suitcases. It required lots of maintenance, which Lev always performed himself, enjoying the process as a boy enjoys playing with a new toy. I thought he loved his motorcycle like a cowboy loves his horse, while I hated it more than I would have hated his mistress. It gave my husband an extra reason to be away from me, and every time he was out riding, I was haunted by the image of a horrific road accident.

At the end of June, Lev finally announced that the village home was ready for Nadia and me—and that I should be prepared to move. I welcomed the change; most importantly, I was hoping that, finally, my husband and I would spend some time together. The previous summer seemed decades away—but good memories of it still lingered.

Two days before the trip, we had our things packed and a taxi ordered, and Lev was in unusually good mood. We knew, of course, that no taxi would venture off the paved road into the forest. We would have to carry the baby, a ten-week supply of food, and all our luggage, for nearly two miles. I did not worry, confident that Lev could solve any problem—but what he proposed made my heart sink: the day before our final departure, he would drive to the cottage alone on the motorcycle and deliver as much stuff as possible. Then the next day we will only have to carry the baby—and ourselves.

Lev left home early in the morning, when Nadia had just woken up and I was fussing around her. I tried to calculate the time it would take him to travel. He would drive about an hour on the paved roads until the turn to Obninsk, the closest district town to the village; then, instead of driving to Obninsk, he would turn the opposite way, and a few minutes later reach the dirt road in the woods. There he would inevitably have to slow down—but how much? It had not rained lately (at least, it had not rained in Moscow), so I expected the forest road to be dry and hard. Nevertheless, if you're gentle on the vehicle, the two-mile ride might take close to an hour. That would make the trip two hours one-way. Once in the cottage, Lev would have to unload the motorcycle, and presumably have some rest. That altogether could not possibly take him more than another two hours. Then two more hours to get back to the city. With all these calculations, I did not expect Lev to be away for more than six hours, probably even less.

It was not yet eight o'clock in the morning when my husband left. At two in the afternoon, I served lunch and was standing at the window impatiently waiting for him to arrive. At three I started getting nervous. At five I became seriously anxious. By seven I had imagined all kinds of horrible accidents that could happen to a lonely man on a motor-cycle. I paced the apartment back and forth, going from the window to the telephone, hoping that the phone would ring, and at the same time fearing that the call would bring awful news... At ten I gave up waiting and called the police, who could not provide me with any information.

Until that day, Nadia had been entirely on breast milk, and I even had some extra to share with another baby. That day she finished her afternoon nursing too soon and was still hungry. Luckily, in prepara-tion for our stay in the village, I had bought a couple of packages of dry baby formula, just in case. During the nine o'clock nursing I had hardly any milk at all, so the formula came very handy. When Nadia woke up at one in the morning, my breast was as dry as if there had never been any milk at all.

Lev called at 1:30 AM, from the train station in Moscow. He said that the mud roads had been impassible, and he literally had to drag the heavy motorcycle through the woods. Once he finally reached the house, he was so exhausted that he needed to sleep for a few hours before starting the trip back. Since the roads were so bad, he decided to leave the motorcycle in the village and therefore had to walk all the way back to the highway. There he waited for over an hour for a pass-ing bus to stop and take him to the Obninsk train station. He had just missed a train to Moscow, and another one was not due for a few more hours...

The following day, when Lev and I walked through the woods to our village, the roads appeared to be perfectly dry and hard, the grass lush and the sun shining—just the way they had been when we, two happy lovers, first arrived at that little paradise exactly a year ago. This time, however, I was walking alone, pushing the expensive imported baby carriage with one hand and carrying my daughter (who had absolutely refused to ride on a bumpy road) in another; my husband, with a back-pack and couple of small duffle bags, was far ahead of me.

8

Our second summer in the village was so different from the first one, that I was beginning to doubt that the previous time had really happened, and was not just imagined by a girl desperately looking for love and happiness. Lev worked all day building a new, bigger house behind our old little cabin. As usual, he insisted that he was doing it "for the family". I did not view it that way at all: I was more than happy with our current modest hut and, given a say (which was of course out of the question), would have preferred that he spend time with me and the baby, especially since we had hardly seen each other during the year before. But Lev wanted to hear nothing about that: for many years he had dreamed of building his own house with his own hands, and that dream seemed to be finally coming true. He was the architect, engineer, and laborer. He made the drawings and the calculations and laid the foundation all by himself. His only aid in building was his sixteen-year-old son Dmitry, who helped for a few hours in the afternoons. At nights Dmitry hung around the village with other vacationing teenagers, and then slept in the attic until past noon the following day.

Once every few days Lev took "time off": he set up a tent in the back yard, far behind the house, and stayed there for twenty-four hours, reading or sleeping. At the same time, he expected meals to be ready for him whenever he got hungry, and all the chores in the house and the garden done, rain or shine. There was no talk of me taking a day off...

So, there I was: the three-month-old baby, who needed to be fed, soothed, and changed (no disposable diapers, mind you—everything had to be washed by hand and dried on the clothes line—pray that it doesn't rain); fetching water from the well; doing laundry (including bed sheets) for Lev, Dmitry, baby Nadia—and preferably for myself (I had not gotten to the point of wearing dirty clothes yet)—all by hand, while remembering to be stingy with water; cooking and serving three hot meals a day, while keeping the hut clean at all times. If it sounds like not enough work, please don't forget to add the garden; that same garden that Lev had shown with such pride to me, his happy bride, only one year ago.

I used to love working at Aunt Olia's land parcel: it was always a creative and fun activity, the main part of which was social interaction with the hostess. I could stop at any time, sit under an apple tree and read a book, go for a walk or for a swim in a nearby river. I had always been looking forward to spending time with Olga at her *dacha*—and beautifying her land was one of the main pleasures not available in the city.

Tending my "own" (well, sorry—my husband's) vegetable garden turned out to be a completely different experience. Lev's being busy full-time with the construction of the new house did not mean that he could allow the garden to go neglected. He had done his share of work in the spring, coming here virtually every weekend to rake, dig and plant. Now it was my turn to take over.

People who have done some serious gardening know very well that caring for a quarter of an acre garden is a full-time job, especially for a person unaccustomed to physical work in the sun. (If you have never done that, please take my word for it!) Vegetable beds needed constant weeding and watering, the water brought manually from the well. Vegetables had to be picked up on time and, if not eaten right away, pickled or marinated for the winter. Berries (that grew in abundance—what a beautiful, mouth-watering, sight!) had to be transferred into jams and other long-lasting preserves. Still, I might have loved working on the land if I could have done it at my own pace—and be praised for small achievements. But as hard as I tried, I could not meet my husband's standards. He was constantly angry with me for disgracing him in front of our neighbors. He could not understand why old semi-literate peasant women had no problems keeping their gardens in perfect order, while his own, college-educated, young and strong wife could not.

He expected leaves and herbs (that could be used as homeopathic medicine) to be gathered in time and dried the correct way. I still remember my husband's fury when I failed to collect flowers from the two lime trees that grew in the garden, three days after he told me to do so. Did I realize that he did not want to have anything to do with a *f-ng spoiled professor's daughter who was so shallow that she had lost all touch with nature?* I realized it very well—and was ready to rush out and pick the damn flowers right away, but, according to Lev, it was too late. I had missed the right stage of blooming and the flowers were not good for medicine any more. That evening my husband spoke to me with such profound contempt mixed with disgust that I could not imagine how he would ever forgive me...

"Meal service" was my only victory. My husband was very demanding, not only expecting an excellent quality and variety of meals (with very limited ingredients to prepare them from), but requiring the food to be ready the minute he walked into the house. Any waiting would have thrown off the tight building schedule he had set for himself. No excuses that the baby had been crying, or that there had not been enough water and I had to go to the well, were ever accepted. Lev got so furious every time he had to wait for his lunch or supper, even for a few minutes, that I finally learned to have it ready by the pre-arranged time and took some special pride in it. I found my own way to be mean: I served lunch and dinner precisely at the hours Lev had set, and if the meal got cold on the table because Lev or Dmitry were late, I would refuse to warm it up. Soon, Lev began to respect that, and started showing up exactly on time. Moreover, he was usually in a good mood during meals, joked with me, and occasionally even complimented me for creativity and timeliness. As for Dmitry, he mostly ate his cold lunch a couple of hours after it had been served, but was advised not to complain.

In any case, Dmitry left after only a couple of weeks, which gave me some relief. Then there were a few days when I had a female guest, the wife of Lev's friend from INION Oleg Gosin. Mentally comparing Marianna with Aunt Olga, I found a lot of alikeness: a scientist with a PhD, a mother of two, a skilled and efficient housewife who at the same time managed to always appear optimistic. I could never reach the closeness with her that had developed with Olga, but I tended to blame myself for that.

The Gosins were the only couple whom Lev would occasionally invite to our house, and whose invitations he never rejected. In short, they were our only family friends. Marianna, twelve years my senior but still much younger than her husband, a decorated World War veteran, expressed little sympathy for my hard work: having grown up in a village, she considered it normal for a woman to work from dawn to dark. "Lev wants exactly the kind of housewife that suits his needs," she used to tell me. "He's already had everything else." "Everything"—

as if I were a thing, not a person... I couldn't imagine failing Lev's expectations. (I had already failed in so many things in my life—I just could not afford any more failures.)

As for Lev's treatment of me, in Marianna's presence he was acting at his best, humorous and charming most of the time—and never raising his voice. Marianna did little work in the garden, and hardly any cooking—but she helped me with the baby. Had she stayed with us longer, that summer might have turned into a completely different experience for me—but she had other vacation plans and left after one week.

During the second part of the summer, there were only three of us—Lev, me, and our baby daughter, who was becoming fussier every day, slept less, and cried more often than before. In spite of that, I had made some progress with the garden (especially making preserves for the winter) and gotten used to fetching water from the well and doing daily laundry. At the same time, I stopped hoping that there would ever be a break, such as hiking together in the woods, or visiting a nearby village, never mind taking a day trip to the Oka River and going boating (something that Lev had been promising all winter).

The most awful days were when Lev took off to run errands. He almost never explained to me what he was doing during his absences or when he was planning to be back. Worst of all, he never gave me any advance warnings. I lived in constant fear of hearing the roar of the motor, then seeing Lev mount his motorcycle and drive away—and that fear was far worse than the fear of his anger or contempt. The loneliness in the little cottage, with no living soul there except the baby, was unbearable. Even worse was my paranoid fear that my husband might get into a terrible road accident and never return.

Strange as it may sound, I was still madly in love with him...

* * *

In spite of my inborn attraction to outdoors, I almost wished for that summer to be over. There was only one thing that made me happy: it was when Lev—always out of the blue—invited me to accompany him on his errands. Those were my only breaks from the hard labor and daily routine, the only opportunity to see the world outside our tiny village. Most importantly, it was also the time of my physical and spiritual reconnection with my husband. Those moments, rare as they were, provided strength for me to carry on...

I can't believe that back then those rare rides did not strike me (or anyone else, for that matter) as insanely dangerous. The open carriage with low sides did not have any seat belts, and no helmet Nadia's size existed, so she wore none. Even a small accident would have caused me fly out of the carriage, together with the baby. A helmet might have saved my life (although it would not have prevented severe disability), but the child would have inevitably been killed.

Even though speed and wind in my face excited me, I considered Lev's driving too adventurous (not that I would have ever said it to him)—but as long as we were together, I could not think of any real danger. As for my husband, I now suspect that he enjoyed risking our lives even more than he enjoyed risking his own. He was a born gambler and childishly admired his own bravery; my veneration increased his self-esteem. At the age of forty-six, he continued pushing his luck in everything he did like a teenage boy, without realizing that one can only push one's luck for so long... Eventually, we would all have to pay a heavy price.

9

Something happened that summer in the village that showed me another aspect of my husband's personality. I had suspected it earlier but underestimated how far he could go. I had mixed feelings about my discovery: partly I admired Lev, but partly I wished that he were not as proficient in that unusual skill. However, many difficult years would pass before I realized that that summer I had only seen the tip of an iceberg.

I hope the reader understands that the following sketch is not just a portrait of Lev Fedorov; it is an important part of my country's portrait. Attractive or ugly?—I am not the one to judge...

The house that Lev was building, like the old one, was made of logs. While most city residents used cheap wooden boards for their dachas, my husband aimed higher: he was not interested in *a dacha*, which would serve mainly as a summer vacation place; he dreamed of a real peasant's home, appropriate for cold snowy winters, like the one he had grown up in Siberia during the Great War. A house of that kind required high-quality, whole, logs. And those were not sold to regular citizens, especially to city dwellers.

Lev knew that probably better than anyone else, but he was not the one to be discouraged by stupid bureaucratic rules, or shortage of supplies. After driving around the neighborhood and talking to different people, he had no trouble finding a local forestry agent who agreed to sell him a few dozen cut logs. There was not enough wood to build even one-third of Lev's dream house, but it was accompanied by official papers confirming that the logs were "legal". Documentation was necessary in case of an inspection, and Lev knew that some inspection would happen sooner or later, no matter how many connections he had in the area. I could never understand how my husband had managed to talk the forester into omitting the number of logs in the voucher (the space was left blank), but the paper had an official stamp—and that made it indispensable. The task of obtaining more logs, and at an affordable price, still remained; but the first step was successfully completed.

Several miles away from our village, there was a tree-felling site where government workers were clearing the ground for some future construction. Lev went over there on his motorcycle and, without much ado, made friends with the guys. As a result, the following Saturday several men in dark blue uniforms appeared at our mini construction site, with a tractor pulling a dozen first-quality tree trunks. After unloading the tractor, the workers stayed all day, working hard at cutting the trunks into neat equal length logs with their gasoline saws. Lev was working with them as an equal, acting as a buddy, joking and carrying on small talk. I understood very well that, at his first slight attempt to act as a boss, the men would leave immediately, taking their gasoline saw along and leaving Lev with all that uncut wood.

The men's presence added work for me: I had to prepare meals for all of them. The day before, Lev had brought a huge piece of pork from the city, and I stewed it, mixed with millet, in a big iron pot. That made a very tasty high-calorie meal, relatively easy to cook. (My American Jewish friends won't appreciate the recipe.) The workers ate lunch outside, sitting on the freshly cut logs. They accompanied their meal with vodka, which Lev had bought in advance. Peeking at them from the window, I noticed with horror that my husband was drinking together with the men, keeping up with their pace. After lunch they requested hot tea, and then continued working for a few more hours without a break, until all the wood was cut. Then they sat down again, and I served them supper. They were eating potatoes with dark rye bread and salt, hard-boiled eggs and scallions, and drinking vodka and laughing, until it got dark.

I had no idea what would happen that night. I knew that Lev had to drink exactly the same amount as the men; missing even one glass would have been interpreted by the workers as "he does not respect us", and he would not get anything from them ever again. I soon found out that I did not need to worry: while Lev's workmates got more and more drunk, my husband remained sober throughout the entire evening. Forty proof vodka seemed to have the same effect on him as a glass of beer would have on another man.

Eventually, when all the workers collapsed one by one on the grass, Lev dragged them into the shed or up the flimsy ladder in the attic, so they could spend their night under a roof—primarily in case of rain. Once again, I thought of how physically strong my husband was: almost all men were taller and heavier than Lev himself. In the morning, he was up at his usual time, not even suffering a hangover, while his workmates were still sound asleep.

The workers left late Sunday morning, having promised to return the following weekend with more logs. So they did, and the entire scenario repeated itself almost exactly. Lev was in a very good mood: he felt understandably happy about having managed to obtain the highest quality construction wood for the price of meals and vodka for five men. He must have been very proud of himself for having been able to talk five adults into not only stealing state property (that never was considered a big deal in Russia), but also and most importantly, spending two Saturdays in a row working for him for virtually no pay. He did have a certain charm about him that made people want to be around him and do things for him; I was not the only one fooled.

As for me, apart from being happy to see my husband in an excellent mood, I had very mixed feelings. I could suddenly see why Lev might have married me: having a beautiful wife the age of his own daughter perfectly suited the image of *I-can-do-it-all* super-guy that he was trying so hard to create. He was determined to make everybody believe in that image, true or not. Most importantly, he wanted to believe in it himself. The latter, strange as it may seem, was not always easy...

10

People who think that women stay with abusive husbands because they have no place to go simply do not understand life. They may hear a woman complaining "I would leave him, if only..." and take her words literally without understanding that she is just daydreaming, often deceiving even herself.

There are a variety of reasons why a woman may choose to stay with a man who mistreats and even abuses her (be it physical or emotional abuse, or both). The main reason is that an abusive man, in fact, is *not always* abusive. There are evenings when he comes home with flowers for her and a loving smile on his face. There are nights when he suddenly turns gentle, affectionate, and makes love to her the way he used to when they were still dating. There are times when he is unexpectedly in a good mood. He jokes and laughs with her, tells funny stories, or plays with their child in a way that would make her friend sigh enviously and think to herself: "what a wonderful father..."

The next day, or even the next hour, his mood changes out of the blue: he becomes grim, angry, critical of everything she does. He starts finding things in the house that are not perfect. He bursts out in a rage of jealousy, because he suddenly remembers that two months ago she came home later than usual, or because she recently bought a sexy dress, or because three days ago a man called her. He can be gone weekend after weekend, leaving her stuck in the house, but when she asks him to watch their child for just one evening, so that *she* can go visit *her* girlfriend, he becomes furious and blames her for being a bad mother. He finds things that he absolutely must do this very evening that will keep him away from home until late. He even suggests that she is looking for an affair (her girlfriend will undoubtedly have single men over!)—and why would a married woman want to go out without her husband anyway? She swallows her tears and forgets the idea, silently promising herself "to leave him as soon as..." The following evening, however, he will come home early and invite her to go for a walk in the park or drive to the river for a swim, as they used to do when they were dating. And then he will cook supper for her as he used to do in their early days, and will talk to her about things that bother him at work, or share stories about his childhood, and then clean the kitchen and sit at her feet in the bedroom while she is singing a lullaby to their child, and look at her with admiration and love...

At night, after they have made love passionately, he will suddenly become furious because she did something slightly differently than before, which is definite proof that she has a lover. In vain, she will try to convince him that she has just read about this thing in a book borrowed from her girlfriend—but he will not believe her (or pretend that he does not believe her). Instead, he will continue finding "proofs" of her adultery: a new perfume, a phone call that she did not explain adequately, a letter that she received last month with male handwriting on the envelope. He will continue to berate her for many hours and will finally leave the bedroom and go to sleep on the couch in the living room. She will spend the rest of her night crying and thinking about the ways she could possibly persuade him that he is gravely wrong. In the morning their toddler will wake up too early, and she will have to get up after a sleepless night, and start dragging herself through the endless day, fearing his return home in the evening and at the same time worrying that he may not come at all.

In a day or two, however, he will apologize. He'll admit that he was foolish and unreasonably jealous, the reason for his jealousy being his overwhelming love for her and his constant fear that she might leave him. And of course, she will repeat all the love words that she has ever said to him, and all the ones he has ever told her, and she will be happy again—for a few hours, or maybe even for a few days, until his next outbreak, which she can neither predict nor prevent.

11

The previous chapter should give you, my reader, a brief summary of my married life. It also might resonate with your own experience—or your friend's experience... Or, if you are lucky, it will not resonate with anything at all.

* * *

Notwithstanding my roller-coaster family life, I was still a social twenty-four-year-old, and I needed interaction with variety of people almost as much as my husband's love. We lived in Moscow, with theaters, museums, art and science exhibits, concerts, private gatherings—Akademgorodok's cultural life, times one hundred; things were happening all over the city—but they could as well have been happening on the Moon... We lived in *Chertanovo*, a relatively new, very green, quiet, comfortable, and boring "sleeping suburb" of the capital. As my dad put it, I was not living in Moscow—but in a place from where one could easily get to Moscow (the nearest subway station was within walking distance from the house)—it only I had freedom to do that... And freedom was exactly what I was lacking. My world consisted of a few neighborhood grocery stores, monthly doctor' checkups for Nadia, a balcony where she could sleep during the day, the bedroom full of books (the one part of Lev's apartment that made it feel like home), the kitchen—and Aunt Katia...

The time when I was hoping to have my husband's aunt as my friend was long gone. She never agreed with me on anything, be it politics, books, music, or raising children (not that she had much experience in the latter...) She was able to turn any conversion around—to stress that the Soviet Union and the socialist system were the best in the world, and that my parents should be jailed for thinking otherwise. She even found ways to praise Stalin and remind that he was the prime reason that our country won the Great War—ideas that nauseated me. She skillfully provoked arguments between Lev and me and appeared to enjoy it when they became heated. She never helped me with the baby (although her presence made it easier for me to leave Nadia alone sleeping while I was doing grocery shopping), but she required special meals to be cooked for her, because of her diabetes (at the same time, she ate all the sweets she could get her hands on). She kept a dozen (not always child-proof) medicine bottles on a low table near her bed, and refused to lock her bedroom door. That last part did not become a problem until Nadia started crawling around and, as all curious babies, grabbing and putting in her mouth everything in sight; I just was supposed to watch my own child—and Nadia had no business coming into her room, in any case... Whatever Lev was thinking deep inside, remained his secret—but on the surface he always supported his aunt.

Aunt Katia's sister, Lev's mother, never visited her—in fact, I still had not met my own mother-in-law. Once a month Aunt Katia's old friend showed up for a courtesy visit, and the neighbor from the first floor would stop by occasionally—but they were the only people I saw in my house, besides Lev. The only exception was the two-three times a year we got together with the Gosins, in our home or in theirs—but they were a strange couple, and Marianna, as much as I tried to like her, never became anything close to a girlfriend.

The reason it was difficult for me to see Tanika (apart from the one-hour subway ride) should be more or less clear from the previous chapter. I knew a few more people (all formerly from Akademgorodok), who currently lived in Moscow and had fairly active social lives; I might have been able to participate in some of their activities, but I was expected to show up with my husband, and Lev had no interest in doing so—neither would he let me go alone. And, even if he hadn't objected, I had no babysitter for Nadia.

Not ready to give up, I started looking at young mothers walking with their baby strollers in our neighborhood. The area between apartment buildings was spacious and very green, with several playgrounds and many benches for people to sit on. When the weather was nice, the benches were occupied by retired old ladies, who sat there for hours gossiping about neighbors and boasting about their grandkids. Young mothers, rocking carriages or supervising their toddlers playing in sandboxes, congregated around the playgrounds. For a while I tried to join them, but eventually I had to give up. They all seemed to have grown up in this very area, had known each other since their childhoods, had husbands their own age who also knew each other, and most importantly, had mothers who baby-sat at night while they and their husbands went out. I felt like a person who showed up at someone else's party without an invitation. I was probably different from those girls for more reasons that that; in any case, the invisible barrier between us seemed impossible to cross.

* * *

In winter, Lev stopped going to the village, so on weekends we occasionally spent at least some time together. My periodic suggestions to get a babysitter and go out or invite someone over to our house, were mostly met with either flat denial or anger, which sometimes turned into prolonged episodes of fury. There were no holidays for us, every work day the same, every weekend like the previous one—except for Lev's changing moods, and my despair about out love and our lives being wasted away. Still, good moments happened occasionally, and I lived in anticipation of those. Plus, the obvious joy in seeing little Nadia growing up kept my *hope* alive. (Remember, *Nadia, Nadezhda*, means *hope* in Russian?)

That wet, cloudy, and snowy Sunday in February started as usual, except that Lev was obviously expecting a phone call. Other than that, he was moderately cheerful and even somewhat affectionate, so I felt almost happy. The call finally came when we had just started lunch. Lev spoke quietly for a few minutes, and then left the house instantly, without explaining where he was going or giving a clue as to when he might be back. I assumed that he would return soon and did not worry too much. However, several hours passed, and he did not come back, or even call. I cooked dinner in an empty kitchen, set the table, and waited. Aunt Katia finally announced that she was hungry, so I served her evening meal. I felt relieved that when Lev returned he and I would be able to eat alone, without his aunt's presence.

Another hour passed, but he did not come, or call. Nadia got her daily bath and went to sleep for the night. I tried to read but could not concentrate on my book. At nine o'clock I finally went to the kitchen and ate my cold supper alone. I was not particularly jealous, thinking that if Lev were having an affair, he would have invented some plausible story. I was getting a little anxious that something might have happened to him, but was mostly pissed that he had again left me alone for an entire Sunday; that fact upset me even more than him not telling me where he was. I realized that he might be testing to see how far he could go and how much more I could accept, and tried to figure out what to say when he returned, without provoking his fury.

When Lev finally came home that night, it was almost 11 PM, and he was cheerful and even friendly. I had to make an effort not to accept his light tone and demanded as calmly as I could that he tell me where he had been. He laughed and answered that it was none of my business. I said that I was his wife and had the right to know. He replied that he had no idea what I was doing all day when he was at work (as if his aunt were not watching my every step)! In any case, he was not the kind of man who sits under his lady's skirt, and reports to her everything he does. I said that in that case, I would like him to buy me a ticket to Novosibirsk tomorrow. He replied: "Fine, no problem," and went to bed in the same good mood. We probably even made love that night.

The next evening when Lev came from work, he handed me a plane ticket for the following weekend.

My parents expected me in the spring and were totally shocked by my impending arrival with the baby in just a few days. Mom said that she was still recovering from a severe case of pneumonia. It was an unusually cold winter in Novosibirsk, and my parents, not having expected any children at their home during the winter months, had neglected to insulate their windows and the balcony door: the apartment was simply too cold for a baby who crawled on the floor. The crib still needed to be bought. In short, it was totally insane for us to arrive at that time of the year and on such a short notice. My mother asked me to be reasonable and exchange my plane ticket for one a few weeks later.

I was ready to be reasonable, but Lev was not. He told me that he was not a boy with whom one could play jokes like that: I had said I wanted to leave, so I might as well leave. However, while talking with my parents, he invented a more plausible story. He told them he was having serious health problems (something that he had never mentioned to me) and INION, his company, had offered him a free voucher to a sanatorium, where he could get some treatment and a necessary rest. He obviously could not possibly leave me alone with the baby for three whole weeks. I was very surprised that he had suddenly become so considerate. And who would take care of Aunt Katia when he was gone? But he had answers to that as well.

The next Saturday Nadia and I were on the plane to Novosibirsk. I was feeling sadness mixed with anxiety and even grief (what if it was the end of my marriage?), and at the same time the excitement of a prisoner who is suddenly granted freedom. I was looking out of the window at the tarmac covered with white snow, at the buildings of the largest airport in the country, at the city that, in spite of all my passionate dreams, had never become my home. Suddenly I thought that I was hallucinating: Lev was walking calmly toward our plane, among parked airplanes, technical service cars, and airport employees, walking as if he belonged to the airport and had all the right in the world to stroll inside the security zone. He stopped across from my window, smiled and waved (he must have calculated beforehand where my seat would be). I waved back, still not believing that even Lev could do such a bold thing.

He continued standing there looking at us, while our flight attendants were explaining the safety rules and checking seat belts. If I had never met Lev before, I would not have had the slightest doubt that he was part of the airport management, possibly even one of the captains. In his fashionable sheepskin coat and fur hat he looked like a polar pilot, strong, handsome and firm, always knowing what he was doing, never afraid of anything, never doubtful, always superior to the petty problems of small people around him. I looked at him with admiration, almost not believing that this radiant man was, indeed, my husband and my child's father.

I could see a flight attendant in uniform approach him, apparently asking who he was and what was he doing inside the security zone. He told her something with a smile, and she left immediately, looking almost embarrassed. Even without being able to hear, I almost precisely figured out their conversation, which Lev confirmed during a later phone call:

"You should know your own management better, miss," he said to the stewardess.

I knew that *that* story was true. And that's why I still loved Lev...

12

For the next few months I lived in an entirely different world. Motherhood could actually be lots of fun, as I had suspected before. The cold weather in Akademgorodok turned to spring a few days after we had arrived. Mama swiftly recovered from her illness, and one of the neighbors provided a crib that her own grandchild had just outgrown. Nadia and I spent half of our daytime outside, watching snow bunks shrinking and turning into narrow fast brooks, where older kids (big enough to walk on their own!) sailed their toy boats. We watched the first grass appearing from under the snow, at the same time as my daughter was trying her first steps. She picked up the first flowers with her tiny hands. Light green sticky baby leaves grew bigger and bigger, gradually filling all the space between the earth and the sky.

Just as in my Moscow neighborhood, there were a dozen young mothers in the yard, supervising babies in carriages or toddlers who had just learned to walk. They chatted, gossiped, exchanged books and cooking recipes, showed each other their knitting, discussed movies and concerts, and visited each other's homes as soon as the sun went down. Only this time I was one of them. They were *my* childhood friends—the girls I had gone to school with or played in this very yard two decades ago.

Maternity leave in Russia had just been extended from fourteen months to twenty, starting two months before the baby was born and ending when the baby reached the age of eighteen months. Young mothers mostly stayed with their own parents, socializing like crazy, while their husbands made a living at work, sometimes in far-away places.

Tanika arrived to Akademgorodok just a few weeks after me; her baby daughter was only a couple of months younger than Nadia, her future best friend during many summers to come. While in Moscow Tanika and I communicated primarily by phone, here we were inseparable again—as if it was our own childhood that returned while both of us became young mothers. We would call each other each morning, meet outside with our children, and frequently end the day going to a concert or a movie together, often accompanied by Anyuta, Tanyusha, and occasionally other young moms.

For the first time since I had left the maternity hospital in Moscow, I was able to see a doctor. She found several health problems, including severe anemia. (If someone needed a sanatorium, it was me, rather than my husband.) My treatment, in addition to daily vitamin shots and rather unpleasant procedures related to genecology, included weekly sessions in the local swimming pool (not to be taken for granted: swimming pools, even in Akademgorodok, were available only to privileged people—or per the doctor's order...). With the help of my neighbor and a former childhood friend who worked in the Novosibirsk University, I could join a group of students who studied French—the language I had begun learning years ago as a future musketeer in Club Victoria, and that I never before had a chance to master.

My mother was still maintaining an open house. As in my childhood, people casually stopped by for weekday suppers; on weekends, we often had "themed" parties with up to twenty-five guests at a time. As before, the hostess and guests discussed unpublished books, watched slides of paintings by artists unknown—or even "forbidden"—in the Soviet Union, read poetry that made fun of the Soviet system, criticized our government, praised life in the West—all accompanied by huge quantities of hot fragrant tea and rich assortment of home-baked pies. (My father, who did not like big gatherings in our relatively small apartment, preferred to spend the time walking in the woods and thinking about his math problems—so he was rarely present.)

As before, my parents' best friend Yurivanych was often the organizer and informal leader of the evenings. He had an amazing ability to "discover" and befriend interesting people, and always brought them to our house. One of the most surprising guests was my ex college adviser Professor Shlomov: it turned out that he and Yurivanych were old-time friends. The professor was charming, and fit right in with my parents and their friends. He said that he had always suspected that Anna Chernetsky, whom he had first met as a freshman in the kolkhoz, was somehow related to the family of Yurivanych's best friends he had heard so much about. Don't I remember him mentioning that he had lived in Akademgorodok for over a year in the beginning of his scientific career? I did not remember that—but was immensely pleased when professor Shlomov called Lev Fedorov one of the most respected specialists in the field of office automation in the country—and congratulated me for the excellent choice of husband.

Unfortunately, Yurivanych (whom my readers might remember as the father of my first childhood friend Allochka), like everyone else, occasionally made mistakes—and that time his mistake may have had long-term consequences for many innocent people.

About a year earlier, Yurivanych was giving a lecture on his favorite artist Salvador Dali (then little known in Russia). He had an extensive collection of slides of Dali's paintings, and, being an excellent speaker, his presentations (although mostly advertised informally) became extremely popular far beyond the city of Novosibirsk.

That evening Yurivanych happened to present in one of the Novosibirsk colleges. As it usually happened, a man with a smart and intelligent face approached him at the end of the evening, expressing his admiration and asking a lot of thoughtful and interesting questions. Yurivanych did what he would habitually do in such cases: he invited his new acquaintance first to his own home in Akademgorodok, then to our family's social-political gatherings.

That man, whose name I forgot, had been coming to my mother's parties for nearly a year before he reported to the KGB. Apparently, he was one of the KGB "part-time" informers, with an official teaching job as his main occupation. Fortunately, there was not enough "material" for the KGB to arrest anyone, but Yurivanych was summoned and interrogated several times. The KGB did threaten to detain him, unless he disclosed the names of all his friends who were involved... Etc.

Yurivanych was distressed and frightened. Being kind, readily excitable, and childishly naive, he had never before encountered an evil force that was stronger than him and could easily smash him. After the first interrogation, Yurivanych, who had risked his life an infinite number of times while canoeing unexplored white-water rivers or hiking in uninhabited mountains, was crying like a child in our living room. I am afraid, though, that even the KGB failed to teach that man in his late fifties with the heart of a child, how *not to trust* people.

The story may disappoint some of my readers: no one was ever arrested, and my mother's parties continued as before, although with somewhat reduced audience. The main practical implication of the incident was that Yurivanych was never able to defend his *doctorate dissertation* (remember, a rough equivalent to the American *post-doc*)— never mind that it had been practically ready and had received the highest reviews from his colleagues all over the country.

* * *

Emerged in that new bursting life, it is not surprising that I was feeling as if I was born anew. There were times when the very thought of returning to Lev's Moscow apartment seemed dreadful. However, I was not ready to leave Lev altogether. I couldn't figure out what I would do after my maternity leave was over, but I also feared pity—if not contempt—of my friends and neighbors in Akademgorodok. I decided to take one day at a time and try not to ruminate about the future. Unfortunately, although always remembering that I was married, I missed my husband very little. And he must have somehow sensed it.

Lev called regularly, every two to three days. One fine day he announced—out of the blue, as my parents viewed it—that he had decided to file for divorce. Since there was no point in my returning to Moscow, he would like to know where to ship my things—to Leningrad, or to Siberia? I calmly answered that I would think about it and let him know—and hung up without further questions. While my shocked mother was expressing admiration of my courage and self-control, I was imagining Lev's disappointment on the other end of the line. I was thinking how desperately he must have been hoping to hear me cry and beg him to explain what I had done wrong and plead with him to forgive me. Instead he met my complete indifference—poor thing!

I was feeling good for a while, until it suddenly dawned on me that my husband might have been serious. Instantly I felt dizzy and nauseous, and the world turned dark, empty and cold. But I forbade myself to think that way, and soon came back to my senses. I was right: in less than two weeks, Lev called back demanding my immediate return *home*. He said that he missed us too much and was tired of being a married man without a wife.

I must admit that I felt some kind of relief. However, I had to finish my medical treatment, as well as the French course. There were also a couple of parties coming up, the most important of them being my own twenty-fifth birthday, an event my family and friends had been preparing for with enthusiasm. There was a certain symbolism in celebrating my Big Birthday in the town where I had grown up, surrounded by people I knew most of my life.

And so, there was a grand party, with chilled campaign, music, dancing till after midnight, lots of beautiful gifts, and an insane amount of food—happening on one of the longest days of the year (although there were no white nights in Siberia, the sun setting as early as ten o'clock at night). Nadia, tenderly cared for by her grandmother, in her beautiful laced dress, Chernetsky large blue eyes, and darkish curly hair inherited from her father, charmed everyone. The day was pleasantly warm, the sky brightly blue, a light wind moving gently through the house, bringing sounds of birds' songs from the canopies of lush green right outside our windows, and intensifying the fragrance of many flower bouquets that filled our two-bedroom apartment...

Nearly half of my former classmates were there, including Igor Scheichman who had arrived from Moscow with his new wife, breathtakingly beautiful but cold like the Snow Queen. Allochka Kotova, Yurivanych's daughter, could not attend: she was working full-time as a theater artist in one of the smaller cities in Siberia, and was busy preparing a new production. Anyuta, who was going through divorce with her son's father and may have felt uncomfortable in Igor's presence, found an excuse to leave early. Which just meant that the following day we, the four musketeers, Tania-Anya of the tenth grade, gathered in her grandparents' garden to continue celebrating my quarter-of-a-century of life, our new adulthood, our old friendship, and the future of our children that we all believed would be wonderfully happy...

And so, despite my mother's persistent encouragements to be a dutiful wife and return to my husband, I managed to procrastinate until mid-August, thus avoiding potential slavery in Lev's village. There were only six weeks left before the end of my maternity leave, so if my husband wanted to have me live in Moscow, he would need to act fast. Whatever my parents were thinking, I knew I would not remain in my husband's custody as an unemployed housewife with no job and no rights, fully dependent on his whim and moods—love or no love...

The day after Nadia and I had returned to Moscow, Lev came home earlier than usual, but furious, screaming at me for a mess in the house and demanding to know why the heck I had come back after he had explicitly told me that he wanted to be left alone. I was standing in the middle of the kitchen, which I had not had the time to clean properly, trying to calm down my crying daughter who had not had an adequate nap because of the jet lag and was probably afraid of the father whom she had forgotten. Somehow, I had to keep on living though this... Or find the strength to break free.

13

...And then there was another New Year, 1984.

As in the famous novel by George Orwell, that year brought a nightmare that none of us could have imagined.

But it also brought some kind of liberation—although not the kind I had been hoping for...

I was not sure whether Lev and I had broken up or not, but we greeted that New Year separately. New Year has always been the most important holiday in Russia—at least as far as I can remember (if you can imagine Christmas and Thanksgiving in the U.S. combined into one holiday, you might come close—but even then, only approximately...) One did not need to be superstitious to believe that the way you spend the night of December thirty-first, will model everything that happens to you throughout the coming year. It was the time of new gala clothes, expensive gifts, magic, surprises, numerous parties for children and adults...

For the first time since I married Lev, I had something resembling a proper New Year party, which was supposed to serve as a good sign. On the other hand, should husband and wife celebrate such a holiday apart from each other?

On my side, I had a "real" party (a lavishly decorated evergreen tree, holiday lights, ice-cold Champaign at midnight, dancing till morning) in my communal apartment in Leningrad—together with Nina, Leonid, and a few of our common friends. (Nadia was there, too—sleeping soundly in the other room, while my mother was celebrating with the family of her childhood friend.) My husband must have spent his New Year night in his Moscow apartment with Aunt Katia, sitting on her couch and watching the holiday TV program—although I would never know for sure.

I tried to persuade myself that it had been me who decided to leave, not Lev who had thrown me out. My twenty-month-long maternity leave ended on October 1, the day Nadia turned eighteen months old.

In theory, she could have gotten a place in the INION day care center (not all companies had their own day care centers, but Lev's one did.) However, that would only have made sense if I had returned to work—and in order for me to be eligible to work in Moscow, my husband had to officially register me as a resident of the capital, using his own apartment as the address. A kind of work permit, known in the Soviet Union as *propiska*.[2] Don't worry if you are still confused; just keep in mind that by registering me in his apartment, Lev would have automatically given me the right to half of it in case he and I ever divorced—and Lev, as you might have figured out by now, did not trust anyone, his own wife including.

Since Lev refused point-blank to even talk about *propiska*, I had no choice but to pick up my daughter and return to Leningrad, to resume my work in Saltykovka. Until the very last minute, I was hoping that my husband would ask me to stay—but he did not. I was not even sure whether he was upset or relieved by my decision—and that was the most painful part.

My coworkers, boss Kharetov in particular, were very surprised to see me back at work in Leningrad. Stanislav Rozov may have been the only person who suspected the truth: at least he did not ask uncomfortable questions. I made some remotely plausible story for everyone else, the major part of which included Aunt Katia, whose permission was necessary for my *propiska*. Since the library did not have its own day care center, and the city-run ones had two-to-three years waiting lists, my only way of working while having a toddler was to persuade my mother to come live with me in Leningrad. She agreed reluctantly, but arrived at our apartment on the same day as Nadia and me.

After all these years, I could not forget my mom's crude interference with Valery—but this time, at least, she was more or less on my side: she considered Lev's behavior despicable and agreed that I had made the right decision. In spite of that, and the very pleasant five months I had recently spent with my parents in Akademgorodok, I could not help thinking that I was exchanging one dependency for another—although certainly a less cruel one. I just had to believe that things would work out. Especially, since I continued to cherish hope that Lev, having realized that I would no longer be his concubine and slave, would change his mind and ask me to come back...

* * *

I spent the fall and most of the winter in Leningrad, wondering if I were still married, or single. Lev called at least weekly, and our phone conversations painfully resembled the ones preceding our marriage two years ago. One week he was apologizing for "having me go through this" and assured of his love and hope that our separation was only temporary; the next week he would ask for divorce, "to make all that nightmare over and done with." Subconsciously, I understood that, in order to stay sane, I should not react to either of his statements—but that was easier said than done. At nights, when nothing distracted me from looking deep inside my soul, I realized again and again that I was still in love with my husband.

With other men, I was more popular than ever: a young married woman has all the attractions of an unmarried girl, plus she is "safe" to court: young—and not so young—men who wanted to date but were not prepared for life-long commitment (including the ones already married), were swarming around me like bees around honey. Had I had any interest in getting a lover, I could have several of them within less than a week. But, as hard as I tried, I could not imagine myself with any other man than Lev. So, I went to movies, concerts, art exhibits, and parties,—but then always reminded my suitors of my motherly duties—and returned home for the night.

Overall, I preferred the company of women much more than that of men; women were safer and more sincere, and I did not need to play any games with them: most of my old-time friends, happy to escape their spouses and children, gladly hang out with me. Nina remained my main emotional supporter and secret-keeper—but Nina deserves a separate story, and this is to come later. Aunt Olga was both mine and my mom's confidant. She came over often and made herself at home, even offered to babysit Nadia in case my mom and I wanted to go out together. She never ran out of multiple advice "that we were stupid not to follow" (which was occasionally annoying), but her presence brightened our lives—the effect she had on most people she felt close to.

14

There is an ancient belief that dead people continue to dwell among us. They can remain loving and protect those whom they cared for in life. But they also can become jealous, envious and even vindictive. I almost began to believe in it myself, after the succession of tragic events of that year had changed our lives forever.

It started with the sudden death of Aunt Katia, at the very end of February, only a week after one of Lev's familiar outbursts "let's get a divorce already and be free of each other!" When my husband called only a few days later, to announce his aunt's passing, he sounded as if he and I were in the midst of the most romantic part of our relationship, about to get married and live happily ever after. I don't know what astonished me more—my husband's unbelievable tenderness, or the death of his seventy-four-year-young aunt, who, although bedridden for the last year, appeared to me as permanent as Lev's violent mood swings or my desperate love for him.

For Lev and me, the weekend of Aunt Katia's funeral turned into a second honeymoon. During the few short morning hours that we spent alone in his empty apartment, Lev pronounced openly what I had been secretly thinking, but had never dared to say aloud:

"Everything will be different for you and me now, without Aunt Katia. She put a lot of pressure on me that caused extra stress. I used to get angrier and more irritable because of her but took it out on you. And she did not like you; you could not have possibly satisfied her, no matter how hard you tried. She kept complaining to me about you, and because I did not dare to get angry with the old sick woman, I got angry at you instead. I don't understand how you could tolerate all of that, with both of us hurting you and you getting no help from anyone. But now we are going to start all over. You can turn Aunt Katia's room into a guest room if you like."

Guest room? I could expect anything from Lev—but him suggesting that we invite guests? Of all the problems that he and I had, his strong opposition to having any company in our house was probably the hardest one for me to deal with... Even when we invited the Gosins, not more often than twice a year, the initiative usually came from me, and I had to put up with endless reproaches for weeks afterwards...

Once or twice I invited my former classmates—but only when Lev was in the village on a long weekend—and even then I had to pray that Aunt Katia would not betray me when he returned...

I walked into the late aunt's room. It had been thoroughly washed and aired to clear the smell of medicine. The big table was covered with a white linen tablecloth set for the funeral repast. It was a nice room, big and sunny, but it filled me with chills when I remembered the horror of two dozen medicine bottles and packages on the bedside table, with the warning labels—KEEP OUT OF REACH OF THE CHILDREN. No matter how much I begged and cried, I could not persuade neither Aunt Katia nor Lev, who always took her side, to make the medicine less accessible. I just had to watch my toddler, they both told me.

It was finally all over. Never again. I stood in the middle of that beautiful room, examining the festive china on the table and wondering if I ever would be able to use the room for anything. I was also thinking that if there were an afterlife, Aunt Katia must undoubtedly be in Hell now...

After the funeral, Lev's relatives stayed for dinner longer than tradition and politeness required. The food was excellent, the atmosphere warm and intimate, and everyone appeared to be having a great time. I was curious to meet my in-laws, most of whom I had never seen before. Lev was reasonably close to his younger brother Sergey, but had almost no contact either with his older siblings or with his other aunts and uncles; Aunt Katia had been a strange exception.

I was amazed by my mother-in-law's speech. I had hardly met her before, since she was not at all close to her late sister (or to her son, for that matter); the only time she visited Aunt Katia after she had moved in with her son, was when the former had become very sick and bedridden. A story that Lev told me shortly after we met, fully explained that coldness.

Aunt Katia's late husband had been a high-ranking government official. A childless couple, they were unusually wealthy and, before they were sent to work abroad, occupied a spacious apartment in a prestigious area of Moscow. When Lev's father, a senior engineer, was arrested in 1938 as an "enemy of the people," his mother, pregnant and with three young children, had to flee their home to avoid being arrested herself. Desperately searching for shelter, she knocked at her sister's door. But Aunt Katia refused to let her sister and nephews in. Sheltering the wife of a political prisoner in her house would have been too risky for her husband's career, and possibly even for his freedom. Aunt Katia gave Lev's mother some money and advised her to leave Moscow on the first available train—advice that the latter had wisdom to follow. That's how the family ended up in Siberia—luckily on their own, rather than under a prison convoy—and in a village, together as a family, instead of a labor camp for the mom and an orphanage for "children of the enemies" for baby Lev and his siblings.

Lev's story, although fitting both Aunt Katia's personality and the cruel times during which it supposedly happened, could very well have been made up. How could anyone forgive that kind of behavior, even from her own sister? I was even more astonished to see tears in my mother-in-law's eyes when she referred to her late sister as "a true communist," and her death as "a huge loss for the Party." When Lev's mother announced that she would miss her sister tremendously, I got close to asking whether the story about Aunt Katia throwing her out on the street with three young children was true. If so, was that her idea of the "true communist's" behavior? But of course, I had enough wisdom to bite my tongue. I did not get another opportunity: Lev's mother and I would never meet again.

* * *

Lev showed up in Leningrad exactly one week later, without any warning. It was the March 8th holiday, International Women's Day, widely celebrated in Russia as well as in most of the world, but for some mysterious reason almost unknown in the United States. Our few guests had just left, and my mother and I were clearing the table. Lev had called in the morning with congratulations, so his personal appearance was the last thing we expected. However, there he was at nine o'clock in the evening, standing in our doorway with two huge bouquets of flowers, one for me and the other for my mother, smiling apologetically and saying: "I came to take you guys home."

He agreed to everything I had been asking for in vain only a few months earlier. I would check out of my Leningrad apartment and he would register me in Moscow immediately. He had already put in an application at the privileged Academy of Science day care for Nadia, and she was guaranteed a spot by next fall. I would have to stay home until then—but starting a new job in the spring and therefore having no summer vacation would be stupid in any case. And this time we would not stay in the village: Nadia was old enough, it was time to show her a different world: we would spend at least a month at the beaches of the Black Sea on the Crimea Peninsular, one of the most desirable vacation destinations in the entire country. Lev would make sure that, upon our return to Moscow, I would have the best professional job my education and expertise allowed.

My mother was shocked by such haste, but my husband responded that he and I had been apart long enough—and that he wanted to wait no longer. The only thing that he had to do before our return, was to buy a car. He did not feel like taking Nadia and me to Moscow by train: there would be too much stuff to take away from the apartment that I was to leave forever. I knew that my "having too many things" was an excuse: driving a new car was a matter of pride for him, a way of asserting his manhood. The motorcycle was only one step toward his goal, and Lev Fedorov was not someone who stopped halfway in pursuing his dreams. I smiled internally at that sign of vanity—and forgave my husband's little fault, like a parent forgives her beloved child.

Money for the car (an unthinkable luxury for most Soviet people) seemed not to be a problem: Aunt Katia had left him enough in her will. Lev had already found exactly what he wanted, a brand new *Niva,* a four-wheel-drive made specifically for muddy country roads. The car would be available within a couple of weeks. Something there made me uncomfortable: why would one have to wait for a brand-new car? If it were a used car, having a wait period would have been understandable. But by that time, I had learned not to ask my husband any questions.

After all, the car was not at all important, and neither was the money he was going to purchase it with. The important thing was that he wanted us back. He came all the way from Moscow to set the date for his wife and his daughter to return *home.*

My life started to look like a fairy tale again. We agreed that Lev would be back in Leningrad in three weeks. By then I would be packed and have all my papers ready. Before leaving the city, Lev and I would go together to Natasha's, my second cousin, birthday party, traditionally held on the last weekend of March. Then everyone would see that we had never broken up!

Lev stayed for two nights and left at five o'clock on Monday morning, to catch the first train back to Moscow. I was half asleep when he kissed me good-bye. I kissed him back but felt too lazy to get up; after all, he could easily fix himself some breakfast. I knew that we would be together in less than three weeks. This time, to live happily ever after...

For the next three years I could not forgive myself for my laziness that gray wet March morning. How much I longed for an opportunity to serve my husband breakfast, or kiss and hug him! That was the last time that year I saw my husband, and much more time would pass before he and I could have breakfast together again...

* * *

Slowly as the time moved, the day finally arrived... The day when Lev would drive to Leningrad, spend one last weekend there with me and Nadia, and on Monday take us away from our communal apartment forever, to a new bright and beautiful life in Moscow.

On Wednesday night we talked on the phone, discussing last-minute preparations; on Thursday morning my husband was supposed to leave for Leningrad. He had already test-driven his brand new *Niva* and was excited as a child who had just received a new toy.

"Do you like beige cars?" he asked proudly, sounding like a happy boy.

I had never thought about the color of our future car, but suddenly thought that I, indeed, preferred beige *Nivas*. Lev mentioned that—in the unlikely case he left later than planned—he might stop in Kalinin (the city that later regained its original ancient name of Tver) and spend a night with Aunt Ella's family.

And then he disappeared.

He had left Moscow, that was clear: he would have called me if his plans had suddenly changed. But he did not call, and neither was he answering the phone in his apartment. I finally called his office in INION but heard what I already knew: Lev Fedorov had taken a few days off and was on his way to Leningrad, to bring his family back home. But he did not come to Leningrad that night; neither did he stop at my aunt's house in Kalinin.

At first my mother and I tried to come up with some explanation that did not involve a tragedy. Maybe, Lev found Tver to be too close to Moscow, and kept driving until he finally stopped for the night in some small motel in the middle of nowhere, with no telephones. On Friday afternoon we were still hoping that the door bell would ring, and Lev would suddenly appear in our living room, as he had done only three weeks ago.

In the late afternoon of the second day, unable to stand the endless waiting, I invented some errands to run and left the house for an hour. It was getting dark when I returned home, but I could see a new beige *Niva* in front of the house, the kind that my husband had just bought. *Nivas* were expensive cars and not very common, and beige was a rare color. My heart jumped into my throat and all the blood flashed to my face. I thought how stupidly hysterical my mother and I had been: of course, Lev had arrived, and nothing bad had happened! There he was right now, upstairs in the living room, playing with laughing Nadia and wondering where I had gone. I lost my breath from sudden happiness, ready to rush upstairs, but for some inexplicable reason, I paused for a second and glanced at the license plate number. In an instant I became so cold and stiff that I could barely move, let alone climb the stairs. The car had a Leningrad number...

Whose cruel joke was that? There had never been any *Nivas* in our poor apartment complex, in all the years I lived there. Why would the one be there on that very night? Parked right next to our entry way, while there were five others in the building? Or at least, why couldn't it be a different color, rather than beige? Was this a sign that Someone was sending me, or simply a bizarre coincidence? In any case, I knew at that moment that my husband would not come that day. He would probably never come—although I could not make myself think about the worst yet.

It took me a good ten minutes to walk up the stairs to the top floor; climbing a mountain with a heavy backpack while I was pregnant had been far easier.

* * *

On Saturday morning, the third day after Lev's disappearance, I finally called his younger brother Sergey, who lived not too far from us in Moscow.

"What do you mean, he has not arrived yet?" my brother-in-law asked, with badly concealed anxiety. "He dropped by my house on Wednesday night, showing off his new car. He was all packed and planned to leave very early Thursday morning. He should have arrived two days ago! He must have gotten into a car accident!"

I said that I had called the police, and no accidents had been reported on Moscow-Leningrad highway. Sergey announced that he would call them himself anyway. And maybe go to Lev's apartment—just in case...

"Otherwise, where the hell can he possibly be?! Now calm down, I'll call you as soon as I find out anything."

It was easy for him to say, "calm down." He was lucky, he was *acting,* while all I could do was passively *wait.* I went back to my room and waited, and waited...

Time stopped. It may have been a few days, or a few months, or a year. My mother took Nadia outside, and I walked around the room like a caged wild animal, desperately wanting to do something, to scream, to run somewhere. My daughter came home, ate her lunch and was put to bed for a nap, cheerfully babbling about "papa coming soon in a big car."

I could not tell how long it had been since I had talked to my brother-in-law. It could not possibly have been the same day; an eternity had passed...

And then he finally called.

I remember the phone ringing in the hallway—and though three families shared the same line, I somehow knew that it was for me.

"Anna," my brother-in-law's voice said, "I have bad news for you..."

I remember how the well-illuminated hallway suddenly turned dark, and the ceiling started slowly moving down, right on my head.

"Is he... dead?" I wanted to ask—but could not utter a sound. And then I heard:

"Lev was arrested by the KGB. They moved him into a criminal prison yesterday: the case is too minor for the KGB. I'll see the investigator on Monday..."

I hardly heard the rest. The lights came back, and the ceiling returned to its place. I think I heard myself laughing.

Will you believe me? That was one of the happiest moments in my life! The terrible uncertainty was over. My husband was alive—and not even wounded! And—whatever his prison term could be, he would come back. Very possibly, there would be no prison term at all. Sergey did not sound particularly concerned.

"Stupid case," he said. "Lev must have been selling our late auntie's jewelry. The old lady had some pretty expensive stuff, so the police understandably want to know where Lev got it from. I hope the old lady left a proper will, so my brother will be able to prove that the junk is his own, not *speculation*. They probably require that the jewels be sold to a government agency—and Lev, of course, was selling them to some private vendor. He may get a fine or a few months in jail, at the very worst. Which will not help his professional career... but will teach him not to get caught the next time.

"Sorry, I could not find out anything else today: everything's closed. The prison clerk gave me the investigator's name, but investigators don't work on Saturdays. I'll see him first thing on Monday morning; then we'll know more. Go to bed now and try to get some sleep. I will call you as soon as..."

I had to wait again: an evening, a day, then the morning of another day. Forty-five hours from now? Forty-two? Or maybe all forty-eight? In any case, that new uncertainty was far more tolerable than the old one. I could try to do something in between, instead of just sitting in my room losing hope every minute. I could kill that evening, for example, by going to my cousin's birthday party. Not much fun, since I had been planning to arrive there with Lev, but still, it would provide some distraction.

Most importantly, I needed to take care of two serious practical matters. I was not worried about having quit my job: I knew that, until the position was filled, Kharetov and Rozov would rehire me. Having checked out of the apartment was a far more serious problem. A passport without a permanent address in it was practically void. Without a valid passport, I was as good as illegal in Russia, not only being unable to get a job, daycare for my child, or medical care, but having no civil rights whatsoever.

Luckily, the bureaucracy worked slowly. When I rushed into the local police department at nine o'clock on Monday morning, my application to check out of the apartment was still sitting in the pile of papers to be signed. The friendly clerk at the reception desk agreed to give me my application back, without asking any questions.

The home phone was tied up all evening: one of our neighbors, Praskovia, as usual was gossiping with her girlfriends. My mother finally lost patience and told her that we were expecting an extremely important call. The neighbor looked very displeased but hung up twenty minutes later. The phone rang almost immediately: it was another one of Praskovia's friends. I knew that this new conversation would last for another hour, and simply lied that Praskovia was not home. "She is always home at this time. Go to her room and check," demanded the lady on the other end of the line. I refused and hung up. I then sat near the phone, guarding it. It finally rang for me. It was Sergey, very annoyed. He had been about to give up, having dialed my phone number ten times in the last two hours.

His news was depressing. Lev appeared to have been trying to sell the gold-dust, which qualified as "foreign currency". That action was legally very different from selling ready-made jewelry. It moved his crime into the category of "state crimes", punishable with much more severity than regular profiteering. The good news was that the investigator appeared friendly. He agreed that people sometimes do stupid things and violate the law unwillingly because of their legal illiteracy. He suggested that Lev's employer write a letter to the district prosecutor, asking that Lev be released on bail. If the prosecutor agrees, Lev's case would look very different in court.

Arriving in court in a prison car under convoy usually means "prison" written on the defendant's forehead; coming on his own, accompanied by an official representative from his company (especially such a well-known and respected company as INION) would almost certainly result in a much lighter sentence.

* * *

While I was falling asleep that night, I suddenly saw Aunt Katia, laughing quietly, her crooked fingers playing with pearl necklaces and diamond rings. The gold-dust was glittering on her dark skirt and on a worn-out carpet under her feet. I shivered and woke from my half-sleep. In reality, I had never seen the late aunt laughing...

15

I got off the train at eight o'clock in the evening. The sun was still high above my head, showing no intention of going down. The big square next to the Moscow Railway Station with a pompous name of the Square of Insurrection (*Ploshad Vosstaniya*) was full of noise, dust, zooming cars, and people with heavy suitcases frantically look-ing for taxis. Peasant women were selling flowers in big bouquets; young people waited for their dates; children pulled their mother's hands, whining for ice cream. Women with shopping bags walked in and out of the small shops that surrounded the square. Buses and trolleys slowly rolled toward their stops and pulled off in a few min-utes, with even more passengers inside; the automatic doors of the city's two major subway stations were opening and closing constant-ly, with crowds of people swallowed and then spit out. In short, it was the part of Leningrad that I hated in some periods of my life, missed at other times, but that was so painfully familiar up to the very last store, to every small kiosk, that I could walk home with my eyes closed. As long as I considered the place where I lived to be my "home..."

I did not remember that it was my twenty-sixth birthday, until I was half-way to the house—walking, instead of trying to squeeze myself into an overcrowded trolley. In the communal apartment on the fourth floor, I was greeted by the dearest and the most unexpected guest: my mother's childhood friend from Kalinin, my beloved Aunt Ella. There were flowers on the table, and the cake in the fridge—and mom said that people kept calling, wanting to stop by... And that, whether I liked it or not, I should call them back and invite them over for tea—after all, everybody wanted to hear about my trip to Moscow, not just my mom and aunt...

I wish my mom could understand that talking about my Moscow experience was the last thing I wanted to do that night—birthday or no birthday. I wanted to forget it all, if only for one evening... Pretend this past year has never happened... Deceive myself that there was a different life somewhere, life outside interrogation offices, courts, talks of prison terms, and interviews with important people who acted as if they could (and even wanted) to help—but at the end did absolutely nothing... Invite my girlfriends for tea, OK—but then try to have a good time...

But no matter how much I wanted to forget, it did not work...

* * *

I remembered my first meeting with Lev's investigator. There were many other meetings to follow, although now I cannot imagine what on earth I was trying to achieve by going over there again and again—except that just sitting close to the man who could see my husband gave me the illusion of some intangible connection with Lev...

The investigator's name was Konev, so later Sergey and I would give him the secret nickname of "Loshadka" (that we used while talking on the phone); both words mean "horse" in Russian. His office, located in an area of Moscow where I had never been before, was not easy to find. I remember walking along a nice wide street, lined with tall trees, new stores, and fruit kiosks. Cheerful women in the kiosks, dressed in white uniform robes, were selling exotic goods: round oranges, miniature models of the sun; small cartons of fresh ripe strawberries smelling of the southern gardens where they had been picked just a day earlier; golden yellow bananas from remote Africa. Other kiosks sold various kinds of ice cream that people were buying and eating as they walked, the sweet milky liquid dripping on their hands...

Women dressed in festive spring coats with colorful silk scarves and high heels strolled in and out of department stores. I could see them through the glass windows picking out clothes, china, or toys for their kids. They came out of stores, bought some fruits or ice cream in a kiosk, and continued on their ways, erect and feminine in their high-heel shoes, carrying their heavy grocery bags as gracefully as their elegant leather purses. Men in shiny fashionable boots, dressed in imported semi-coats, and carrying briefcases, walked with an air of self-importance. They rarely bought groceries, but often stopped at pay phones to call someone who obviously was not in jail...

It was Moscow, beloved by its citizens, admired and cursed throughout the country, causing envy in those who were not lucky enough to live there: the city with exciting jobs, world-class museums, and stores full of wonderful goods and food that most of the country could only dream of.

It was a real, residential Moscow—far from its historical downtown infested by tourists and desperate shoppers from neighboring towns. Moscow, where every remote area was made close to the rest of the city by the web of speedy sparklingly clean subways, like a healthy body is connected by blood vessels into one single organism.

Less than a year ago, I was proud to be one of its privileged dwellers; now I felt as if I had arrived on the moon, where mystical creatures were engaged in some meaningless rituals. How could people buy new clothes? Make superficial phone calls? Leak melting chocolate ice cream off their fingers? Smile?

I was moving among those people as an invisible shade, a being from a different world, a small vessel of grief, despair, and hope mixed together. I stopped once or twice to ask for directions. I did not dare to ask for the district office of the Ministry of Internal Affairs, as if people could guess why I had a business there. I kept asking for the street address, which no one seemed to know.

I finally found a modest brick two-story building, well hidden inside an apartment complex among tall trees, cozy benches and playgrounds. I had to wait in a long gloomy corridor outside the row of closed doors, while Lev's investigator finished his previous appointment. The inside of the building made me think of a prison, except that I could leave any minute, and the ones in prison could not.

The investigator wanted to interrogate me, if I did not mind. No, I did not *have to* answer any of his questions. I did not have to come there and take his precious time, either. He made it clear that if I wanted to learn anything about my husband, I had to talk myself. Expecting some kind of a trap, I tried to be careful with my answers. The questions, however, seemed totally innocent and referred mostly to our family, the property we owned and when and how I had seen my husband for the last time. The investigator was writing down my answers in a thick notebook with a ball-point pen. Sometimes he frowned and flipped a few pages back, apparently in order to compare my answers to the ones Lev had given. In one case our answers must have been so different that the investigator could not hide his surprise.

He wanted to know about the purchase of the car.

Did I know where my husband had gotten the money? Inheritance from his aunt? Did I have any idea how much cash she may have left him?

Obviously, I had no idea.

Ok, what about Lev's previous car? We did have a car before, didn't we?

Yes, but only for a few months: it was only good for asphalt city roads, and performed poorly on the mud ones, especially after rain.

Where did the money for the first car come from?

I did not know; I assumed that Lev had borrowed some from his friends, and probably partly from his aunt. He had also gotten a bonus from his work. In any case, that was a used car, and a much cheaper model than Lev's new *Niva*.

The investigator looked dissatisfied. He didn't seem to believe that I did not know the answers. I suddenly thought that it was probably better if he decided that I was lying: what kind of an image was my husband creating, having so many secrets even from his own wife?

What happened to the old car, then? Had Lev sold it?

No, as far as I knew, he had an accident that totaled the car, although Lev himself was lucky enough not to get injured. Then Lev just received insurance payments, so there was not even a need to sell.

That's when the investigator raised his eyebrows. He flipped a few pages back in Lev's case, and showed me the sales agreement which stated that Lev Fedorov had sold his *Moskwich* for this and that amount of cash to such and such... "Sold a used car for more than its store price," muttered the investigator, although without much reproach. Cars being in a huge deficit, market price was higher than the government one, and all attempts by the authorities to make such profiteering illegal remained fruitless.

I felt terrible. I did not care if the investigator considered me a liar, but it was obviously bad for my husband's case that my answers differed so much from his. And why, for heaven's sake, why, why had Lev lied to me? Had I ever asked anything about his money? Had I ever judged what he was doing?

The investigator was silent for a few minutes, flipping through the pages of the case record, probably deciding what to make of the numerous differences in Lev's and my answers. He lifted his head and looked at me inquisitively for a few seconds. Then he wrote a few more lines at the end of my testimony and asked me to sign. I had read enough literature about imprisonments, arrests, and interrogations to know that I should never sign anything without reading it first. I read the entire thing slowly. The investigator seemed annoyed but did not interrupt me. The last paragraph, the investigator's summary, caused me some discomfort: it was not exactly what I had said. I pointed it out to him, but he shrugged his shoulders.

"Do you want to sign: yes, or no?"

I said that I did want to sign, but I'd like him to change the last paragraph.

"I am not going to change anything," he said calmly, "but, of course, you do not have to sign anything, either. We can just throw your entire testimony away, as if it had never been given. However, I thought that you might want it to be included in the case record. Some things that you said might actually benefit your husband."

"They know how to work," I thought helplessly. "They cannot torture people anymore, so they must have learned some psychology..." I wished I could ask someone's advice, or at least think the situation over and come back later.

"Probably, none of that is important, after all," I finally decided, and reluctantly signed my testimony. I did not want to alienate the investigator. My strongest feeling during the entire interrogation was, *this man has just seen my husband.* He had been sitting in the same room with him, talking to him, watching the expression on his face. I wished I could somehow change places with him, become him, if only for one day; I envied him, and wanted to turn into his shadow to follow him into the prison. I would have signed worse things, just to have that man like me.

"Could you take a note to my husband?" I asked before leaving.

"Oh, of course, no, but I can give him an oral message."

"Not even something simple, like "I love you and I will wait for you?" I could not understand his bureaucratic stubbornness: how could such a note complicate the inquest process?

No, notes were not allowed, period. But the investigator would be happy to convey the message orally.

"Here, I am writing myself a note, and putting it in your husband's file. You see: 'Tell inmate Fedorov that his wife loves him and will wait for him'. Don't worry, I won't forget. It was nice meeting you. Have a good day now."

* * *

A few days later, after having returned home to Leningrad, I got hold of a copy of the Criminal Procedural Code of the Russian Federation and read it from the first page to the last as I had never read any novel. I still remember a paragraph, which stated clearly that a person under interrogation had the right to write down his or her own testimony or make corrections to whatever the interrogator has written. I scolded myself for having gone to the investigator totally unprepared. Well, I would know better next time...

Within a few weeks I studied the Criminal Code as well as the Criminal Procedural Code well enough to be a lawyer. I could not get a copy of the Commentaries to the Criminal Code, though. Those were more strictly guarded.

16

After Lev's arrest, I suddenly started noticing men with young children. Fathers with little boys and girls were walking on the streets, riding in buses and subway trains, hanging around playgrounds. I heard the toddlers' excited screams: "Papa! Papa, look!" and watched fathers smiling back, fixing their offspring's clothes, wiping their noses, and then, most importantly, going home with them. Home, where no one would be able to take them away from their children. Why, why was my daughter any worse than all those kids? Was she less deserving of a normal family? Has she committed some terrible crime, to be deprived of her father as a punishment? Even assuming that Lev Fedorov was a hundred times guilty, why should his toddler daughter be punished? What civilized society punishes children for the crimes of their parents?

And how can all these people keep walking around smiling, making phone calls, doing shopping, enjoying ice cream, acting as if the world is perfect? As if nothing has happened? Don't they know that Injustice, like a vulture, has spread his giant black wings over all of them, looking for his next victim?

* * *

I lost count of how many times I went to Moscow during the first ten weeks following my husband's arrest. After talking to the investigator Konev, I reached out to Lev's immediate supervisor in INION. That man was fairly accessible and always sympathetic but kept insisting that he could do absolutely nothing without the approval of the Academician Vinogradov, the company's president. After an endless number of seemingly hopeless attempts, I was finally granted a meeting with that almighty man. I can still see his fashionably dressed secretary, his spacious office with a giant window facing a wide sunny boulevard where neatly cut trees were just beginning to gather leaves, as if it happened yesterday.

The president could not hide his surprise that Fedorov's wife turned out to be so young. (I was so embarrassed by his comment, that, for the first time in my life, I lied about my age: I said that I was twenty-nine and just had a youthful look, which I could not help...) Vinogradov nodded understandably; he expressed sincere consolations and apologized for not seeing me earlier. Of course, he was very concerned about Lev's case: it was a very uncomfortable situation for the company to have one of its senior staff arrested for a government crime. Unfortunately, he was not ready to authorize signing the required letter of bail, the only thing that might have helped my husband to get out of jail. The academician needed more information; he had to find out what the issue really was.

The fact that a man with no legal education had sold his own gold-dust to a private buyer, not being aware that it was forbidden, did not seem like too much of a crime. Vinogradov was more concerned with the fact that my husband had bought a brand-new car just a few days before his arrest. Where had he gotten the money? He received a fine salary, sure—but it certainly would not have been enough for such an expensive car. Had Mr. Fedorov been engaged in some illegal activities? That was what Vinogradov needed to find out before committing himself to signing any important legal papers.

The INION president could spend all the time in the world "finding out": he was not the one in jail. I was half-listening to the academician, looking over his head out of the window. There was a stream of cars on the boulevard, used ones and brand new ones, red, green, white, gray, cheerful under the spring sun like colorful balloons. I noticed a few *Nivas*, and a few even more expensive *Volgas*. The academician may have found me rude when I suddenly interrupted him—but he did not show it.

"Do you believe that the owners of all these cars should be arrested and imprisoned, while the government investigates where the heck they have gotten the money?"

Vinogradov replied that that would not be a bad idea at all.

"Then let's arrest them all," I said. "Justice is only justice if it is equal for everyone. Even if my husband is guilty, why should he alone be punished while thousands of others continue to go free?"

The president did not have an answer. He was sorry that this tragedy had happened to one of his best employees. He had profound sympathy for me, since I obviously had to go through so much. He promised to continue to be on top of events and to do all he could to help. When it came to court, he would seriously consider sending a representative from the company who would act as a public attorney. He regretted that they had been unable to provide the bail letter, but I had to understand...

* * *

Unfortunately for everyone, I refused to "understand." And neither did my father—even though he was a *doctor of science* in physics and mathematics, and therefore must have been smart by definition. It is possible that Grandpa Solomon, a famous criminal lawyer, would have understood something, and even explained it to us—but grandpa had been dead for a few years...

And so, my father went to the person he respected more than anyone else in the world: the former president of the Leningrad University, who many years ago supervised writing his Ph.D. dissertation, and later brought him to Akademgorodok; the man who had been my dad's boss and his teacher, his immediate supervisor in the Institute of Mathematics and his personal friend: Academician Alexander

Danilovich Alexandrov. Alexandrov, a full member of the U.S.S.R. Academy of Science, a poet and a translator of Shakespeare in his spare time—in short, not a stupid person by any measures—could not comprehend Lev's story. More than that, he felt it to be his moral obligation to help, so he began thinking of people he might engage in the case. That is how my dad and I met Kerimov.

Kerimov, a long-term friend of Academician Alexandrov (I believe in their youth they climbed the Pamir Mountains together), was not just a scientist, but also a lawyer. Alexander Danilovich called him "one of the country's most prominent law scientists." He must have been from Azerbaijan, judging by his last name and appearance, although it did not matter where he was from—or did it? He lived in Moscow now, and his best friend was the Minister of Internal Affairs—a man who could set my husband free with a two-minute phone call.

That's how I ended up in Kerimov's pompous study. For my first meeting with the famous lawyer, my father flew all the way from Novosibirsk, just to accompany me and provide moral support. Later I would come there alone. I found the enormous size of Kerimov's office, with its antique furnishings, to be somewhat tacky and showy. Nevertheless, Kerimov was always respectful and extremely sympathetic; unlike Vinogradov, he promised definite help; he even gave me his home phone number and encouraged to call.

During one of our phone conversations, he told me that he had discussed the matter with his friend the Interior Minister and the latter assured him that my husband would be free within two days. When I called three days later, Kerimov expressed great surprise that my husband had not been freed yet and promised to call the minister again. Nothing was happening, though. Neither my parents nor I could understand why Kerimov was playing that game with us. He had wasted a lot of his personal time talking about Lev's case—and never even hinted that helping was a problem. But it was obvious that he had done nothing.

Alexander Danilovich was so surprised by his friend's inconsistent behavior, that he called him again. Many years had passed since he and Kerimov had been close, so calling Kerimov was not a routine thing for Alexandrov to do. But he believed that *when the matter is about a grave malady or jail, there is no such thing as politeness.* He insisted that we must not feel obliged to him or even grateful. Doing what he could to help in such a tragedy was the simple duty of any human being.

Unfortunately, that was not what I have heard from many other people later in life.

But I still believe the late Academician Alexandrov. I also believe that people like him, rare as they are, are responsible for the fact that this world has not yet completely gone to Hell...

As for Kerimov, it took me many years to understand what neither my naive parents, nor Academician Alexandrov—who, like many great scientists, had the heart of a child—could figure out. The prominent Moscow lawyer, born and bred in the Middle Asia with its very specific mentality, simply wanted a bribe.

I wonder what would have happened to all of us if we had figured out Kerimov's game. It may not have changed anything on a large scale: my parents, as much as they were prepared to sacrifice for me, almost certainly would not have been able to come up with enough cash to interest a person in such a high position. It would have saved my father and me the time and expense of going to Moscow, just for one-hour interviews with Kerimov. It could have spared me from cherishing unreasonable hopes, and then being devastated when those hopes crashed. But if we had managed to bribe the minister's friend and Lev Fedorov had not been sentenced to four years in prison, my entire life (and therefore, Nadia's) would have gone completely differently...

Would it have been better or worse?—I am not the one to answer...

17

There is no place like home...

Never in my life had I felt that commonplace truth as strongly as that first summer after my husband's arrest. Like a wounded animal returning to heal its wounds to the cave where it had been born and bred, I came back to my parents' home in Akademgorodok, finding consolation and relief in waking up in the same room, having familiar books and familiar things all around me, looking out of the same window at the same trees and the same squirrels, hearing the same sounds, walking on the same streets, and buying groceries in the same shops as I did when I was a child.

The air there smelled of woods, grass and earth, not of car exhaust, dust and urine, as in our Leningrad neighborhood. Nadia was laughing again, playing in the tall grass and running around like a puppy, having suddenly discovered the warmth of the summer sun, the coolness of the shade of hundred-year–old trees and the delight of building pyramids and castles in a clean sandbox. My mother's soups and pies recreated their former delicious tastes; the sky turned blue again. I was finally able to pick up a fiction book and forget myself enough to get involved in someone else's story.

* * *

Before leaving for Akademogorodok, I did the last—and almost certainly the most important—thing I could have done for my imprisoned husband: I hired one of the best criminal lawyers in Moscow. She happened to be an old friend of Oleg Gosin, Lev's friend from INION; she was a highly sought-after attorney who would never have taken a case "that minor" (per her own words), if it were not for Oleg's coworker and friend. Svetlana Semenovna Gunina, a middle-aged, low-key woman, turned out to be indispensable. Not only she helped my husband to get the lightest possible sentence, but she provided moral support to our entire family though the long ordeal of the inquests and courts, and ended up as close to becoming a personal friend as her position allowed. But here I am running ahead of my story.

The summer was almost half over when I finally realized that there was nothing I could do in Moscow to help my husband. The investigator had asked for a two-month extension in the inquest: he needed more data. That meant that not only I, but even Svetlana Semenovna, Lev's attorney, would not be able to see Lev Fedorov for at least two more months: a person under investigation in the Soviet Union was not supposed to have any contacts with the outside world, including his own lawyer.

There was also Nadia I had to be concerned about: even though she and I spent most weekends at Aunt Olia's dacha, there still were five days each week to stay in the city, where my daughter acquired all possible ailments, from multiple allergies to poor sleep and appetite, bed-wetting, and overall crankiness. My mother was losing her head, ready to collapse from exhaustion. We clearly needed to leave. I had used up all my vacation time on back-and-forth trips to Moscow—but all-understanding Kharetov signed a six-week unpaid leave for me, without any questions.

* * *

It was hard to imagine that only a year ago, I was reluctant to leave Akademogorodok to spend summer with Lev; I would have given up half of my life now to have that opportunity. I also wished I could share my grief with my friends and neighbors. However, no matter how I looked at it, merely pronouncing the word "imprisoned" turned out to be impossible. Academician Alexandrov was the only one who knew the secret, but he would never give it away—and no one would think of asking him, in any case. Our neighbors, most of whom were my father's coworkers and who knew me from the age of three, felt all but insulted that my mom and I were clearly hiding something from them. My girlfriends wanted to know more than "things between me and Lev have gone sour, so we've decided to take a break." It was not a Russian custom to keep personal things away from your friends.

I ended up reducing my social life to the absolute minimum. Considering the stress and grief I had just gone through, spending time by myself or with Nadia was mostly what I needed. Even Tanika, whose daughter played with Nadia daily, did not know the real story. I told her that I had decided to continue working and living in Leningrad instead of moving back with my husband, for reasons I was not ready to discuss. I had never called her in Moscow that past spring, but stayed with my parents' friends who by then had severed all their ties with Akademgorodok and therefore were "safe."

To compensate myself for the limited interactions with my childhood friends, I wrote long letters to Leningrad, especially to Nina, who knew everything and was not only understanding and sympathetic, but sincerely concerned. She usually responded right away—and if you remember that it was a pre-email era, when letters came written on a regular paper, both sides covered with small handwriting, you may be able to imagine the excitement of finding an envelope with a Leningrad stamp in my mail box...

One unexpected interruption to that tranquil, if not content, existence was a sudden visit of Igor Scheichman. One day I answered the door bell, and there he was—with a large bouquet of flowers and looking very serious—not a trace of a smile or anything suggesting possible romance. Igor's and mine mothers had recently become close friends, so I knew that the Snow Queen had left Igor for another man, and that their divorce was now complete. I had no idea, however, that my mother had chosen Maria Scheichman as a confidant, and that the entire story of Lev's incarceration was now know not only to her, but also to her husband and, most importantly, to her son.

"I can only imagine what you have been going through," said Igor, without any introduction. "You don't need to worry: your secret is safe with me and my parents... You know, I am not the one who likes to gossip... Especially in a situation like this... I just thought... maybe some flowers would cheer you up—even if just a little bit... Yes, I do want to see your daughter... Nadia you're saying her name is? *Nadezhda*... Good name! We all need a little bit of *Hope* to keep going, don't we?.."

I told him I was very sorry about his divorce. He replied that he had almost gotten over it—and now thought that the final outcome might have been for the better...

Neither one of us wanted to discuss our recent pain, but knowing that we did not have to keep any secrets from each other was very consoling. For the two weeks Igor spent in Akademgorodok, we saw each other almost daily, mostly walking through the woods with Nadia in a toddler carriage, going for a swim in the Ob Reservoir, or sometimes watching a movie together in the Houses of Scientists' grand hall. Those were the very things I had been hopelessly dreaming of only a few years ago... Wait, how many years?... A century ago, I suppose—considering how many events had occurred since we both graduated from high school and went our separate ways...

Igor was now a post-graduate student in a rather prestigious college in Moscow, successfully working on his Ph.D. I wished I could also boast some career advancements—but could I have said that my currently imprisoned husband had promised to help me with writing my dissertation? That would have opened a huge bag of worms—and was unlikely to gain me any respect from Igor, while his pity was the last thing in the world I wanted...

It may have been a totally wrong question when I asked whether his last name Scheichman had ever been a hindrance to his scientific career. He frowned.

"You know, Anna—we have already been through this topic more than once—haven't we? Ok, you have won on one point: some anti-semitism does exist in this country... Maybe not just *in this country*—what do we know about the rest of the world? However, it is limited to certain places and certain occupations. I just look hard before getting myself into a situation where I can get slashed because of my last name...

"Does it help that your nationality, after all, is "Russian?"

"I have no idea. The truth is, that I *am* a Russian... And so are you, for that matter. And so are our fathers, regardless of their last names... Any person with a tiny bit of brain will understand this!"

"And you would not want to work for people without any brain at all... Or without any honesty "—I forced a half-smile. "I haven't reaped any benefits from being *Anna Fedorova* versus *Anna Chernetsky* yet... Even though right now my documents... are as perfect as they can be—at least as far as the nationality is concerned..."

"With an uncle in London?"—interjected Igor. Damn, he knew that, too... On the other hand, was I ashamed of Uncle Victor living in England? He had gone through all the nine circles of Hell intended for new immigrants—and he seemed to be making it there... I should be proud of him, shouldn't I?

"Just don't tell anyone that you are proud of your uncle. In case—in a very unlikely case—you are ever asked... I mean, officially."

So, things were more complicated than Igor was trying to present them. Of course, he would defend his candidate's dissertation and get his Ph.D.—all Jewish scientists did, sooner or later. Moreover, both of our fathers had achieved much more than that, they were both *doctors of science*, a significantly higher rank, while enjoying all the privileges that came with that title—at least in Akademgorodok: higher salaries, access to the specialized grocery store, the privileged policlinic for the whole family... None of us wanted to discuss that part, though. Our country was based on equality—or at least that is what both of us had learned at school—and, for the sake of our fragile relationship, it was much safer to leave it at that.

So, we continued talking about books, movies, new subway stations in Moscow—all irrelevant stuff, as far as I was concerned. Sometimes we spent hours together, barely talking at all. We did not even gossip about our common classmates. No bringing up the fact that Anyuta was single now, for example (although, if Igor had asked me, I would have had no choice but to tell him that Anyuta was dating again—but he never asked, did not even mention her name). We just invented our own, a very secluded world—and dwelled there. For the whole two weeks. After that, Igor departed, to spend the rest of his vacation climbing the Caucasus.

We promised to write to each other: I wanted to know all about his climb, of which I was envious; he wanted to learn what would happen when Lev's investigation ended, and how would things go with the court.

We both kept our words. Already back in Leningrad, I received a letter of several pages, with the account of his mountain climb and a couple of photographs. One of them showed Igor—broadly smiling this time—with a heavy backpack, against the background of a mountain stream, with a butterfly sitting on his outstretched arm; on the other photo, he was standing with a girl—but their figures were small and far away: the picture mostly depicted snow-covered mountain top with a spectacular drop-down.

Chapter Four
THE TRIAL

1

"ATTORNEYS ALMOST NEVER DIE IN their beds," said Svetlana Semenovna Gunina. "They die from heart attacks in courts, being shocked by their clients' tough sentences."

The investigation was finally over, so Lev's attorney was preparing for her first visit with the defendant. I was already back at work in Leningrad when she called me with the news. Two days later, Gunina and I met in a small garden in Moscow, two blocks away from the prison where my husband was kept. She said that we needed a private place to talk, so here I was, right from the overnight train.

"But some of them do make it to retirement?" I asked, quite insensitively.

"Those are either lucky ones," replied Svetlana Semenovna, "or the ones who do not care. There are not too many of those, thank god. You do not want a lawyer who looks at your husband just as a *client*, someone who enables him to make money—rather than a suffering person who needs a friend and a protector."

For a few seconds, I thought of my late Grandpa Solomon—but brushed that thought away.

Per Svetlana Semenovna's suggestion, I had written Lev a five-page letter. The law strictly prohibited carrying letters to the prisoners, but attorneys violated it constantly.

"I am responsible for your husband's emotional state just as much as for his legal defense," explained our lawyer. "Anything that will make him feel better must be done. Write the most loving letter you can. Just don't address him by his name or mention that he is in jail. If I do get caught with this letter, I should be able to say that it was addressed to me, and I just forgot to leave it at home."

Svetlana Semenovna would have lost her license if she had been caught carrying a letter to her defendant. Attorneys were routinely searched while entering and exiting prisons, so even my "careful" letter to my husband (without any names, dates, or mention of arrests and imprisonments) was carried by attorney Gunina in her underwear.

She also suggested that I give her some food for Lev.

"They do not have enough to eat in jail," she explained, "not to mention the quality. At least half of the modest amount of food that comes with the government supplies is stolen by prison employees. One good lunch is not going to make a difference in your husband's nutrition, of course—but it may lift his mood, at least for one day. Do not bring any more food than he can eat in the few hours I am with him, however. He will not be allowed to take any food back to his cell; moreover, I am not supposed to give him any food, and will be severely reprimanded if your husband gets caught eating anything that came from outside the prison."

"What happens if a guard comes into the room while he is eating?" I asked.

"I'll wait until the guard on duty is someone I know," smiled Svetlana Semenovna. "Then he will not come into our cell, or at least he will give me enough warning..."

Never in my entire life had I prepared any food with so much care, imagination, and love. I bought the most expensive fruits at the market; I made Lev's favorite salad; I wrapped small sandwiches with caviar and tongue—delicacies unavailable in Moscow, and especially Leningrad, stores, but that I had thoughtfully brought from Akademgorodok, from my mother's emergency supplies.

Lunch for Lev was easier than the letter: Svetlana Semenovna did not have to hide it her underwear. The law did not oblige lawyers to eat in the prison staff cafeteria; they were allowed to bring their own food. The only thing they were not supposed to do was to share their food with their clients.

"Oh, do not thank me, please!" she told me when I handed her my little parcel. "All attorneys do that. It is an essential part of the job, our moral duty as human beings. If you are not prepared to risk, you do not take this job."

I thought of my late grandfather again—but this time it was so unpleasant that the thought made me blush. Attorneys in the Soviet

Union were paid per case, not per hours they worked on it; and the government fee was standard. How could my grandfather manage to amass so much money during his years of practice, except by charging his clients "extra" under the table? Svetlana Semenovna either did not notice my facial expression—or chose not to ask questions that seemed irrelevant to her client's case.

It made no sense for me to wait for her outside the prison, she said. Her meeting with my husband would almost certainly last all day. She would call my friends' house, where I stayed, in the evening. If Lev writes me a letter, she would carry it the same way she carried the one from me to him: hidden in her underpants. Was I capable of waiting until the next morning? If not, she would find a way to meet me in one of the subway stations on her way home...

✱ ✱ ✱

When I visited Moscow a few years ago, I suddenly realized that I had forgotten where *Butyrskaya Prison* was. I knew it was somewhere around Novoslobodskaya subway station, but where would I go from there? It is very well hidden inside a ring of apartment buildings, so one could walk past it, without having any idea that one of the most notorious prisons in Russia is right there...

In Russian folklore it is known by its nickname: *Butyrki*. I used to feel its overwhelming presence everywhere in Moscow, no matter where I was. It dominated the city—its shadow hanging all over it, darkening the sky, blocking the sunlight, poisoning the air. I could hear the moaning of people confined inside its granite walls. No matter what I was doing, I could not stop thinking of how many of its inhabitants were innocent of the crimes they were accused of, and how many hearts were bleeding, how many bitter tears shed outside of those walls by the ones who loved the inmates, guilty or not guilty.

Now I am asking myself: why is *Butyrskaya Prison* so special? There are many infamous prisons mentioned in Russian, and especially Soviet, folklore: *Petrovka, Lubyanka, Kresty*. Numerous poems and songs have been written about those taken inside, often never to come out. Even before Lev's imprisonment, I knew many of them by heart. When my husband was arrested, those verses cried out my grief, and I kept repeating them to myself as a pious person repeats a prayer.

> *Here, bird-song*
> *is unknown;*
> *here one learns patience*
> *and the wisdom of stone.*
> *I have seen no color*
> *except lingonberry*
> *in the fourteen years*
> *I have lived as a prisoner.***
>
> . . . .
>
> *It happened like this when only the dead*
> *Were smiling, glad of their release,*
> *That Leningrad hung around its prisons*
> *Like a worthless emblem, flapping its piece.****

Butyrki was special *to me* because *my* husband was imprisoned there... I was convinced that, even if I lived for another thousand years, I would always be able to find that building resembling a medieval castle that concealed itself in the midst of modern, festive and bright Moscow, with my eyes closed. I would never stop hearing the cries of anguish and pain of those suffering innocently. The shade of that building would always follow me. I would never be able to escape from it, nor forget its existence for even one minute...

But I did forget...

2

Isn't it strange? I had always known that my country had bad laws, but at the same time was convinced that prisons were mostly filled with people who deserved to be there. Intelligentsia had been crying out about the lack of political freedom; everyone considered incarcerating

---

* *Varlam Shalamov*, translator unknown
** *Anna Akhmatova*, translator unknown

dissidents in mental institutions and correction facilities unjust and cruel, disgraceful and debilitating for the country. The very same people, however, believed that criminal prisons (unlike political ones) served the noble purpose of protecting honest citizens from thieves and murderers.

My husband was not a political prisoner. Moreover, he was guilty of the crime he had been accused of. Nevertheless, he was in no way a criminal. The fault was not with him, but with the ridiculous, unjust, undemocratic laws. Nowhere in the civilized world were people punished for selling their own possessions, whatever those possessions might have been, and whoever the buyers were. But the Soviet Union was different. There, one could sell one's own house, a car, furniture, china set, or even an item of jewelry. But nobody except the government had the right to sell or exchange money. "Currency" was a terrible word, associated with the darkest, most dangerous crimes—crimes against our Soviet state, crime against the people. "Violation of currency operations" was one step short of high treason—and, according to some bizarre logic, gold-dust was considered a "currency."

Lev Fedorov was detained under Article 88 of the Criminal Code of the Russian Federation, with the scary title of "Violation of the Rules of Currency Operations." The minimum punishment under that article was three years in prison, with the confiscation of property; the maximum, for repeat offenders—death by execution.

The "currency" that he had sold was not American dollars, or British pounds, or German marks, or any money of a foreign country. It was one hundred grams of gold-dust, an inheritance from his late aunt.

Unfortunately, said Svetlana Semenovna, there was more to the story than the one-time mistake of selling a handful of gold-dust. Lev's case appeared to be far less straightforward than his lawyer had originally believed. My husband had a history of a business relationship with a professional profiteer, a person who had been sought by the KGB, not just by the *Militsiya* (police), for a long time.

Her name was Kirova—and, unfortunately for Lev, she was at least a decade older then him. They will be tried together as collaborators in the same criminal case, explained Svetlana Semenovna. And no judge will ever rule to issue the same punishment to a younger man and an older woman; his punishment must be more severe ("political correctness," Soviet style). "So, if she gets the minimum sentence of three years, your husband will be sentenced to four. Luckily, I know this woman's lawyer; he and I will work together on getting her the lightest sentence possible..."

Lev was arrested in Kirova's apartment, less than an hour after he had left his brother's house and was supposedly driving home in his new car, to get ready for the morning trip to Leningrad.

"There was a copy of the Criminal Code of the Russian Federation on the shelve right above his head," complained Sergey later. "Why on earth couldn't he look at it? That always-know-everything brother of mine... He could have just read that one stupid article—and he would know enough to deny that he had ever seen the damn gold-dust..."

But Lev never opened the Criminal Code. Neither did he tell his brother about having sold the gold-dust. And, of course, he had no idea that his buyer, Kirova, had been arrested by the KGB just a few hours earlier, caught "red-handed" while transferring the jar with the gold-dust to some shady character in one of Moscow's busy subway stations. Her buyer, who was said to be a professional profiteer from Azerbaijan, was probably tried in a different court for a different crime; or maybe he managed to escape in a crowded subway, and the KGB had to spend many more months trying to find him.

Kirova, taken to the KGB prison and immediately interrogated, naturally tried to cooperate with the investigation. Unfortunately for her, she could give only an ambiguous answer to their main question: where had she gotten the gold-dust?

"His name is Lev Alexandrovich, and I do not know his last name. I have his phone number written in my notebook at home, but that is all I know," answered the poor woman. She knew that she had no proof, and the investigator was unlikely to believe her. But then a happy idea came to her head:

"Actually, he is supposed to come over to my place this very evening. I gave him three hundred rubles extra for his gold, and he promised to return the debt tonight..."

Unfortunately, it was the truth. After saying good-night to his brother, Lev did not drive straight home, as Sergey and his wife believed. He needed to stop at Kirova's place on his way—just for a few minutes, to return the debt of three hundred rubles. He had no intention of ever seeing her again. Their business affair was over: having bought his dream car, Lev did not need any more money and most importantly, had nothing more to sell.

Those *few minutes* changed our lives forever. Instead of the friendly lady of the house, Lev was met by stern KGB officers. Not giving him any time to get over the shock, those well-trained professionals began their questioning immediately. Was he the one who had given the gold-dust to Mrs. Kirova? If Lev had said, "No, I've never seen it," his case would have been over and done with right then. But Lev said, "Yes". That one word converted a free man, a respected citizen with a good job, beautiful apartment in Moscow, a family, and even a new car, into a prisoner with no civil rights. One word that ruined his life forever. The one time in his life when he should have lied, but—contrary to his nature—did not. That made no sense to anyone who knew him well... Maybe, it didn't make sense to him either. But then it was to late.

He admitted that he had sold Kirova the gold-dust. And then nothing could have taken those words back.

The only explanation I can come up with was the one that Lev gave me later: he did not think that he had done anything illegal, and he did not want to let down the old woman by denying that he had sold her the gold-dust. If she couldn't explain the source of the gold, her sentence would have been even tougher. As for Lev himself, he had his aunt's will as proof of the gold's legitimacy, backed by his entire family who, if needed, would have testified that the gold had been in the late aunt's possession for as long as they remembered her.

* * *

Pieces of the puzzle of my husband's life slowly began fitting together. I remembered Aunt Katia asking Lev repeatedly about her jewelry. She had given it to him to store in a safe place, but it had to be a place that she had access to. I remembered Lev being annoyed at her inquires. He had told his aunt many times that he had placed her jewelry in his office, in a fireproof safe with a secret code. It was insane to keep things of that value in an apartment that could easily get broken into... And, after all, Aunt Katia's will clearly stated that all her possessions would go to her nephew Lev Fedorov, so Lev had considered it his personal business to keep his future inheritance safe and sound.

All of that was true, but I felt somewhat uncomfortable thinking that my husband was denying the old woman her last joy, regardless of how unreasonable she was in wanting that jewelry back, and how much I disliked her. I certainly would have felt much worse had I known that Aunt Katia's precious necklaces, bracelets, and earrings were slowly moving from the safety of Lev's office to the pocket of an enterprising Moscow lady, who later made a profit by reselling them for a much higher price. By all logistics of the Soviet law—and the Russian mentality—she was a real criminal: *profiteering* meant making a living without working, getting money for doing nothing productive...

Now I finally knew where Lev's big money had been coming from. First, for the country cottage that Lev bought only a couple of months after he had moved in with his aunt. Then for the motorcycle with a side carriage. Finally, for his first car, a used *Moskwitch* that gave us so much trouble on muddy country roads, and that he later "totaled" in a very fortunate accident, without receiving a scratch himself... I was always surprised that my husband was able to afford all those expensive things with the salary of a senior research assistant, one quarter of which went to pay child support. But he was not a man who discussed his finances with his wife.

"You're used to dealing with shit, aren't you?" he once asked contemptuously. "Well, now you're living with a *real man*—and real men have money..."

* * *

"Real men have money..."

Aunt Katia's father-in-law (or was it her grandfather-in-law? Or her uncle-in-law?) must have been a real man. An employee of a gold mine somewhere in Siberia, he managed to steal a handful of gold-dust (and probably not just gold-dust) and carry it past all the tsar's inspectors to the privacy of his own home. The Revolution did not favor rich people, so the gold that had not been transferred into money under the old regime was passed on to the next generation as a souvenir, or maybe some kind of insurance, the last resort in case things get really bad... Things never got bad for Aunt Katia's successful husband, and, in any case, neither he or his wife would have ever done such a stupid thing as trying to sell the gold-dust; unfortunately, they were not careful enough—or forethoughtful enough—to get rid of it altogether. After all, it was not a big deal: some glittering metal in the bottom of a small glass jar. It was possible that Aunt Katia had forgotten about it. Or maybe she had not— otherwise why was Lev waiting for her to die to sell it? He had no remorse selling most of her ready-made jewelry while she was still alive...

Where had Lev kept the gold-dust? Our three-bedroom apartment had almost no storage spaces that I could not have accidentally accessed. Was it the redwood cabinet in Aunt Katia's room? Oh, how much I wished I had known it was there! It would have been so easy to pull the jar out while Aunt Katia was outside, and flush the damn gold down the toilet... They would have never found out what happened to it... One hundred grams of stupid metal—and your whole life is ruined... The family is destroyed; the child grows up without a father... And Lev—what will become of him? How will he survive the shame of imprisonment? Years of forced labor in camp? He will be at least fifty when he comes home—will he remain in good health?

Oh, how I wished to have a Time Machine... Just to move a few months back... How could I *not have known*? There was a time bomb in my husband's house—a bomb ticking quietly, bringing all of us closer and closer to disaster with merciless certainty... It would have taken me only a few seconds to disable it, destroy it forever...

* * *

I could see the whole scene of the search almost as if it had happened in my presence. I saw my husband arriving at his own home at four-thirty in the morning, accompanied by three KGB officers. A black car waiting patiently outside, the driver dozing behind the steering wheel. Not a prison car yet, just a black *Volga* with an official government license plate number... The officers are not wearing uniforms; they are dressed as civilians, although their coats, shirts and ties are identical, as well as their posture and facial expressions—well-programmed robots, not human beings.

Formally, Lev Fedorov is not a prisoner yet, even though in fact he is. I can see him opening the front door with his own keys—opening it for the last time in many years. Three dark coated figures stand close behind him, watching his every movement, breathing down his back. His hands are probably trembling, and he can't get the key into the keyhole right away. He asks the men to move away a little, not to obstruct the hallway light. The door is finally opened, and Lev walks in first, the three dark figures following him silently. He pauses in the hallway and takes his coat off. He tells himself that there is nothing to fear, he'd committed no crime. His uninvited guests will leave in a few minutes. Or maybe it is just a nightmare. He is too tired. He has not slept for almost twenty-four hours, and he cannot think clearly. Too bad he's spent a sleepless night: he must drive to Leningrad in the morning, he should be well rested and alert.

The officers need two witnesses, it is required by law. One of them rings the doorbells of the adjoining apartments. It is five o'clock in the morning, and the neighbors are disturbed and displeased. The first one refuses to help and locks the door in front of the officer's nose. A middle-aged lady from the other apartment, however, hastily wraps herself in a big flannel robe and comes over. She has hair-rollers in her grayish hair, her unwashed face still traced with wrinkles from her pillow. This neighbor used to be friendly with Lev, but now she avoids meeting his eyes; not as much as "good morning" comes out of her mouth. She is looking at the officers' faces like an obedient dog, waiting for their orders.

They still need the second witness. Finally, another neighbor shows up, from an apartment one floor below. He is dressed less casually than the lady, and therefore it took longer for him to get ready.

The aliens begin the search of our apartment. They take their time, raking through Nadia's toys, ransacking our summer clothes that I did not bother to take when leaving last fall. They study bookshelves, examining the spine of every book. They rummage through drawers and kitchen cabinets. They take inventory of every piece of furniture, every silver spoon, Aunt Katia's old fur coat, even the modest earrings that my mother gave me for my twenty-fifth birthday in the hope that one day I might have my ears pierced. After the trial, the government officials will come back to confiscate all valuables—unless the owner is acquitted, which almost never happens.

Ah!—Here they found something interesting. The officers livened up after almost two hours of the monotonous and tedious travail. On the bottom of one of the drawers, they found a folder with a typewritten book in it. Underground literature? Indeed so! Not a novel by Solzhenitsyn, just a collection of essays by different dissident authors. Next to it lies a notebook with verses by Naum Korzhavin—mostly lyrics, but several poems make fun of the Soviet government and the socialism... Everything "home-published"—classical *samizdat,* underground literature...

That part makes me feel the worst: the poetry notebook was mine. Will samizdat found at home complicate my husband's criminal case?

Svetlana Semenovna dismisses my worries.

"It's too minor for the KGB to open a political case and has nothing to do with his criminal case. If I were you, it would be the least of my worries. If they had found *Gulag Archipelago,* that would be a different story..."

3

One of those early days of September, shortly after I had returned from my first meeting with Lev's attorney, Stanislav Rozov asked to talk to me in private. I had expected that my coworkers would have questions—although I still cherished hope that they did not know the real answers.

"I know what happened to Lev," said Rozov, without any preamble. "And I understand and respect the reasons you did not want to share that grim story. You seem to have done a lot trying to get your husband out of the mess he had gotten himself into—but I assume it did not help.

"I am your friend, you know... Maybe even more than you realize..." His face had a soft, even kind expression, very unusual compared to his habitual skepticism.

"How many people know?" I asked, almost in whisper; I could not find my voice, and butterflies in my stomach were all going crazy. Still, Rozov's words, especially the tone they were said, caused some kind of reassurance, if not relief.

"Officially, only me and Kharetov. And the Library director, of course. And the local 'First Department...' If you mean our wonderful coworkers... No one has believed the story you invented... They are annoyed at you for making things up; they are intrigued... and of course they are gossiping. But I doubt that anyone guessed the real reason.

In any case, by the time they figure things out (if ever), you will not be working there... So, it won't matter.

That is when my heart stopped.

The library remained the last island of safety and predictability left for me in the world—and now I was going to lose even that...

"I will not be working here? Because of taking too much time off?"

"No, that is not a problem. Between you and me—there is not as much to do in this department as our boss is trying to convince the management... You did a very fine job here... with whatever could have been done. And taking time off is expected from a woman with a young child...

"The reason you need to leave is... well, the Boss (he frequently called Kharetov "the Boss"—which in his case sounded affectionally)—the Boss has been invited ... You know, to the First Department—with the library director present, of course (and he had not forgotten your crazy trip to Tallinn, which made the entire library talk about you...) They obviously had the information directly from its main source... Official version of it—which does not sound nice, to say the least ... From the Moscow KGB, if you want me to be completely blunt. And they conveyed to the Boss... In a friendly way, of course... that the wife of a political prisoner has no place in our "ideological" (he stressed the last word with his usual sarcastic tone) organization—our beloved library. The Boss is now required to ask you to leave... Or... if you don't leave voluntarily, he is allowed to find a way to lay you off... (In which case we'll lose the position—which you understandably don't care about.)

"In any case, Kharetov was very upset—he has a kind heart, you know... and a soft spot for you. He could not bring himself to ask you to resign... You were going on leave, so he was relieved to be able to procrastinate. But now, when you are back... The poor guy cannot summon the courage to tell you... So, he asked me..."

"And how do *you* feel saying that to me?" Whatever you might think, it was a rather desperate question (was I hoping for the decision to be reversable?); it couldn't sound anything but rude—but Rozov took no offence.

"I am used to solving difficult situations, you know," he said without a smile. "And everyone in the department knows we are friends... I hope you understand that I *am* your friend—regardless of what happened to your husband... And I have a plan to help you. There is some time, you don't need to leave tomorrow... Just reassure Kharetov that you are looking for another job—and he will be satisfied. I will back you up, no one will rush you. But you do need to start looking, OK?"

Before I had time to answer that I had no skills, Rozov presented his rescue plan.

He had always admired my intelligence and was convinced that library automation was far below what I could have achieved.

"You may not have the brains like your father... (very sensitive thing to say, thank you!)—but certainly enough to learn some computer programming. So, I will teach you. Yes, right here, right now. The Boss knows what we'll be doing; he will not bother either one of us with petty assignments. I can teach you basic programming in two-three weeks. No, we don't need a computer for that. And then you will be able to get a job as a computer programmer—there are plenty of openings for that... No, you don't need to be good at it—the demand is high enough... and we probably can pull some strings..."

Rozov tried to hide his bitterness behind irony when he commented on my husband's behavior during the interrogation.

"I can't believe that Fedorov could be such an idiot to admit his fault to the KGB! He must have thought that, as soon as they have proof that the gold was his own and not stolen or bought for profit, they would let him go! As if the KGB turns down potential victims easy as that! Oh, I understand! Your husband must have decided to play a noble knight toward that woman—at the expense of his family, not to mention his own freedom, career, his entire life. Not that she seems particularly deserving of such sacrifice... God, what an idiot! *Violating stupid laws is the duty of any man with common sense. But an intelligent person must have enough brains not to get caught!*"

* * *

During the next three weeks, Rozov and I were working diligently together. He decided to teach me programming in PL-1, in which he was proficient (the language has been long dead—as dead as all the technology of the 1980s; but you can still Google it and see that once it was a real—and widely used—programming language). Instead of a computer we were using pen and paper, drawing algorithms. Rozov was immensely pleased: "It is in between learning a foreign language, and thinking mathematically," he said. "And you sure have a strong mathematical logic—from you dad or from your school? Never mind your language abilities."

I had no idea how to look for a job—so three weeks later, my mouth dry from embarrassment, I dialed the home phone number of Professor Shlomov. The next day, he and I met in his office in my former alma mater. Professor Shlomov had heard rumors, which he had a hard time believing; he was upset to find out that Lev Fedorov, whom he greatly respected for his scientific and technological achievement was, indeed, incarcerated. "What a stupid thing to do for such an intelligent man," he kept repeating. He also promised to help me find a job.

"Give me a day or two—and I will call you with a couple of options," he said.

That is how I ended up in the SRC—Scientific Research Center belonging to our very own Institute of Culture. There were a few dozen employees, many of whom had long-term relationships with each other. The programming department was considered the backbone of the company and was the most respected one. I had doubts that I could last there for more than a few days—even less that I would ever fit in socially...

"Don't worry," reassured Shlomov. "They will not lay you off right away—and by the time they are ready to do that, you will have learned enough to justify your existence. That is a real, 'alive' job, after all—and I hope that it will distract you from ruminating about your husband's fate."

* * *

I was terrified and barely kept myself from bursting into tears when, on my very first day on the new job, I received an assignment with a two-week deadline, and realized that I did not have the slightest idea of how to write the damn program. After staring at the piece of paper for an hour and trembling every time my supervisor appeared behind my back, I dared to ask his permission to write my program at home, in a more relaxed atmosphere. He reluctantly agreed, and in the evening, I rushed to Rozov's apartment. My friend laughed at my miserable state and wrote the entire program in less than one hour. It took him much longer to explain to me the function of each individual command.

There was a good hour of commute home from his place, but in spite of inadequate sleep, my second day at the new job was a lot easier than the first: I was busy at the keyboard, typing Rozov's program. At the end of the day I ran it, praying that it would work the way Rozov had explained. Of course, it did not. I spent the last half an hour of my working time pretending to study the printout and trying to find a mistake. In the evening I was at Rozov's place again. This time Stanislav took the program more seriously. His professional pride was hurt: the mistake had been his. He explained to me that these things happened often, and I must not get discouraged: in real life, a program rarely acts the way the programmer thinks it should. At least, not with the first run.

He found the mistake. He explained it to me. There were more trials and errors to follow before the program was complete, but I did meet the deadline, and eventually began to correct at least some of the problems on the spot, without Rozov's help. I continued reading manuals of the programming documentation, and they gradually began making more and more sense.

Rozov helped me to write the first drafts of my programs for several more months, but I felt more and more secure, more capable of finding and correcting mistakes on my own. Meanwhile, my teacher and I got closer and closer, and soon we both felt a need to see each other regularly, for reasons that had nothing to do with work: Stanislav Rozov was the only person with whom I could talk about Lev's imprisonment without shame or fear to overwhelm him; for him, I may have been the only person with whom he could talk about his own imprisonment—and he was at the point of his life when he desperately needed an understanding and empathetic listener.

Stanislav's was the story of a young man's romantic belief in the new democratic after-Stalin Russia; the story of his arrest, a few-months-long inquest, his trial, the years in labor camp, the struggle for his place in the society after he returned.

"They were all worshiping Nikita Khrushchev[3]," he said. "The guy had the guts to publicly denounce Stalin, close off political prison camps, and... well, he took a lot upon himself to allow some "free speech" in this country. But criticizing the head of government was still far beyond what Russia would ever allow—and I learned it the hard way..."

I was fascinated by the way Rozov talked: there was no anger in his words, no bitterness. It seemed that Stanislav viewed the time of his imprisonment not as lost years, but as an invaluable experience, an important school of life that helped him understand the world and himself. I thought that after knowing Rozov for four years, I did not know him at all. That small man with a body of a thirteen-year-old boy and funny-looking triple-lenses glasses was a giant.

As for my work with SRC, Professor Shlomov appeared to be right. By the time my new bosses could fire me, I had learned enough programming to keep up with the job. During my second year in the company, I worked almost independently, turning to Rozov for consultations only in particularly difficult cases.

4

There was still no trial. The prosecutor considered the case ready, but Svetlana Semenovna chose to procrastinate. "In criminal cases anything that delays the trial is good," she said. "No logical explanation, just experience. The government policy might change, the courts might start giving milder sentences for currency violations. In any case, your husband has a good four years to go; the more of his term is served in Moscow, the better. No need to rush to the labor camp."

I had mixed feelings about postponing the trial. According to our lawyer, there was no chance for Lev to be acquitted, but I was impatient to finally be able to see him, to write and receive letters. The lawyer got angry.

"We're talking about your husband's life, and you are concerned with a one-hour visitation! We are now heading toward winter—and it is much better to be on *the train* in the spring."

I had forgotten about *the train* for a while, although I should have remembered. A prisoner had to be transported from the investigation prison to his "final destination," the labor camp, where most of the term was served. And Russia was a very, very big country... I had read enough books about the transit (underground literature, of course—which made it only more memorable)—but somehow was hoping that things had changed, that prison trains in the 1980s were different from the ones of the 1930s…

"They aren't all that different," said Svetlana Semenovna. "The prisoners are expected to make it to their destinations alive, and most of them do—but that's about it. The conditions there are still horrible."

"Don't they heat the cars at all?" I was still hoping for some reassurance. But Svetlana Semenovna was not in the mood to reassure me.

"Practically, no. But a cold train is not the worst. The cars are too crowded for the prisoners to freeze, even with no heat. But they are transferred from one train to another on the way, and often must wait outside for a long time. I'd rather spare you the details. Just take my word for it: you do not want to travel under guard in winter…"

* * *

Svetlana Semenovna built her legal case on the assumption that her client may have been insane while committing his crime. She herself doubted that it was true, but her beliefs did not matter: if she succeeded in convincing the judge that her defendant might be mentally impaired, Lev would be sent to a mental hospital for evaluation, before he could even be tried. The evaluation, together with the waiting time for the hospital bed, would take close to six months.

"Conditions in the hospital are much better than in prison," she said. "It will be sort of a rest for him. In any case, I can't allow a man to be sent to a labor camp when there is even the slightest chance that he might be mentally ill. And even if your husband is one hundred percent healthy, he might be able to fool the doctors. In that case, he would get some treatment and be set free; no trial, no criminal records. He will be restored at work, with all the back salary paid for the time he was forcefully detained. Please, don't count on such a happy end… but we have nothing to lose and, in either case, some definite win. So, we'll go for that—and you can wait for your date and letters…"

At that "mock trial" (since our lawyer had no doubt that the judge would grant her request, I did not consider that trial to be "real"), I saw my husband for the first time in six months. He was very pale and noticeably thinner, but seemed very calm and self-confident. He looked around the room, nodded to me, his brother, and the few acquaintances who came as witnesses, without smiling or distinguishing anyone. He wore a multi-colored sweater that I had knitted for him for his birthday—the one he must have been wearing on the night of his arrest—and that had more significance to me than any smile would...

I felt caught in the middle, having to testify before the judge about my husband's insane behavior while he could hear my every word. I kept reminding myself that Lev had agreed to play the role of a mentally sick person. Nevertheless, I felt awful. During the two hours that my husband and I spent in the same courtroom, he never looked me in the eyes, or expressed any feelings. I wanted to run to him, hug him, tell about my love, about my nightmares of the train, ask about his health and the conditions in the prison, reassure him that I would always wait for him, healthy or sick, a patient in a mental hospital or a prisoner. But he was behind the bar, with two armed guards standing at his sides, separated from me and from the rest of the world, just as if he were behind the ten-foot thick stone walls of Butyrki.

While my husband was waiting for the bed opening in the Kashenko Mental Hospital, the largest psychiatric facility in Moscow, I had to figure out what was there left for me to wait for... Should I hope for the "happy end," as unlikely as it was? Or look forward to the one-hour date in prison, after Lev is found guilty—which will inevitably be followed by him leaving Moscow on *the train?* Counting the days, weeks or months until the hypothetical date when he finally will have served his term and return home? Then we might be able to pick up broken pieces of our lives, and, putting them together, start everything anew...

But there was a caveat there—something that none of us (save, maybe, Lev's lawyer) had ever thought of: how on earth could Lev retain his (technically government-owned) apartment while being incarcerated and therefore having no civil rights? Had Nadia and I been registered there, the apartment would be considered "occupied," regardless of where we actually lived. But—thanks to Lev's endless procrastination—we were still residents of Leningrad, and there was no way to change that, until Lev was free and legally restored in his Moscow home. Catch-22—no matter how you look at it...

If this does not make sense to some of my readers, you are in a good company—and I don't want to take your time explaining all the complexities of Soviet housing laws (which, as most laws, only made sense to those who wrote them). The important thing to understand is that incarcerated person (guilty or not) would lose all his civil rights—and, upon release from jail, had to start his life anew—or commit another crime and return to jail.

Even before Perestroika[4], some brave journalists managed to publish articles describing the tragedy of ex-convicts who did not have immediate family to provide *propiska*, or "registration" for them (and only immediate family members were allowed to do that—on the provision that they themselves had enough square meters), and therefore ended up with passports without addresses, which in the Soviet Union was a crime in itself. Their passports being invalid, their owners could not get an official job, which turned them into outlaws.

And that is when we thought of Lev's son, Dmitry—the kid who helped him build his dream house in the village. Spoilt as he was, he remained Lev's son. And, although living with his mother, his *propiska* was with the father. So, after all, Lev was not the only one registered in the apartment—even after his aunt's death. The problem was, that Dmitry was turning eighteen in the spring, which made him eligible for the summer military draft. Military rules had changed in the country since the days I finished high school; being a full-time college student no longer guaranteed exemption from the draft. Of course, serving in the military was an honorable occupation—so, after the two years of service, Dmitry would return to Moscow with all his prior rights—except that the government would give him a room in a communal apartment to live in—in exchange for the large apartment he will have lost, which was way too big for one person...

Of course, if Dmitry somehow manages to avoid serving in the army, the apartment will remain in the family. But even Svetlana Semenovna did not believe it was possible: Dmitry was a healthy young man, and the army service appeared as inevitable for him as a jail term for his father...

5

The trial was finally scheduled for the end of February.

Lev was back in Butyrki. As Svetlana Semenovna had predicted, he was found mentally healthy, but we had won some time. The criminal courts were swamped, and after being released from the hospital Lev had to wait for another good two months. He must have used that time efficiently, charming people whom he depended on. It was undoubtedly a challenging job: this time he was dealing not with blue-collar woodcutters, but with the prison's top management.

A few days before Lev's trial, Svetlana Semenovna visited one of her other clients in Butyrki. She ran into an officer she knew, who stopped her in the corridor and asked:

"You are Lev Fedorov's lawyer, aren't you?"

"Yes," said puzzled Svetlana Semenovna.

"Is there any chance that your client will get *no more* than five years imprisonment?" asked the officer.

"I certainly hope so! Why?"

"Because we (the officer meant the prison's management) want him to serve his term here. He is too valuable a specialist to let him go to camp. We can really use his knowledge and expertise in jail. And of course, if his sentence is more than five years, we will not be able to do that. You know the laws…"

Svetlana Semenovna certainly knew the laws. Soviet prisons, Butyrskaya included, were meant for pretrial investigation, not for serving as correction facilities. After the final court hearing, convicted prisoners were sent to serve their terms in labor camps. Economically, however, prisons were supposed to be self-supporting; they received very little, if any, government subsidy. Therefore, prisons could keep some of the felons to work in the prison itself. There were significant restrictions to that privilege (such as the kinds of crimes, the terms of incarceration, etc.)—and, of course, the number of "qualified candidates" greatly exceeded the demand. The lucky convicts for whom the impossible dream came true, did *not* have to spend many exhausting weeks on the prison train; they were *not* subjected to the cruelty and tyranny of the convoy guards; they did *not* risk their health, and sometimes their very lives, working in unsafe and very poorly regulated mines in the cold northern climate. They stayed in clean, warm, and safe prisons, got a fair nutrition, prompt medical care if needed, and could count on at least some protection from the harassment of other prisoners.

Most of those lucky people were employed in housing services. They cleaned bathrooms, cooked for their fellow inmates, washed dishes and clothes. The most qualified ones worked as plumbing or electrician's assistants, reporting to free-hired civilians. My husband, however, was considered too valuable a specialist to be wasted on such low-skill labor: he would be assigned to maintain electric and phone security systems inside the jail. (Eventually, he ended up doing even more than that, and was rewarded generously, although indirectly, by the guards and even the prison's top officers. That part of his life, however, was still in the future, and no one, including probably Lev himself, could anticipate it back then.) The news that happy Svetlana Semenovna conveyed to me, was:

"Your husband is not going to the labor camp! No train, no convoy. No leaving Moscow!"

Oh, selfish, selfish human nature! From that moment on I stopped hearing *the train*. I was almost ashamed of it; I kept telling myself that, at least for the sake of others, I must not forget. But I kept forgetting, first for a few minutes a day, then for a few hours... And at last, I was not thinking about it for a few days in a row. It was still moving along the tracks somewhere, and someone else's spouses, siblings, and children were moaning inside its stifling cars. But, hard as I tried, I could not hear it anymore...

* * *

Another remarkable thing happened that winter: my stepson Dmitry obtained an exemption from the army. This was not a temporary deferment, but a permanent decision that he was not fit to serve in the armed forces. With the firm enlistment rules of the Soviet Union, for a healthy eighteen-year-old man, who was not even a college student, escaping the draft seemed next to impossible. Nevertheless, it was done for Dmitry Fedorov, and done by nobody else but his imprisoned father. None of us have ever learned what connections Lev managed to establish in the Kashenko Mental Hospital, but not too long after he had returned to Butyrki, his son was invited to an appointment with one of the top psychiatrists in Moscow. The latter, bypassing Dmitry's primary doctor, issued a verdict that Dmitry had a mental disorder that completely disqualified him from ever serving in our glorious army.

There must have been further steps, to get more signatures on the document: the army officials would not have accepted the diagnosis of a single psychiatrist, even a prominent one. Svetlana Semenovna was shocked and upset: up to that moment she believed that her client was an honest citizen who had made a mistake due to a common legal ignorance. She considered him a very difficult defendant, but attributed it to his character traits rather than his criminal nature. The incident with Dmitry changed her perception of my husband's personality. "He is not the man I thought he was when I took up his case," she told me, sounding very distressed. "There are too many things about him that I do not want to know, if I want to be able to defend him..."

There were things that I did not want to know, either.

I wished I had not seen the sales agreement for the car that my husband had allegedly "totaled" during a road accident. I wished Svetlana Semenovna had not told me that "he lies so badly that he can't remember his own lies". I wish I had not read my husband's autobiography, written for the prosecutor, in which the facts of his former employments were drastically different from the legends he had been telling me during our short romance.

From the semi-god whom I met almost four years ago, Lev Fedorov gradually turned into a human being—and a very imperfect one, not to say more. If I were to continue loving him, I had to do some hard emotional and mental work, putting together bits and pieces, and creating a completely new picture of my husband's personality. It looked like I should have plenty of time for that work, and I was optimistic that I would eventually succeed.

At least there was one part of the former Lev that I loved, cherished, and was incredibly proud of: in his criminal case Svetlana Semenovna found a Thank You Letter from the district attorney, addressed to INION, Lev's former company; it expressed gratitude from the Ministry of Internal Affairs, the office of Public Prosecutor, and all citizens of Moscow, to the INION employee Lev Fedorov, for his heroic behavior in risking his life while helping the police to arrest a dangerous criminal. The story about Lev breaking his arm while saving a young policeman from two offenders who were trying to take away his gun, appeared to be completely true. Despite Aunt Katia's mocking and putting me down for having believed in it...

* * *

I can picture the day of the trial as if it happened yesterday: cold, windy, with dry white snow crunching under my feet: the way you imagine late February in Northern Europe...

The courthouse was located in some remote district of Moscow, where I had never been before. That's where Lev's business acquaintance used to live, and where the crime of selling the gold-dust had been committed.

The courtroom was full. Most of the spectators belonged to the other defendant's party, so I did not know them. There were a few of Lev's former coworkers, including, of course, the Gosins, who came to provide moral support to both Lev and his wife. An official representative from INION, sent by the President Vinogradov, acted as a public attorney. Sergey, Lev's younger brother, was the only member of the large Fedorov family—except for his children Dmitry and Elena, who were sitting separately from everyone else, pretending that they did not know me.

I remember my husband walking into the room, his back very straight and his head up. He was required to keep his hands behind his back, but there were no handcuffs, nor any other visible physical restraints. Two armed guards in uniforms followed him half-a-step behind. Lev went straight to the dock, without looking at anyone or trying to figure out who was in the courtroom. I imagined how incredibly humiliated he must be feeling, knowing that his coworkers, his wife, and his children were seeing him in that condition. But whatever he felt, he did not show it.

Once he sat down, he started slowly scanning the room with his eyes, lightly nodding to people he recognized. I kept looking at his face, afraid of missing the moment when he finally looks at me. It seemed to take him forever. He nodded to me the same way as to the others, without any special expression, and suddenly I saw not a criminal defendant brought to court under guard, but a speaker who was about to deliver his presentation at a conference, in front of a highly respected audience.

He looked almost like he did on the day he defended his dissertation: formal, distant, tense and calm—except that then he was dressed in suit and tie, not in a home-made sweater. The guards in the background did not interfere with the picture.

But when the judge started talking, I was forced to remember that we were in court...

Svetlana Semenovna built her legal defense on Lev's remarkable qualities as a hard-working person, a talented scientist, and a valued employee of his institute. She spent a good ten minutes listing his awards, including numerous statements of gratitude Lev had received from various companies he had ever worked for. She asked the honorable court how often they had an opportunity to try a person who had received a personal Letter of Gratitude from the District Prosecutor for having fought dangerous criminals. She reminded them that her client had sold his gold below the government price; that the only reason he could not possibly have sold it to the appropriate government agency was that the waiting list for the sale of gold was over a year long, and Mr. Fedorov needed the money much sooner. Lev Fedorov was a man his country had to be proud of, not to lock him up with criminals.

The trial went on and on... The second attorney, who defended Kirova, delivered an even longer speech. I knew that Kirova's lighter sentence was in my husband's best interest, so I tried to concentrate on her case, but could not understand it. The judge finally announced a lunch break, and Svetlana Semenovna came over to me and the Gosins, to tell us that everything was going well. Kirova would almost certainly receive no more than three years in jail: her lawyer was doing a great job. Both lawyers understood that it was Kirova, not Fedorov, who was a real criminal deserving severe punishment; their job was to assure the minimal sentences for both defendants, so they combined their efforts to reach that goal. I had no idea where our lawyer was getting her confidence, but she clearly knew what she was talking about.

* * *

The low winter sun had not set yet when we left the courthouse. It was very, very cold—the last temper tantrum of Mother Winter who did not want to give way to Spring... We stood outside the tall apartment building that housed the district criminal court, in two separate groups: the Gosins, me, and Svetlana Semenovna in one group, Dmitry and Elena Fedorov with their uncle Sergey in another one. We were all waiting for Lev to exit the building, to wave good-by to him—and possibly even shout some words of support. But there was no prison car in sight and, therefore, no Lev. Svetlana Semenovna finally went back inside to talk to the head of the convoy. She had learned that there were some technical delays, so we could be waiting for at least another hour before the car arrived to take Lev back to Butyrki. None of us could stand the cold for that long; the Gosins had plans for the evening—so we decided to leave. After all, everything went according to Svetlana Semenovna's expectations: Lev was sentenced to four years, one of which he had already served. He will not be deported from Moscow neither during the remaining years of his imprisonment, nor after his term is served. In addition to all those wonderful things, in my pocket I had a written permission for a one-hour date with my husband, signed by the judge himself.

I remember waiting for a streetcar on a wide, white, freezing prospect. The sun had descended close to the roofs of the remote buildings, but not yet disappeared. Sergey Fedorov had said goodbye to all of us and left on a bus. I watched Dmitry and Elena, my stepchildren who were almost my age, climbing into their trolley on the other side of the street. They looked quiet, somewhat slouchy, and very lonely, distant even from each other. They suddenly reminded me of two half-frozen birds who had failed to find a shelter on a cold winter day, and now must cuddle with each other to keep whatever little warmth their tiny bodies still contain, without much hope for survival. Unexpectedly, I felt sorry for both of them, especially for Dmitry, who from now on had to live his entire life with the label of "mentally sick", as a payment for his father's having screwed up his own life...

6

The judge's permission for the date was valid the next day after the trial, but I could not use it, no matter how impatient I was. Butyrki was under quarantine due to a flu epidemic, and all dates were suspended until further notice. I had to return to Leningrad and wait again.

According to Svetlana Semenovna, I had no idea how lucky I was: epidemics in prisons did not prevent convicts from being sent away to labor camps. Many inmates would leave for their thousand-mile-long trips without exercising their only chance to see their family. There will be many wives, mothers, and children who will cry their eyes out, unable to ever use their precious permissions for the one and only post-trial date. As for me, I could wait all I wanted: my permission would still be good when the quarantine was over, no matter how long it lasted: my husband was in no danger of being sent away.

Svetlana Semenovna called me a few weeks later with the news that the epidemic was officially over, and the dates resumed. However, due to the recent quarantine, thousands of people eligible for dates were besieging the prison daily. Most of them did not even know whether their family member was still in Butyrki or had been sent away to the labor camp. "People kill each other in that line," warned Svetlana Semenovna. "You can either wait for a couple of more weeks—just make sure that your permission doesn't expire—or be prepared to come very, very early—and hold your place in line firmly."

Of course, I decided to see my husband as soon as possible.

On the day of the meeting, I arrived at Butyrki in a taxi at two o'clock in the morning. I had slept for a few hours at Tanika's house (I had finally revealed to her my shameful family story) and felt more agitated than tired. The prison reception room was closed, and at least a hundred people were waiting outside, hoping to be the first in line to see their loved ones in the morning. By daybreak the number of people with permissions reached several hundred, and the last ones had no chance to get in that day.

It was mid-March, and the night temperatures still fell below freezing. Dark indifferent apartment buildings surrounded the prison, creating an extra wall between us and the rest of the world. We were standing inside that circle in complete silence, crowded near the prison gate and stamping our feet in a futile attempt to keep warm. I started wondering if my watch was broken, or whether it was the time itself that stopped moving, when someone discovered a hallway door in one of the apartment buildings that was accidentally left unlocked. Immediately, several dozen people moved in, and took positions on the stairs. It was warmer inside, and people began to talk.

They came from all over our huge country, just to see their brothers, sons, and husbands (or, in some cases, mothers, wives, and daughters) for a short hour through a thick glass wall, in a few-day period between their trial and the beginning of the exhausting journey to the camp. Those who did not know anyone in Moscow, spent their nights at train stations. Everybody was talking of prison terms and camps, trying to guess where their loved ones were likely to be sent. I learned a lot about different camps that night: that one had a better head of the guards, but the trip there took over two months; in the second one, the conditions were milder and the labor lighter, but it was even farther away and not accessible by any transport, the nearest train station being over a hundred miles away. That camp was the closest to Moscow and the train stopped nearby, but the labor was hard and unsafe, and the guards were all beasts...

At six in the morning the door of the prison waiting room finally opened, and several hundred people, including those who had not been lucky enough to fit in the hallway, finally moved inside.

There were still a good three hours to wait before the office opened, and people continued talking. Each convict was somebody's child, spouse, parent, sibling. Mostly men, but sometimes women. I was hearing their jail terms: "twelve years," "ten years," "eight," "seven"... "Six years" was met with an envious silence.

And all of a sudden—how can I explain it?—I realized that *I did not belong there.* I was too damn happy, too damn lucky, I just did not have any right to be among those people who considered me one of them and tried to share their grief and their humble sandwiches with me. Several women asked me whom was I visiting. The husband? "Oh, poor thing, you are so young! Any children? Only three years old? Oh, poor girl, alone with such a young child..." And then someone asked me:

"How much?"

And I answered humbly:

"Three more years".

"Do you know *where*?"

And I had to say:

217

"Yes. Here, in Moscow."

And instantly there was a silence and emptiness around me. Women who had just been so warm and sympathetic, turned away and stopped noticing me. And I was almost glad, because I suddenly felt as if I came dressed up in a fancy evening dress and jewelry to a gathering of starving homeless people...

Lev and I talked for an hour on the telephone, looking at each other through a dusty glass screen. Coming up with topics for the conversation became more and more difficult: but there was nothing else to do except talking—and knowing that our every word was being recorded, did not help. The only thing that we really needed—a chance to touch, to hug, to simply hold each other and say nothing for a while—we could not have. We parted, feeling both frustrated and relieved, having reminded each other that our next dates would be "real," that Lev had an unlimited right to correspondence, and that it only takes three days for a letter to get to Leningrad from Moscow.

It was well after noon when I finally walked out of the prison. It turned out to be a beautiful spring day: the sky was bright blue, and the sun reflecting in the melting snow hurt the eyes. Birds sang their love songs like crazy, or maybe they were just happy—without any particular reason. And I was only twenty-six ...

I stopped at the nearest kiosk and bought myself a large ice-cream bar.

7

Spring finally came to my life after what had seemed an endless winter. I achieved some kind of inner peace where things were clearly divided into black and white, and I knew with confidence what I should and should not do. My husband had been convicted, but since the hope for his acquittal had died long ago, his conviction did not feel like a tragedy. On the contrary, the term was less than I had feared, and most importantly, he was serving it in Moscow. The image of the horrible train stopped torturing me, and all knowledge about labor camps, acquired during the last year, had become useless.

I knew that I must wait for Lev and try to give him as much moral support as I possibly could. But I also knew that I did not have any obligation to continue being miserable on his account: he had brought me too much pain when we lived together, and now it was his turn to suffer. As for me, after having done everything I could to relieve his suffering, I had to make the most out of my own life. I wanted to enjoy sunshine, to advance in my work, to learn new things, to reconnect with old friends and possibly make new ones.

At first, I was getting depressed and anxious when there were no letters from my husband for more than a week. Then my feelings became more complicated: I was equally afraid of finding the mail box empty, and opening Lev's letters. There was too much hatred in them, and although that hatred was not obviously directed at me, the overall tone made me feel threatened and insecure. One of the most shocking things was that Lev blamed attorney Gunina for his four-year sentence. He turned everything upside down and analyzed his legal case in such a perverted way that Svetlana Semenovna looked responsible for his unjust imprisonment. I tried to tell him that he was wrong, but soon realized that arguing was pointless. As a judge whose mind is made up long before the trial, Lev Fedorov, having blamed someone, did not care to listen to any objections. I was happy that at least he was not accusing me of deliberately having picked the wrong lawyer; he decided to blame his friend Gosin instead. But I could sense that I would be made responsible for many other things—as soon as my turn comes.

Lev devoted several letters to his early childhood memories, but even those were full of anger and contempt toward people who should have been close to him. His imprisoned father was the only one who escaped accusations of betrayal and deceit. There was no one about whom my husband spoke with love or gratitude, his own mother not being an exception. I realized that I was temporarily exempt from that list of evil creatures only because, at that moment in his life, Lev Fedorov found it convenient to keep me on his side.

* * *

Nadia remained in Akademgorodok with my parents. Contrary to the dire predictions of multiple pediatricians and child psychologists who followed her during her first year of life, she appeared to be developing normally—both physically and mentally. I was in Leningrad during her third birthday, but my mom threw her a proper birthday party, and I mailed a big box of colorful building blocks. When on April first I called my daughter to wish her happy birthday, her "Hi, mama," sounded so indifferent that at first I got hurt and thought of buying a plane ticket and flying to Novosibirsk immediately. But I had a new job and lots of plans for the next two weeks—so I quickly forced myself to take my mind off that phone call: my daughter was happy, and doing fine. I had my own life to figure out. As my beloved Aunt Olia loved to repeat: "Everything is for the best in this best of all worlds..."

"Everything is for the best in this best of all worlds," I said to Rozov, after I found a mistake in the program he and I had been working on together, which he had missed. "Thanks to you, I am now a computer programmer, not some miserable librarian."

"You must thank your husband," he replied, with his habitual barely detectable irony in his voice. "Had he not gone to jail, you would be in Moscow now... Doing what?"

As usual, it was impossible to figure out whether Rozov was serious or mocking; and if he was mocking, then whom? Himself? Me? The world?

We were drinking tea with cheese sandwiches in Rozov's small kitchen, when I noticed that it was nearly one o'clock, the subway closing time.

"Is anybody waiting for you at home?" asked Stanislav. "And you don't have to be at work tomorrow until... Five o'clock in the evening?"

He was correct on both accounts: no one was waiting for me at home—and the computer time the SRC rented from a more serious company, did not start until their own employees stopped their work for the day. My work schedule was unpredictable, ranging from working on weekends to evenings and even all-nighters—but, without a family to worry about, it suited me just fine. I had lots of hours to work at home (which was my favorite place), and I could do all my food shopping during late morning hours when the stores were empty, without lunch-time, and especially evening, queues of angry housewives, impatient to get home to their kitchens and their families.

As for Stanislav's wife, they had what he called "an open marriage." She had her own little apartment in a quiet and green suburb of the city, close to her job, and they visited each other on weekends and holidays. "We are more friends than husband and wife," he explained. "We may have sex a couple of times a year, if at all... Of course, she is a young woman, and needs much more than that... So, I don't come over there without giving her a fair warning..."

I had never seen such an expression on Rozov's face—or maybe I did, but preferred not to notice. I didn't feel that I was ready to cheat on my husband... Or was I? In any case, it was not happening tonight...

"I will sleep on the couch in your living room," I said. "Or go home in a taxi."

"The couch had protruding springs in it." Now I could see a trace of a smile on Stanislav's face, and his momentary blushing went away. "I will set up a folding bed for you. The same one my better half sleeps on when she is visiting," he added casually.

"And, by the way, I should tell you something else: I know your husband quite well... Maybe, in some ways I know him better than you do... certainly much longer. You don't need to believe me—but I can assure you that, even if you stay celibate for the next three years... which would be very stupid, if you want my opinion... But *even if you do*—he will never, ever believe it... What do I mean? Lev Fedorov likes women—and they like him (I am not telling you anything new, am I?) And he is not... Well, he does not have enough imagination, to understand that other people could be different from him... So... Do you think if you were away (in jail, or wherever) for four years, he would stay faithful to you?"

I was surprised how long it took me to fall asleep that night. Not that the folding bed was particularly uncomfortable, or the temperature in Rozov's living room was not right... But Stanislav's words stirred something in me... Well, they stirred a lot of things—feeling, thoughts, memories—more than I could deal with in one night...

Lev Fedorov would never believe... I remembered his letters from prison, full of anger and distrust of other people. No, he would not... He will not! In fact, he was not faithful even when we were together, and I was madly in love with him, cherishing every moment of closeness... Those long weekends in the village... His absences that he never explained. And, most of all, the way he talked about a couple of his women-friends... I was so naïve, so blind from love not to see it back then—although things were so obvious. All those jealousy scenes that came out of the blue... And that evening, when he called me "a whore," only because a neighbor had presumably complained to him about his own wife having an affair... "All women are like that... all of you! Don't try to persuade me that *you* are different. I am not a fool..."

The thought that my husband almost certainly had a mistress—and possibly more than one—upset me surprisingly little. As if it was just one more piece of puzzle that fit in his new portrait—fit so snuggly and tightly that removing it would take an enormous effort. And, of course, he will never believe that I did not sleep with anyone else. That I do not sleep with someone else already... And can I blame him? Who in the right mind would believe that a healthy twenty-six-year-old woman can live without sex for over a year?..

And could I, really?... Maybe I could not have... should not have...

It was already getting light outside, when I finally dozed off.

The next time when I came to Rozov's apartment, we spent the night in the same bed.

Chapter Five
"Everything is for the Best in This Best of All Worlds..."

1

As much as I tried to fit in with my new coworkers, I failed to make any friends in SRC. Female colleagues viewed me with unkind suspicion: what sort of woman wears a wedding ring to work, but never talks about her husband? From my terse answers they had no difficulty figuring out that I was living alone. I occasionally mentioned my toddler daughter, but never her father. A divorced woman would have been socially accepted—but I said I was not... And why the ring?

Men, as it turned out later, considered me stuck-up: a beautiful woman who thinks she is above everybody else, just because of her looks.

Still, I had friends: Rozov and Aunt Olia were as important in my life as ever. But the person I spent most of my time and felt the closest to, was Nina.

Nina, who seemed so happy to everyone else, had her own secret tragedy, her own pain, hidden from everybody, even from her family. For a long time, I was the only one who knew: she had fallen in love with another man.

When I first learned about it, I felt shocked, and almost certainly overly critical. I was still with Lev, trying to figure out how to turn our roller-coaster relationship into something resembling a normal family life—and mostly blaming myself for failures. I was too wrapped up in my own problems, to be able to see that my best friend's marriage had turned to be very different from what she had dreamed about. It still seemed fine on the surface, but Nina was as lonely with her quiet, intelligent Leonid as I was with my volatile Lev. Unlike me, she was not stuck in her house with a baby: she lived with her mother who was always available for babysitting. Leonid was not somebody who could ever insult a woman—or any human being, for that matter. He almost certainly loved Nina in his own way. The problem was, that he loved his job by far more. He always came straight home after work; unfortunately, he often did not leave his office until midnight.

He was a talented software programmer. In other times and in another country, he could make millions—if only he had the drive and ambitions. However, he was not an ambitious person; he was not after making big money or career. He was a pure scientist, in love with his science for the sake of science. He actually may have treated his programming as art even more than a science. And, as any artist, he lived in his creations.

He had a little closet in the apartment, with no windows, lit by a hundred-watt bare lamp hanging from the ceiling. A square table occupied almost the entire space. That's where Leonid lived when he was not at work, smoking cigarette after cigarette and studying his computer printouts. He came to bed when his young wife had long been asleep. Most of his weekend time was spent in the closet. He would come out to eat after multiple invitations, but rarely talked to anyone during meals, impatient to get back to his programs. He was writing programs even in the bath tub.

When Nina and Leonid went out together, they made an impression of a beautiful and happy couple. They indeed were comfortable with each other—in rare moments when they were together. Unfortunately, while their marriage grew older, Leonid spent less and less time with his wife. The worst thing was, that even after he had promised her to go out, she could never count on him: he had a habit of canceling his plans at the very last minute. Numerous times he put her in an awkward situation when, minutes before departing for a party or theater, he suddenly announced that he did not feel like going. Having expensive tickets did not mean anything to him. Many times, Nina had to call her friends frantically, offering a ticket to a play or concert that starts in an hour, and often ended up going by herself. Even more awkward were cases when she had to come alone to a party and lie that her husband had suddenly fallen sick or had an emergency at work.

Eventually she stopped counting on him, and started making plans with her girlfriends, or rejecting invitations to parties where she was expected to come with her husband. Still, she frequently was put in a situation when she had to go alone—and she hated that. Leonid did not seem to care. Most of the time he probably did not even notice whether she was home or not.

Had Leonid been even slightly less distant, Nina would have never started an affair. But she was then twenty-four years old, a very outgoing, social girl, and in the beginning she probably just thought "why not?.." She was sure it would not go anywhere. She still loved her husband. She may have hoped that if he got slightly jealous he might finally notice her. She never lied to him, she always told him: "I am going to meet Boris, for coffee, movie etc. Would you like to come along?" But Leonid, who at some earlier point had been Boris's friend, always said "No. Have a good time".

The tragedy was that Nina did not have "a good time": she fell in love head over heels, with a cold, selfish, and irresponsible man, who, she knew, would never love her. (After knowing him for many years I began to suspect that the only person he was ever capable of loving was himself.) Nina had a rare fragile beauty that you had to look hard to notice, but once noticed, couldn't take your eyes off. She was a prestigious girlfriend for the bastard who had everything else, including a stunningly beautiful wife. He also had a peculiar social position: once a talented and successful engineer, he had become a *refusenik*—i.e. a person who had applied for emigration from the Soviet Union but was *refused* by the authorities. At the time I first met him, he had quit his engineering job and was working as a boiler room operator—an occupation that gave him a lot of free time and privacy, if not any significant salary...

Boris was hurting Nina immensely, by disappearing for weeks and months in a row, right after he had made a date with her. He kept her waiting for his calls for hours, days, weeks. Many times, she thought it was all over, started to calm down and think of the possibility of not having him in her life. And then he would call, or even show up in their apartment without warning, but with some fascinating story, a funny joke, an interesting book. He intended to keep her, and finally she learned to just be patient and wait...

Their affair lasted for many years and ended with his immigration to the U. S. To his honor I must admit: he kept calling her and writing to her and promising her definite help in case she ever decided to emigrate. I really don't know how he could have helped—so promising probably was not worth much...

* * *

I last saw Boris in San Francisco, several years after Nina died. He had not changed a bit, did not even age: still the same confident smile, same stylish clothes, casual talking about his successful business, his wife, his son. He had met me at the airport and was driving me to the house of a mutual friend where I was supposed to stay, so I had to tolerate his presence. But every time I looked at him, I saw Nina's narrow face, saw her eyes full of pain at times she came over to my place after Boris had not shown up for a date.

I am sure that he was partly responsible for her early death: she wore out her heart.

But Boris's presence in my best friend's life eventually changed mine: I would almost certainly had never gotten to the point in my life where I was granted the Political Refugee status by the American Embassy in Moscow, if many years earlier Nina had not met Boris. Therefore—for better or for worse?—I would have never come to America.

But who could have known it back then?..

2

That spring I read the *Tanakh* for the first time in my life.

I had not been planning on reading it, was not even thinking of it. It happened accidentally. I was sitting in Nina's living room, talking to Rahel Naumovna, her mother. The conversation drifted from subject to subject, from foreign languages to old books. Nina's mother, who among her other weird ideas, did not believe in home libraries, had one book that she treated as a family relic. It was a nineteen-century edition of the Tanakh (the part of the Bible that Christians call "Old Testament") which had originally belonged to Nina's great-grandfather. When my hostess handed me two heavy volumes with golden letters running across fancy leather covers, I opened the first one more out of politeness than because of any interest to the subject.

The text was in two languages—Russian and Hebrew. I had never seen Hebrew letters before and found them almost artistically beautiful. The paper had turned yellow from time, but the printing had not faded a bit. I read the first few lines of the Russian text, but could not take my eyes off the strange script on the opposite page. And suddenly something turned inside me, something I could not define in words: it was almost subconscious—the desire, no—the need—to read that book from the first page to the last, not skipping a single line. I sensed a hidden poetry in the old-fashioned language; there was a mystery hiding behind every page, and that mystery was waiting for me to solve it.

"Unfortunately," said Rahel Naumovna, "the book cannot leave the house. It has been in my family for three generations. It survived the Revolution and the three wars. You are most welcome to come here any time and read it, but I can't let you take it home."

Most of the time, Nina and I met at my place or on some "neutral ground," but from that day on I became an almost-daily guest in her apartment—even when my friend was not home. It felt almost like a second job. The atmosphere in the house was somewhat distracting, with constant invitations to share family meals, watching Leonid disappear in his "computer closet," trying to figure out who was calling on the telephone—in short, my progress was extremely slow. I continued reading the Book more out of stubbornness, than because I really enjoyed it.

It all changed in one day, when Nina showed up at my place with the first volume of the Book. Her mother, having considered the matter, decided to let me read in the privacy of my own home. I was the first person in Nina's memory who had won such an outstanding trust with her mother.

For the next two weeks I looked forward to being alone at home and not writing any computer programs. Reading Tanakh, and especially looking at the Hebrew part of the text, turned me on as if I were drinking some magic wine.

Like most Soviet citizens of my generation, I was raised not just in a secular, but an openly "anti-religious" society. Of course, like most of my peers, I had tried to read the Bible—but it was mostly parts of the New Testament, sacred for Christians but not for Jews. The stories I had read and heard from the Old Testament, were adapted for the contemporary reader to convey the plot only, and thus give the necessary knowledge for understanding great works of art. Needless to say, such adaptations stripped the stories of poetry and philosophy.

Like most of my friends, I was turned off by the striking injustice of *Adonai*. I could not comprehend how anyone could worship God who punished innocent people for crimes committed by others and de-stroyed entire nations for the sake of his "chosen" people.

And suddenly I saw the whole narrative in a totally different way. Instead of seeing *events* that may or may not have happened, I started seeing *symbols*. Instead of reading Biblical stories as guidelines for the way life *should be*, I began to read them as symbolic descriptions of the ways *life really was* at that time... Which, in turn, made me won-der how much had actually changed in the subsequent few thousand years. Real life has never been fair or just; crime, committed by indi-viduals, usually reflected on the entire nation, often through many generations.

Examples were numerous and overwhelming. The Bolsheviks' revo-lution in my own country, which threw millions of its contemporaries as well as generations to come, into the abyss of political repressions, malfunctioning economy, and perverted mentality. I thought of a hand-ful of German Nazi leaders, who not only killed six million Jews (many of whom were their own German citizens) but pushed half of the world into the bloodiest war in history. Fifty million people died, and Ger-many itself ended up in ruins: desperate mothers searched in vain for the graves of their teenage boys, who had perished fighting for ideas they often did not share, or even understand...

The Book, written thousands of years ago, was telling me about the Tatars burning Russian villages and massacring women and children, because of the greed, cowardice, and narrow-mindedness of Russian princes, their rulers. It was talking about medieval witch trials and in-nocent people tortured and burned at a stake, because those in pow-er needed to keep their power. I thought of peaceful and prosperous countries turned into places of disaster and despair, because of the misdeeds of a ruling group, sometimes only a few powerful individuals. The Book I was reading was not trying to give answers about the way the world *should be*; its stories, written by different people in different historical epochs, simply registered the way the world *have been*—and probably will remain—for as long as humans inhibit this planet...

My own story with Lev Fedorov suddenly turned petty and unim-portant—although logical—as a grain of sand in a huge desert...

Before returning the volume to Nina's family in exchange for the second one, I decided to read it one more time. On the second reading, I found another layer: instructions about proper living in society, sketches of what later would become criminal laws, attempts to define morality and separate good from evil in human behavior. It could not be anything more off-putting for a modern person than the legends, stories, and morals, taking place in a society based on slavery. But wasn't slavery the only socio-economic system that existed during the times the Tanakh was written? Had the authors tried to describe a more just society, the Book would have turned into an interesting utopian treatise but would have lost its value as a reflection of life the way it was...

At first, I was happy reading the Book alone, but soon I felt a strong need to discuss it with someone. I had too many questions and very few answers. I tried talking to Nina, but she had never read the Book and, although she listened to me with polite interest, could not offer her own opinion. Aunt Olia complimented me for "reading the book that every educated person should read" but, as a true scientist, rejected the idea that the Bible was anything more than a collection of stories that had inspired great works of art. Rozov simply suggested that I should read a manual for programming language PL-1, instead of wasting my time on "stupid ancient tales."

I finally gave up. I turned my attention to the history of the country where the Book had been written—and realized that I knew nothing. It was the country of my ancestors, just as much as Russia. But Russia was all around me—and no matter how many lies and biases we had to learn at school and hear from the TV screens, there were things to see, hear, smell, touch, experience—far more information than could be found in a thousand books. At the same time, neither libraries nor the largest bookstores, offered any literature about the history and culture of Israel; there was no embassy in the Soviet Union, citizens of Israel did not come to visit, and those who went there from Russia never returned to tell about life on the other side...

I wandered around bookstores, the way a hungry animal searches the forest looking for food. Anti-Zionist brochures were the only literature where the country of Israel was even mentioned. Out of desperation, I finally decided to buy one of those paperbacks. After all, in order to criticize, the author had to offer some real information. That information would undoubtedly be perverted, the facts turned upside down and misinterpreted. However, having graduated from a Soviet high school and a Soviet college, I knew the rules of that misinterpretation well enough to be confident that I would be able to do a "reverse translation".

I remembered the game my father and I used to play when I was in sixth and seventh grades at school and had to prepare "political information" reports. Dad gave me the summary of the world's news the way he had learned them from different foreign radio stations, jammed and outlawed by our government. I was then supposed to "translate" them into the language that my school teachers wanted to hear. For example, if the "Voice of America" or BBC reported that "Soviet troops, in violation of the international laws, crossed the border of an independent X** country," in my "translation" the news sounded like that: "The people of the Republic of X** asked the fraternal Soviet people for help in fighting bandit groups backed by the U.S imperialists". My father corrected me if I translated "too much." As a result, I always got "fives" (i.e. "A") for political information at school.

Having decided that I should have no problem in "translating" an anti-Zionist brochure, I finally picked up the one called "Zionism: the face and the masks". It seemed to have a larger history section than others, although written in a tone just as appalling as the rest of them. I swallowed the book in two days—with disgust, but nevertheless having found some useful information about the history of Israel and its political structure. I got an impression that the author, with all his dirty language and constant accusation of Israel as an undemocratic and peace-threatening country, knew the subject well. I even thought that if, by some miracle, I had an opportunity to talk to that author privately, he would be able to tell me many interesting things and would answer at least some of my questions in an unbiased way.

Having memorized everything in the brochure that seemed worth memorizing, I decided that there was no point in buying any more of that kind. I needed real books on Jewish history; I wanted to see Israeli movies, hear Hebrew songs, read contemporary Israeli literature. I suddenly realized that, with all my extensive education, that part of the world remained a well-guarded white spot. That white spot now drew me towards it like a forbidden fruit attracts a sinner. The Book I had just read, taught me that every person carried responsibility for his or her nation. There was a part of me, hidden from everybody (including myself), which was responsible for that tiny piece of land and everything that was happening there.

Had I been braver, I could have gone to the synagogue and tried to find someone to talk to, but I was too shy to even attempt that. Besides, having already lost one job on the account of my husband, I was not prepared to risk accusation of "ties with Zionism." Tanika's story with the cross was still fresh in my mind—but Tanika got in trouble for wearing a Christian symbol which, like it or not, was an essential part of Russian history and culture. I could not even begin to imagine how authorities might react to a young woman who demonstrates affiliation with the religion of an enemy country.

Still, I had a strong feeling that something *must* happen, and the white spot would somehow turn into colors. I just had to look hard.

That was when I met Michael.

3

He looked as if he had just stepped down from the pages of the Book that I was studying so passionately, an ancient Hebrew dressed in imported jeans and a modern shirt. He had a black curly beard and hair, and eyes that looked right inside you. He spoke softly and slowly, not wasting words, but a hidden passion in his voice made me think of a Hebrew prophet.

The minute he walked into my living room, I knew that something had changed in my life. We sat down and talked as if we were close friends who had known each other for many years and needed to catch up on the recent events of their lives. He asked my permission to smoke, but, other than that, seemed to feel at ease in my house, as if he had been there many times before.

It was May First, the day that the government treated as a big international holiday, and everyone else regarded as a reason for two extra days off. Young people usually had parties—not out of solidarity with world proletarians, but simply because it was a four-day weekend, and the weather in the north of Russia was still not warm enough for camping and other outdoor activities. Nina and I, both lonely in our own ways, also decided to have a party. There were only four of us: Nina, her friend Boris, Boris's best friend Michael, and me.

Many events had led to that day. First, five years ago, Nina and Leonid met Boris during their honeymoon in the mountains of Pamir where Boris had a summer job as a tour guide. What started as a casual vacation friendship, continued after all three of them had returned to Leningrad. Unfortunately, while the marriage progressed, Leonid became less and less social, and left his young wife alone more and more often. Their friendship with Boris was beginning to fade, and Nina was very surprised when the latter suddenly invited her and her husband to his birthday party. Leonid said that he would go, and asked Nina to accept the invitation. So she did, only to face an awkward situation when, five minutes before they were to leave the house, Leonid suddenly announced that he did not feel like going. Nina had already gotten half-used to her husband's mood swings, but this time she was very upset. Boris was not her close friend, and she felt extremely uncomfortable arriving at his party alone. Since it was too late to cancel, she spent a good half an hour crying and trying to persuade her husband to go—all in vain.

She finally went alone, and having arrived at the party late, invented some story about her husband needing to finish urgent work that very evening. Unexpectedly for herself, she ended up having a good time. The conversation was interesting, the people warm, and Boris was clearly glad to see her. Unfortunately, there was one guest, perceptive enough not to believe Nina's explanations about her husband having to work on Saturday night. That guest was Michael. At the end of the party, he found a moment when Boris's wife was not around, and whispered in his ear:

"You are an absolute idiot! This is a gorgeous girl who seems to be married to a turkey... Where are you looking?"

That evening started a romance that changed Nina's life forever. She resisted as long as she could. She tried to persuade herself that it was "just a friendship". The fact that Boris lived with a strikingly beautiful woman whom he referred to as his wife, made that self-deception even easier. Every time Nina had a date with Boris, she asked her husband to join them, but he almost always preferred to write his programs. At first Nina was seeing Boris because he was an interesting person; but gradually his presence in her life started filling the emptiness created by an unhappy marriage. She must have missed the fine line that separates "liking" from "loving", and when she realized that she was on the other side of that line, it was too late...

After that memorable birthday party, Nina met Michael several more times. Every time she saw him, she somehow thought of me. She could not explain why: it was a kind of intuition, an image of Michael and me together. She finally told Boris about it; Michael did not mind meeting Nina's "unusual friend", but it was hard for him to find the time.

Michael and I finally met in my house on May first, 1985, thirteen months after my husband had been arrested, and nearly two years after the beginning of Nina's bitter affair with Boris.

A few days later Michael brought me a bunch of books about Israel and Judaism. Most of them were *samizdat*: typewritten or photo copies of real books. One book was published in the U.S. and therefore was in English. I swallowed all of them within a few days, as a thirsty person in a desert gulps water, without even feeling its taste.

* * *

Michael and I saw each other several more times before parting for the summer. There was absolutely no romance; at that time, I would not even have called it "friendship," but rather "acquaintance"—at least by Russian measures. I was almost surprised when he called me again in September and invited me to his place to listen to Israeli records. (His family being away, that was the one and only time Michael invited me to his home.) Out of the record player came melodies of the desert, ancient as the Bible itself. There was an unspeakable sadness in them, profound loneliness, and longing for eternity. Then we listened to modern Israeli songs, full of joy and hope for the future, in spite of the bitter history of the country that had given birth to them. That night I heard the sounds of the Hebrew language for the first time in my life. Michael pronounced and translated the phrases that were repeated most often: "*Yerushalaim shel zahav*"—Jerusalem made of gold, "*kama tov*"—how good, "*eretz*"—the land, the country... After that short lesson, I could recognize these words when I heard them. The letters on the records' covers were the same ones I had seen in the Bible, only here they were talking about contemporary, commonplace matters; they were part of everyday life, and that made them even more fascinating.

I asked Michael if he knew how the letters sounded. He brought me a photograph of a page from a text book, displaying Hebrew alphabet with names and transliterations of each letter. I could hardly believe my luck when he allowed me to keep the photograph: he did not need it, he knew enough Hebrew already. Later I found out that Michael was boasting about his knowledge of Hebrew. He did know the alphabet and a couple of dozen of the most common words and expressions, but could not read a text without vowels. He was, however, my first Hebrew teacher.

After some hesitation he started lending me his records, so I could copy them onto a tape and play them at home whenever I wanted. He gave me his own interpretations of Judaism that I now find bizarre, but then his ideas influenced me a lot. His understanding of God and the universe, his attitude to life and death, were a weird mixture of Judaism, Buddhism (which I suspect he knew very little about) and his own philosophy. He frequently sounded as if he had answers to all questions—a quality that would have been more appropriate for me at twenty-seven than for a grown-up man in his late thirties; but he also was a good listener, and accepted disagreements with subtle humor and sufficient degree of respect.

Michael was certainly a very interesting and intriguing friend, but, like Boris, extremely unreliable. I could never be sure that he would show up for the date he had set up himself. He could disappear for a few weeks in a row without any warning, and then show up on a half-an-hour notice, and spend the long evening with me, being as much at ease as if we had seen each other the night before.

Unlike Nina, I was involved but not in love, and although Michael's broken dates and sudden disappearances distressed me in the beginning, I got used to them quickly, and started taking them for granted. I tried not to make other plans for the evenings when Michael promised to stop by, but I left the house a few times when he was not there at the agreed time. That did discipline him: he still missed dates, but at least learned to call me when he was late.

* * *

Like his friend Boris, Michael was a *refusenik*. He had applied for emigration some ten years earlier, when many people were given permission, but was rejected... or, better say, *refused.* He had graduated from a good technical college, and for a few years worked as a space engineer, involved in research that required security clearance. Following the unwritten rules of the Soviet government, he quit his official job a year before applying for emigration; during that time, he cleaned restaurants at night. His wife was then a junior engineer with a symbolic salary, and they had a toddler daughter. In order to survive financially, Michael, who had always been interested in photography, started his own mini-business photographing wedding couples laying flowers on the memorials to war veterans.

The refusal to allow his emigration must have been a blow to his family; there was no logic, no explanation, except the standard bureaucratic phrase that *Mr. Levin's emigration is considered unreasonable at this time,* and very little hope that the decision would be reversed any time soon. Did they consider that Michael knew more "state secrets" than thousands of other applicants who were, despite their former "secret" jobs, receiving *permission*? Or was it just a lottery, where some people had to lose, to keep the game going? One could only guess...

Later I learned that Michael Levin's name was known to many human rights activists worldwide. His story frequently appeared in foreign media—in articles concerning Jewish emigration and human rights violations in the Soviet Union. Having never set foot on Israeli soil, Michael had been granted Israeli citizenship by a special decision of the Knesset. There were demonstrations in front of Soviet Embassies in Europe, demanding permission for Michael and his family to leave the country.

It is only natural that the KGB took interest in Michael. Simply arresting him would have been difficult because he was too noticeable. Therefore, he remained free, but never left alone. One of Michael's favorite stories referred to an early stage of his life in *refusal.* After having quit a night job in a restaurant, he was formally unemployed for a while. An unemployed adult under fifty-five was considered a *loiterer* in official bureaucratic language, and loitering was punishable by law. Michael would not have been the first refusenik imprisoned for not having a job after his employer had fired him for his desire to leave the country.

When Michael was summoned to meet the investigator, he went well prepared. The law, he reminded the officer, required *one of the spouses* to work; the other one could stay home doing household chores. There were no indications that the working spouse had to be the man, and Michael's wife was employed full-time. The investigator admitted that it was correct. However, he insisted that Michael must have had an unreported income: otherwise how could his family survive on his wife's salary of ninety rubles a month? That question was the investigator's big mistake.

"Do you mean," inquired Michael, "that in the Soviet Union a person with higher education working full-time does not make enough money to support a family of three? Do you realize that such a statement discredits socialism and the entire Soviet system? I will make sure that those who may be concerned know about your views..."

The young investigator, who was hoping to use Michael's case to get a promotion, was happy to get rid of the difficult defendant, and the case of loitering was closed forever. But that did not mean that the authorities gave up on Michael.

Several years after I first met Michael Levin, I came across an old article in some English-language newspaper, describing his arrest for "possession of bullets" that had been stealthily hidden in his room by the KGB officers conducting a search. That resulted in a few days of detention, after which Michel had to be set free "due to the lack of evidence"—or perhaps because Soviet authorities did not feel like generating too much commotion abroad on behalf of Mr. Levin's release.

4

Michael and Boris had met while taking a course to become boiler-room operators. The most common jobs for highly educated refuseniks were, strange as it may sound, night watchman, street cleaner, and operator of a boiler room. At those jobs, traditionally held by blue-color proletarians, one could meet a sophisticated well-read engineer or scientist, most often a refusenik, or sometimes an unrecognized artist or an unemployed philosopher whose philosophy did not fit the official government school. Members of those informal groups knew each other instantly and frequently formed profound friendships. The example of Michael and Boris illustrates that pattern.

One of the world's most breathtaking architectural ensembles, the Palace Square of St. Petersburg, will forever remind me of Boris and Nina. Boris's boiler room in the basement of the General Staff Building, across the square from the Hermitage Museum, provided the greatest contrast one could find in a big city: the square bursting with tourists, the boiler room warm and quiet, its semi-darkness creating a feeling of complete isolation from the rest of the world. Occasionally, Nina asked me to accompany her there: apparently, she was not always comfortable facing her lover alone. The basement provided a safe and convenient place for a date—absolutely private and very cozy, especially during long northern winters with their almost perpetual darkness. The boiler was fully automated, and Boris's job of watching the instruments' readings was easy, leaving plenty of time for personal matters. Nina must have spent the most meaningful hours of her life there. Meaningful does not mean happy: many times, when she stopped at my place on her way home, her eyes were red with tears. For me, however, it was a fun place to visit, always a mini-party that generated mostly positive emotions—and resulted in a few fun photographs and bitter-sweet memories...

The place I visited more frequently and with much more complicated feelings, was located in an apartment building at the outskirts of the city far from its historical architectural ensembles: it was Michael's photo studio. I forgot the reasons why Michael had never made it to a boiler room operator, but at the time when he and I met he was running his own "photos for passports and documents" shop. To make ends meet—and also out of love for the art of photography—Michael photographed everyone who was willing to pay, and even more often did work for people from whom he did not expect any payment at all. Nadia's and mine best pictures from those years were done by Michael, and he never charged us a ruble. Running his own photo shop served two major purposes for Michael: it gave him an official "employment," and provided an excellent well-equipped photo lab for whatever extra work he wanted to do. It was also his private office, his personal space where he could do whatever he wanted.

Photography was the love of Michael's life, but the shop generated more expenses than income. Private enterprises were poorly developed in Soviet Russia, and the regulations behind them were insufficient and ambiguous. Even more ambiguous were rules of taxation, which each official interpreted according to his or her individual preferences.

Michael lived and supported his family on unreported income but had to be clever not to get caught. He almost certainly received some financial help from foreign Jewish organizations, but that assistance could not possibly have been regular. Michael's family puzzled me a great deal. At the time he and I met, he had two children fifteen years apart, the younger one being only slightly older than my Nadia. His wife was reported to be beautiful, intelligent, and gentle, but like any proper oriental patriarch, Michael kept her inside the house. She had worked for a few years after graduating college, but then he insisted that she stop, even before their second child was born. Michael must have been making enough money to provide for the family, but he hardly spent any time at home. The time to reach him began at midnight, and very often calling at twelve-thirty in the morning I heard his wife's friendly voice: "He is not home yet. Please, try in half-an-hour". Liza Levina knew me as her husband's English teacher and later as a fellow refusenik, and we occasionally had friendly chats on the phone; but, until the day the family was finally leaving the Soviet Union, I never met her personally. Michael's family belonged to a different part of his life, and I was not privileged enough to be allowed into that sanctuary.

* * *

I had plenty of opportunities to get to know the Levin family many years later in California, when I visited them in San Francisco. Liza was a very nice person, but I could never figure her out as a woman. Her facial features were perfect: she had nice hair and a splendid figure. Nevertheless, she seemed plain to me: always wearing dark clothes, always feeling cold, smoking cigarette after cigarette, reluctant to learn English, afraid to drive a car, not daring to look for a job, relying on her husband's opinion in every possible matter, she caused more pity than admiration. Immigration does crush some people, so she may have been different in Russia, although I cannot imagine her ever being radiant, wild, sexy, independent, as I had always imagined Michael's wife should be.

Michaels' life in the United States did not go as everyone who knew him had expected. He was never able to return to his main profession as a space engineer. He was undoubtedly talented, had received a world class education and had successfully worked in the field in the Soviet Union. Unfortunately, he had missed too many years and was probably too old by American standards. Had he been able to emigrate in his twenties when he first applied, his professional life would almost certainly have been different. Eighteen years of living as a refusenik hardened his character, made him famous among Jewish and human rights activists worldwide, and brought him new friends, but in many ways, they were years stolen from his life.

Fourteen years after he set foot in this land of great opportunities, Michael is still working as a manager in someone else's photo shop. He has long become indispensable to the owner, but having no proper credit history and no guarantors, has been unable to get a sufficient loan to start his own business. What had been possible under a suppressive Soviet regime, appeared to be impossible in free America. His wife Liza died a year ago from lung cancer, which went unnoticed until it was too late: Michaels' employer did not provide health insurance.

If Michael feels bitter about his crashed hopes, I've never heard him complain. He has always been reserved in matters concerning personal emotions, and never expressed any regrets about having left Russia. Michael remains my only Russian-American friend who has not gone back to the city where he was born and had lived most of his life, and where he still has relatives and friends.

What surprises me the most is that he never went to Israel, not even for a short visit. I once asked him why.

"Why have another dream crashed?" he replied. "Maybe I want to have one illusion, an image of a perfect place on earth, an ideal country, that I do not want to ruin…"

Looking back at those long-gone years in Leningrad of the nineteen eighties, I feel nostalgic. In spite of all the hardships and bitter experiences, we were still so young, so naïve, so full of hopes for the future, with dreams so vivid that it was hard to separate them from hopes. We knew very well what was right and what was wrong; we knew whom to trust and whom to avoid, without mistake; we could spot a potential friend in the crowd instantly, as well as see through a hypocrite, no matter how well disguised. We were still in our own country.

And, most importantly, we were all alive.

5

It was late evening in the fall when I got out of the subway station in a new development area in Moscow, to spend the night with Tanika and her family. It was pitch-dark, and I was feeling scared and very lonely. I dragged my small suitcase, which was becoming heavier and heavier, through the narrow unpaved pass under the trees, fearful of the empty darkness around me, even more than of meeting a male human. Apartment buildings were close by, but I could not see them behind the dark trees. There were lights in the windows, and behind those windows people who had no idea about my existence were having company, drinking their late evening tea, watching TV, bathing their children, preparing for bed—living normal lives not realizing how happy they were.

Tanika had apologized profusely for not being able to meet me this time—but, after all, why should she? I was about to cry, when suddenly I thought about thousands, tens of thousands of women who, in order to visit their beloved ones in prisons (or, more often, in labor camps), had to ride for days and days on slow trains, sleeping at godforsaken stations, then travel for hours on mud roads on passing trucks, and still were grateful for those three days in a tiny private cell they could share with their husbands. How dreadful the way back home must be for them, even longer and lonelier than the way to the camp, because there was no reward of seeing their loved ones at the end of their journey...

Compared to them, I was unbelievably happy. I had had only an 8-hour train ride from Leningrad, plus a night on a comfortable couch in my childhood friend's cozy living room. And tomorrow I would see my husband, see without thick dusty glass separating us, see him so close that I should be able to hold his hand, maybe even hug and kiss him...

I had been dreaming of that date for months, imagining everything that we might say to each other, touching him, looking in his eyes...

Now, when it was finally so close, I could not believe that it was, indeed, about to happen. There was an eternity to live through between tonight and tomorrow morning. Ten endless hours, six hundred minutes—and what if something goes wrong at the very last moment?... What if I had the wrong day, or my husband would be denied the date at the very last minute?

What if I don't feel all the emotions, all the love for him I am feeling now... What if?...

I thought of my previous date with Lev, the night spent on the stairs while waiting for the jail to open in the morning, remembered women with faces stiff from grief who suddenly stopped talking to me, because I was too damn lucky to belong to their sisterhood. I remembered my promise never to forget that, no matter how miserable my life seemed to me, there were many people infinitely more unfortunate than I was. I had broken that promise too soon. I felt ashamed—but it did not make me feel any better. That trick was not working any more: simple understanding that my situation could be much more desperate, was overwhelmed by another one: that I could, in fact, have a *normal family*. I could be living my life like everyone else, never having to learn about prison camps and jail terms. Just like Tanika, or like my other girlfriends who now felt obliged to feel sorry for me...

* * *

No matter how long the night had seemed, it was finally over... I did have the date right, and was at the prison office on time. I was now passing through a dozen armored doors, each one guarded by an armed police officer. Every officer spent at least two minutes checking my papers and then finding my name in his list of free citizens granted the privilege of entering Butyrskaya Prison that day. My heart was beating faster and faster, not from fear, but from anticipation of seeing my husband in a few minutes. Now, when I was finally inside the prison and all the guards had my name on their lists, I began to believe that my date with Lev was real, and that he was, indeed, waiting for me at the end of that endless corridor...

And there he was, dressed in a dark blue prison uniform that actually looked good on him. He was neatly shaved, slightly pale but not noticeably having lost weight. He smiled and stepped toward me. We held each other, and stayed like that for a few minutes, saying nothing. The supervising guard did not seem to care. There were two other couples in the same cell, and only four chairs. The guard said that he would fetch more chairs and left. The door to the cell stayed wide open. The bathroom at the other end of the corridor implied that all of us were free to walk out of the cell if we had to.

The doors of several other cells were opened into the same corridor; each cell accommodating two or three dating couples. Two uniformed guards walked lazily from one cell to another, but they did not seem particularly intrusive. Our guard returned in a few minutes with apologies for not having been able to find more chairs. That was just fine with Lev and me: I happily sat on his lap. Another woman sat on her husband's lap. The cell was large enough for all three couples to have relative privacy: if we talked quietly, our neighbors could not hear us. The third couple soon disappeared: they must have found a less crowded cell. We now had enough chairs, but nobody was in a hurry to change position. The guard left after a few minutes and did not show up again. "He is Ok," said Lev. "I know him. You can get your food out..."

Lev certainly did not act like a starving man. It was getting close to lunch time, so we both ate with a healthy appetite, but taking our sweet time to enjoy the food. The sun shining brightly through the open window made our meal feel almost like a picnic. The grills on the window seemed completely out of place.

I finally could see the prison courtyard.

"Is that where you guys go for a walk?" I asked.

Lev smiled. "It's a big prison, honey. There are many courtyards here. I do walk through this one as well—each time I need to go over to another building."

"You mean, you can just walk out of your building and wander around the jail?" I was amazed.

"Well, I have to get permission, of course, and I can't leave my building after six at night—but I do need to visit all the buildings in order to do my job..."

According to Lev, he was responsible for all internal telephone communications and electronic signalization inside Butyrki. If that were true, it meant that he supervised free-hired workers, maybe even some junior prison officers. Knowing my husband's ability to invent stories, I did not completely believe him. I was wise enough, however, not to show my doubts.

Later I found out that I was wrong not to believe Lev. He may not have been the top manager, but he was, indeed, doing highly qualified engineering work and had at least one prison officer who reported to him. His position was unusual for a prisoner; many officers treated him as a coworker, rather than as an inmate. He reinforced that relationship by doing small favors for them, like fixing their personal electronic equipment. They did not have to (and actually, could not) pay him money for his work; they rewarded him with extra food—and not an additional prison ration, but meals bought in the staff cafeteria, or even brought from their homes.

Overall, I know very little about my husband's life during his years of imprisonment. He befriended several of his prison mates, and those who were released before him told me a few stories. I had to trust my intuition and knowledge of my husband's character, to choose which parts of those stories to believe, and which to reject. After Lev's release, I heard a few of his phone conversations with people he had met in Butyrki, including top prison officers. But I never collected enough pieces of that puzzle to compose a complete picture.

* * *

That date was very different from the ones I had read about in the books by Solzhenitsyn. Lev and I soon got used to the fact that the guard was not bothering anybody and became fully relaxed. Instead of a traditional one-hour date, Lev was granted two hours—a reward for "good behavior". During the second hour we were alone in our cell and could do whatever we wanted, except close the door. I found the requirement as stupid as most bureaucratic rules anywhere in the world, but there was nothing we could do about it, so getting upset made no sense.

Our biggest problem was coming up with new topics for conversation. Asking my husband about internal jail life did not make too much sense, since I could not trust his responses anyway. Telling him about my life in Leningrad was almost impossible: I was afraid to provoke his jealousy by describing my new friendships and meetings with interesting people. And I did not feel that complaining about my difficulties would be appropriate. I mentioned that I had recently read the Bible for the first time and that it had a great impact on me, but Lev reacted negatively. He called religion "a collection of tales for old ladies and the apparatus used by power-greedy clergy to keep people under their control." It was almost the opposite of the statements he had made earlier, so I was surprised and upset, but found it wiser not to argue.

I carefully attempted mentioning the books I had read about Israel, but that caused an even worse reaction. Lev immediately became stiff and asked if I was planning to run off to Israel with his daughter, leaving him alone in prison. He did not believe my reassurances, so I changed the subject as fast as I could. The basic problem in our relationship was not my husband's imprisonment: it was, as I had had many opportunities to understand, the lack of mutual trust.

By the end of the second hour finding topics for conversation became almost painful. Luckily, we were alone in the room, and had the option of just hugging and kissing without saying anything. However, neither one of us became particularly passionate. When our time ran out, I left the cell with mixed feelings of relief, disappointment, emptiness, and some dull pain. I knew that a long time would pass before my husband and I had another date and an opportunity to try again.

6

That night, Stanislav and I spent hours looking for the reason my program hadn't worked the way it was supposed to—before, exhausted more emotionally than physically, we collapsed in bed together. At that point of my life, those evenings with Rozov were probably the best part of it. I could tell him everything—but he always accepted it when I left some details of the story untold. He never asked intrusive questions; he never lied to me, or gave me reasons to lie to him. We saw each other infrequently, but each time was a holiday for my soul, mind, and body...

I had already told Rozov as much about my first date with Lev as I was comfortable telling; that means, all the facts, while omitting some subtle feelings that I had trouble putting into words. One of many wonderful things about Stanislav was that I could talk to him about my husband lying in bed with him, just as easily as at the tea table in the kitchen. For tonight at least, we were done with the topic—or so we both thought. I felt happy and light, Stanislav's skin cool and smooth next to mine, and me feeling stupidly happy and almost weightless—I thought if I wanted, I could just fly...

"I am so sorry," said Rozov. "Age... you know... I am no longer thirty. Please, don't take it personally..."

"What are you talking about?" I asked sleepily. "Do you think I stay here only for intercourse? There are many more things to enjoy in bed... with a good friend."

He chuckled. "I know, I know... Still, *she* is trying to be nice, isn't she?" Rozov occasionally talked about me in third person in my presence. Was it to mask some awkwardness, or stress his affection? I never bothered to find out. It was just part of Rozov; always fun, never boring—and never embarrassing...

"When she is all excited... And he can't perform his duty..."

I covered his mouth with my hand.

"Your duty was to help me with the damn program—and you've done that splendidly. And now you are offering me a comfortable place to sleep..."

"I just can't stop thinking about my friend... *her* spouse. He is exactly my age—but I can't imagine him ever having that kind of problem... consider that jealousy, if you wish." It was supposed to be the end of Rozov's apology—but suddenly I became tense—so tense that lying down was no longer comfortable; I sat up as if someone gave me an electric shock.

"What do you mean?"

"You know what I mean... Even though you are married to a man the same age as I ... You must have never..."

"Never what?" It was absolutely clear what Rozov was talking about—and my question could have been rhetorical, if only... I suddenly felt hot, then cold, then hot again. "You must tell me what you mean! Using words!"

Stanislav must have understood that he had gone too far—but there seemed to be no return. He was now tense, too, probably scared by my reaction.

"My friend Lev, *her* husband," he said in a whisper, "never had erection problems—or did he?.."

My mind was racing. "No... at least I had never..." Instead of that, I said something unexpected even to myself.

"Ok, you said—on multiple occasions—you know him well; that you *understand* him. Now, let's imagine—just imagine—that he—occasionally—had this very problem... as most men do sometimes, as you say... How do you think he would behave? Get angry at himself? Apologize? Using ... what words...?"

Rozov was quiet for so long, that I began to doubt that he understood my question. Or, that maybe I had just thought of asking it, but never actually had. But when he finally spoke, I knew that he had been thinking hard about his response—and it was not easy for him to pronounce the words.

"He would get angry *at her*,"—he said. "At his wife—just at the moment when she is all excited, her entire body ready to accept him... and he suddenly—at the last moment—realizes that he might not be able to satisfy her... The last thing on earth he would do, was to let her notice... God forbid, she would think that he is not a superman... that he might have faults as a male... No, he would never apologize—he would start blaming her... Not for his own impotence (even though very temporary)—no: he would think of something else to blame her for: remember something she had done—or could have done—earlier that day... or that week... or that month... He would make an ugly jealousy scene... Say cruel words... Make her cry, make her ask his forgiveness... And then, while she is meek, and week, and crying, his erection would come back—and then he would make love to her. And then he would say that he "has forgiven" her, that he believes her—or that it all does not matter... because his accusations have already done the job he wanted... he does not need them any more... Until the next time it happens..."

I think I said something about needing to go to the bathroom. I was gasping for air, I needed some space—I needed to be alone... Digest what Rozov had just said...

Because I now knew that he was right... That is exactly what was happening. How blind I was, not to see it back then? Why would my husband suddenly become extremely angry and unreasonably jealous in the hottest moment of our love-making?.. And how unfair it was... How painful... how I cried and begged him...

It all came back as real as if it was happening now... It was not Rozov back in the bedroom... It was Lev Fedorov... And I did not want, could not return there...

I had to run away... As far as I could—now, before it was too late... Too late for what?

I was standing in an unheated hallway of Rozov's small apartment, my head pressed to the wall, and crying, and crying... I did not realize I was crying, until I had to pause to catch my breath... my feet and hands became cold—after all, I was almost naked... In my mind, I ran outside—and I could see myself as if I were someone else.. "She" as Rozov called me. *She was running along empty street, in the autumn rain, barefoot, her long dark hair disheveled by the cold wind, her thin white nightgown transparent, her body barely protected, barely covered... But she had to run... There were no people around—or maybe they were looking at her from behind their closed windows, from behind their half-drawn curtains... A crazy girl, like a ghost, in long white robe, which did not even cover her breast... running away... From the man she loved... whom she now hated... from herself... from her shame...*

Stanislav's touch was lighter than a summer breathe, and his hand soft and warm on my shoulder. "Ok, ok... come back to bed, you will catch cold here..."

I did not resist him, but let him lead me into the bedroom. I suddenly felt so tired, that my eyes, still swollen with tears, closed by themselves. I must have fallen asleep instantly: I don't even remember my head hitting the pillow.

*   *   *

It was late morning when I woke up. The sun shyly lit the small messy room, the almost-bare tree outside the window was dropping off its last leaves. Strong and fragrant smell of coffee was coming from the kitchen.

"Aren't you late for work?" I asked Rozov.

"I called there and said I had ... some family issues. The Boss never asks any questions, you know... I will get there when I get there... I am leaving the place anyways... I want a real job... Writing programs with you made me feel nostalgic, I decided to return to my own computer programming... Yes, I will be busier than I am now... But I will still find time to help you—don't worry."

The coffee tasted great, and so was the toasted bread with cream cheese. I felt well rested, not even sure whether the last night happened, or was a nightmare...

All I knew, was that I would never, ever feel about Lev Fedorov again the way I used to... Not in bed, not anywhere else... But the thought did not bother me anymore. I was OK with it... At least for that morning.

7

The previous winter, Grandma Galia, my mother's only living aunt who used to take care of me and my second cousin Natasha, slipped on ice and broke her arm. She lived alone, in one small room in a communal apartment, which she shared with five other families. In theory, she should have had a fair amount of help from her adult neighbors—but the Grandma managed to have sour relationships with all residents of the apartment, regardless of their age or family configuration. Natasha's mother and my mom's first cousin, Aunt Irina, was at Grandma Galia's place at least three times a week. She had to come after a full day of work, and listening to her old aunt's endless complaints often made her irritable; as a result, none of the women enjoyed the interaction—although Aunt Irina's sense of duty would not falter. Natasha and I took turns visiting Grandma Galia on weekends. Still, accompanying Grandma to doctors' appointment (which always happened during the work day) was not always possible; besides, even though Grandma Galia's six-story apartment building had an elevator, it was out of service more often than not—so the old lady had a very hard time climbing stairs to her fourth floor.

The recovery was long and painful, but Grandma Galia won. At the end of the treatment, she was feeling so well that she spent the summer at her usual dacha, with her usual girlfriends. She lacked her former energy and strength, though—which became more obvious when the dacha season ended, and she returned back to the city. The shorter the days became and the closer the winter, the more anxious Grandma was getting, unsure of herself, complaining of loneliness, and fearing that she would not survive another ice-fall and another breaking of a limb. We, relatives, tried to reassure her—but none of us truly believed in our own promises that "Grandma Galia would be OK." After all, she was nearing eighty—and her generational stamina developed during the Civil-War childhood and the Great-War adulthood, was beginning to wear out...

The rescue-thought that came to my mind, appeared suddenly and unexpectedly. At first, I was so shocked, that, not believing myself, I called my Aunt Irina. "What would you think if I try to move in with Grandma Galia?" I asked. "Yes, I mean *apartment exchange*: my two rooms plus her room—for something bigger, that we both could share..."

Aunt Irina liked the idea in general, but was doubtful that I could find anything decent in exchange for our three rooms: after all, in the real estate language, none of them was a valuable residential property. Both Grandma and I lived downtown, in close proximity to subway stations and other public transport—that was a definite plus. Grandma Galia's room was small, in a very populated apartment. On the positive side, it had all conveniences, including a full bath and large kitchen, and her windows were facing a quiet green inner yard—but five more families sharing the same facilities? My two rooms, on the other hand, were spacious, and the communal apartment relatively small: only two more rooms with neighbors—but the windows faced a very busy and noisy street; worst of all, there was no bath, or even a shower, in the apartment—a very serious drawback according to the housing standards of the 1980s... Still, my aunt suggested that I should advertise— and see what responses we get. After all, what did I have to lose?

Stanislav Rozov advised me to forget it: no one, he said, is going to move from a private apartment (even a very small one) to a place without a bath tub. "Your rooms may have grand ceilings with stucco molding, and redwood floors—but who cares, when the place lacks the basic conveniences? Don't even waste your time on advertising and looking—better use it to improve your programming skills." Aunt Olia was of a different opinion: Many families were desperate to split up; a young couple may not be put off by the lack of shower in the apartment—after all, there were a number of excellent public *banyas* in the neighborhood—and I myself lived there for years, without missing the bathtub too much...

Of course, it was aunt Olia who offered to talk to my mother: after all, nothing could happen without my mother's consent: she was *registered* in the two rooms with all the same rights as I was; moreover, Aunt Galia was *her* aunt—so the authorities considered them "immediate family," while a great-aunt (which Grandma Galia was to me) was not "close enough a relative" to share the title for the new apartment. So, without my mother's explicit consent, we would not be able to get the common title, which would make the entire enterprise useless.

Aunt Olia called my mom from the comfort of her office, which (unlike her home) had a telephone. At first, my mom's reaction was negative: after all, our apartment building was scheduled to go for "capital repair" sometime in the near future—which meant that all residing families would receive government-owned single-family apartments—so moving out of our current rooms was outright stupid. Aunt Olia's counter-arguments were based exactly on the same premises: first of all, once the date for the capital repair is announced, all exchanges would be "closed," so both we and Grandma Galia would lose the only opportunity to improve our living conditions, never mind moving in together. Second, the capital repair—and therefore moving of the residents—may not happen within the next three years; and in three years mom's daughter and granddaughter (i.e. Nadia and I) would both be gone to Moscow; my mom will remain the only one registered in the two large rooms—so there is no way the government would give her a single-family place; she would just receive another room in a different communal apartment, with almost certainly lesser square footage, and possibly more numerous neighbors. As usually, my mom gave in to Olga's strong mathematical logic, and reluctantly agreed to consider the exchange—provided that I could "find something decent."

So, that fall, in addition to establishing myself in a new profession and desperately trying to figure out my constantly changing feelings toward my husband, I got busy looking for a new place to live. I spent hours and days advertising, showing off my two rooms, and visiting single-family apartments where residents wanted to split up so desperately that they considered moving into communal flats. At first, it seemed as if Rozov was right: as soon as people learned that my apartment did not have a full bathroom, the deal was off before it went anywhere. Following Aunt Olia's advice, however, I continued to advertise and to show. (Thankfully, Aunt Irina, mom's cousin, took care of all the talking about and showing her aunt's room—so at least I did not have to deal with Grandma Galia's part).

"Rolling stones gather no moss"—or maybe we were just plain lucky—but eventually we ran into a family who agreed to consider the exchange, in spite of all the faults of mine and Grandma Galia's places. The young man who came with his parents to look at my two rooms, happened to be a professional plumber. A closet, filled with junk that no one needed for years, caught his sight right away. He knocked on the walls, studied the water and sewage pipes—and announced that he saw no problem turning the closet into a shower-room; it would take him and his friends just a few days, and probably very little money, if at all (which implied that the materials would all be stolen—an assumption that did not surprise anyone). I was honest enough to warn him that the neighbors might object to destroying their closet, and that, as far as I knew, none of them had any interest in having a shower room, etc... The young man gave me a look that made me feel sorry for my current neighbors; at the same time, his short and careless whistle caused some malevolent feelings that I was not proud of. But I would not be there when that happens—so Klava and Praskovya would not even be able to curse me...

As for Grandma Galia's small room, the young man had a separate plan: he was about to officially marry the girl he had been already living with; the girl was now pregnant. He would first register in the small room alone, and then add his pregnant wife; as soon as the baby was born, the room would become too small for a family of three, so the government would have no choice but putting them in the fastest-moving queue for a new single-family apartment. As for his two parents and younger sister, they could live comfortably in my large two rooms with a new shower, until the capital repair of the house would move all three of them into a nice individual apartment in a new area of the city. Win-win, no matter how you look at it.

The place they offered me in exchange, was what people called "*Khruschevka*": a tiny three-bedroom, with a go-through living room and a separate kitchenette; and of course, a full bathroom, albeit small but with a bath tub. The legend had it, that Nikita Khrushchev after visiting the USA, decided that Soviet familied deserved comparable living conditions: so, he "copy-catted" the design of American apartments, at the same time significantly decreasing their sizes. (Later, I had many opportunities to wonder whether Americans were as well situated as the Russians had believed—but then it did not matter).

The apartment was in an excellent area of the city, but in a very poor condition, and required significant repair—but here I had lots of volunteers to help. A few of my friends, including, of course, Aunt Olia, Nina's husband Leonid, and Rozov—all said that they had experience in beautifying and bettering apartments, and promised their free labor to support me in that new adventurous endeavor.

The building did not have elevator (none of *Khruschevkas* did)—but we would live on the fourth floor, and with much lower ceilings it would be a shorter distance for Grandma Galia to walk up the stairs. Besides, for the next two or three years, at least, she will be living with me—and after that we could always find a boarder to move in one of the bedrooms, in exchange for taking good care of aging Grandma. Another one-hour phone call to Novosibirsk from aunt Olia—and the deal was done. Aunt Irina acted as my mom's official representative, when the six of us: Grandma Galia, Aunt Irina and I from the Staheyev-Chernetsky family, and the three adults from the other side, signed papers in the presence of three government officials, finalizing exchange of our residential places. I was now an official resident of a one-family apartment—small and rather dirty, but mine. Grandma Galia, after having chosen the room for herself, allowed me to do with the rest of the living space whatever I wanted. I was overexcited: being busy had always been my main coping strategy, whatever the problems; and repairing my own apartment—even with the shortage of materials—was a creative process, which I always enjoyed. In addition, it was a great excuse to see more of my busy friends, as well as the chance to have Aunt Olia, Nina, and Rozov finally meet.

8

Lev and I saw each other every two to three months, and the time between our dates seemed shorter than I had feared. Apart from visiting my husband, I had another reason for going to Moscow: I was suing the Soviet Government.

The matter was not as dramatic as it may sound: I just followed the standard procedure. After Lev's arrest his property, including the brand-new car and the bank account, was confiscated by the government. Legally, however, the property of a married person did not fully belong to him. Fifty percent of goods and money acquired during marriage belonged to the spouse. I had not been arrested or tried, so my property could not be confiscated.

The problem, however, was that the government took everything, as if assuming that the defendant was single. After Lev was sentenced and the confiscation of property finalized by the court, I had a right to appeal that decision by reclaiming my part of family assets.

Indispensable Svetlana Semenovna recommended a good probate lawyer, a quiet middle-aged man who treated me almost as a personal friend. He explained to me that goods confiscated from a person sentenced to jail were sold at special stores at prices way below their actual value, and only employees of the court system and correction facilities had access to those stores. Judges, therefore, had a vital interest in confiscating as much as possible, while appraising confiscated goods as low as possible.

In the case of the car, however, the price was fixed and did not depend on the judge: the car had documents. So, even though I had lost most of the furniture and jewelry (including items I had before my marriage), fifty percent of the car money was pronounced to be mine.

I had to wait for several more months before the money granted me by the court made it into the Moscow Central Bank. My husband had been imprisoned for almost two years when I walked out of the bank carrying in my purse a heavy load of cash. That very evening, I visited my parents' friends, to whom Lev Fedorov owed a significant sum of money, to return the long overdue debt. Then I opened a special bank account, and deposited the remaining three thousand rubles—all that was left from my husband's former wealth. Whatever the law may have said, I considered the money to be Lev's and wanted to make sure it would be there for him when he came home. The only treat I allowed myself was a pair of imported leather boots, and a return ticket to Leningrad.

* * *

There were many prison visits in the years of my husband's incarceration, but I do not remember them distinctly. My memory still holds selected pictures, some of them as vivid as if the event has just happened, others vague—and I can only guess what details may hide behind fragmentary images.

I remember the date when Lev introduced me to one of his fellow inmates. That inmate, in his early forties, had an intelligent face and a mild pleasant smile. His prison uniform hung on him as clothing looks on people who have lost lots of weight fast. He looked straight in my eyes when he shook my hand.

"That's Alexey, my friend," said Lev. "And this is his girlfriend Rina."

There was something in my husband's tone that implied that he wanted me to remember that couple. I had no idea why, and it was hard for me to concentrate on other people when I had come all the way from Leningrad to see Lev. There were only four of us in the cell, but the atmosphere was tense. Our warden was unusually strict. He kept walking into the room and interrupting us with petty cavils. He tried to make sure that Rina and I were not feeding the prisoners—and was as zealous as if his own nutrition depended on our compliance with the prison rules. Unlike Lev, who seemed to want food from outside the prison mostly as defiance against authorities, Alexey appeared really hungry. I noticed pain on Rina's face as she watched him quickly swallowing small pieces of sandwiches and fruits that she pulled one by one out of her purse. While Lev and I did not have much to say to each other, and therefore did not mind spending most of our time sneaking the food behind the guard's back, Rina and Alexey looked like they really needed to talk and were frustrated.

When I walked out of the jail with the usual feeling of disappointment mixed with emptiness, Rina was waiting for me outside. She was a small, very slim artificial blond in her mid-forties, who tried very hard to look ten years younger. She was dressed very expensively and according to the latest fashion, her jewelry matching her makeup, and shoes matching her dress. She had a fancy imported overcoat that she left unbuttoned to show the tight dress. She took my hand, and started speaking hastily and passionately.

"Our men want us to stay in touch. Alexey has told me so much about your husband—it's good that they are together. There are all sorts of people in prison who are not Alexey's kind at all, but Lev has been a wonderful friend for him. He helps people whom he likes... He has connections, you know... (I did not know anything about Lev's connections, and could only wonder what Rina meant.) It is so rare to meet an intelligent person in prison..."

Alexey had a car accident. He hit a pedestrian who was acting as if he were drunk. It was dark and rainy—Alexey could not possibly have stopped in time. But that guy was an off-duty police officer. So, the police report said that it was Alexey who was drunk, and that he was speeding. "I know how Alexey drives," added Rina hastily. "He never speeds. And he was not drunk that night: he had spent the whole evening with me, and had nothing but tea. And he never drinks alcohol when he has to drive, anyway..."

It was a sad but rather typical story. I had little reason to doubt Rina's words, especially when I remembered Alexey's sad intelligent face.

"What is his term?" I asked.

"Six years. You know, they don't let people stay in Moscow if they're sentenced to more than five years, but they made an exception for Alexey because it was just a driving accident. He's already served four years, and they are going to let him out on parole. The case is in court right now, so he may be home in two or three months..."

I felt dull pain of envy: "home in two or three months..." Oh, happy, happy woman! I had two more years to wait. After today's date, when Lev and I spent most of our time trying to fool the prison guard and therefore did not have to search for topics of conversation, I felt much closer and warmer toward him. I had never doubted that, after Lev has served his term, we would live together—maybe not forever, but for a significant time... So, as far as I was feeling that morning, I would rather have him come home sooner than later...

"Do you live together?" I asked, remembering that Rina had been introduced to me as Alexey's "girlfriend".

"Oh, he was in the process of divorcing his wife when he was arrested. He does not love her; he's wanted a divorce for many years, but did not have enough courage. He finally filed for divorce when he met me. Now she is hoping that he will come back to her; stupid woman! He does not even want her to visit him in jail!"

There was too much pain in Rina's semi-hysterical voice, not to doubt that she was sure that Alexey would not return to his wife. One thing was clear: as different as they looked, Rina was madly in love with my husband's quiet cellmate. I stopped feeling envious: Rina's situation was worse than mine. I briefly felt sorry for Alexey's wife: was *she* waiting, too?

"You must take my phone number," said Rina. "Please, feel free to stay at my place when you come to Moscow. If I am not traveling, of course. But if you call me in advance, I'll arrange to be in town."

She opened her fancy leather purse. I expected to see a piece of paper and a pen; but instead, Rina took out her wallet and handed me a business card. I had heard of business cards before, but had never met anyone who owned one. Not even Academician Alexandrov. I studied Rina's card with curiosity. She appeared to be an editorial staff member of a well-known journal. A journalist. Now I understood where her fancy imported clothes had come from. She belonged to a different social class; she was part of the Moscow elite, far, far beyond my reach. Interesting: Alexey did not seem to belong to that aristocratic circle any more than Lev or I. Maybe he will return to his wife, after all. But this woman looked like she really loved him. This weird lady called Life plays funny jokes on people...

"Wait, I'll write my home phone number here," said Rina. "You can call me at work, but... I won't really be able to talk to you. They know nothing about Alexey. Actually, they think I am still married to my husband. We've been separated for a while, and I live alone now, but legally I am still married. It's better for my job this way..."

I thanked Rina, and put her card in my purse. I figured I should probably keep it, just in case. I would almost certainly never call her, unless Lev specifically asked me to. When she and I were saying goodby, I looked at her hands: they were covered with expensive jewelry, but the wedding ring was missing. I thought that she must be wearing her ring at work, to preserve the image of a married woman that was so "good for her job". She took it off to see her lover in prison.

I looked at my ring. I remembered Lev's first words when I walked into the cell, and he took my hand to kiss it:

"Do you wear your ring all the time, or only *here*, with me?"

"I always wear it," I said.

I told the truth: I would feel that I was betraying Lev if I left my ring at home every time it was convenient. Lev did not seem to believe me. Judging other people by himself, as his friend Rozov had said... I was hurt, but it made no difference. I was not wearing my wedding ring for my husband any more. I was wearing it for myself. Taking it off would have made my life easier, but it would also have meant that I had submitted to the system, and recognized that it was stronger than I. And I was too proud to accept that.

And so, I had to pay the price.

9

In any given social group in Russia, being too private and reserved about your personal life is just as bad as it is to be too open in the United States. My former boss from Saltykovka, Kharetov, used to start his work day by complaining about last night's quarrels with his wife, and even hinted about his inadequate sex life. He was respected as a knowledgeable specialist and a good manager, but his public confessions gained him a different kind of popularity: his employees *loved* him because of his openness. Kharetov's frank talks about his personal life made people feel that he was *one of them*.

One of my fellow programmers at the Scientific Research Center was a recently divorced woman in her late thirties named Stella. A weak programmer, not particularly attractive, she was, nevertheless, one of the most popular people in the company, a welcome member of any small group of friends. The key to her social success was her habit of telling her coworkers intimate details about her personal life that often made me blush. Stella's colleagues may have pitied her, but she was almost certainly unaware of things said behind her back. Stella was always surrounded by people who wanted to have lunch or tea with her, exchange books, or have a small chat.

The majority of employees in the SRC had known each other for years through work, school, or a common circle of friends. That created a very informal atmosphere in all offices, because personal relationships overwhelmed business ones. A few people attracted my attention to the extent that I dreamed of becoming their friend. I increasingly enjoyed my programming work, and could have been happy in my office, if I—consciously and voluntarily—had not chosen to ruin everything from the start.

The problem was that I could not bring myself to tell my superficially curious coworkers that my husband was serving a prison term. My bitter experience in the Public Library had made me cautious: I did not want to risk losing my new job. That fear, however, was a secondary reason for my silence: unlike the Public Library, SRC was not considered an "ideological institution", so the "moral face" of its employees was not scrutinized as strictly. Neither was my husband a KGB prisoner any more, and regardless of how his crime was qualified by the Criminal Code, its severity in the eyes of the authorities was greatly reduced by the fact that he was serving his term in a criminal prison rather than political one.

In short, it was not the fear of losing my job that kept me silent, but the thought that everyone in the company would discuss my husband's imprisonment for mere entertainment. Imagining women in my group bombarding me with stupid questions and comments was intolerable. I did not want to have to justify my husband's behavior to anyone. I came to the office every day wearing my wedding ring. I mentioned that I had a three-year-old daughter. But I never talked about my husband, or how I spent time after work. My coworkers sensed that I considered my personal life none of their business. It was a very "non-Russian" attitude, and I was not forgiven.

* * *

December was coming to an end, which meant the approach of Russia's biggest holiday: the New Year. To me, it was the third New Year without my husband, and the second one after his arrest.

Parties at companies, clubs, schools, and day care centers started in the middle of December, and continued at least one week into January. The northern city of Leningrad, dark at this time of the year for eighteen hours a day, brightened with festive colorful lights. People were spending hours in lines for fir trees, and their homes smelled sweetly of forest, pine needles, and home-made pies.

Everyone was buying presents, dressing up, feeling younger and happier. Neighbors and coworkers were sharing their New Year Eve's plans with each other. Women were making new party dresses. Hairdressers were all booked weeks in advance. The closer the Big Night came, the more excitement there was in the air. Offices were closing earlier, and instead of working, employees were having their first pre-holiday parties: women shared recipes for homemade delicacies, men opened bottles of wine, and music and laughter filled the rooms.

Women smelling of expensive perfumes and shining with makeup and jewelry were competing for the admiration of their male coworkers. Nobody worried about "sexual harassment": the idea simply had not made it into the heads of naive Russians.

On the city streets one could meet Grandfather Frost (*Ded Moroz*), cousin of the Christian Santa Claus, dressed in a long red robe lined with white artificial fur, his thick white beard hanging below his waist. Behind his back he carried a heavy sack full of wonderful presents for children. He was always accompanied by his granddaughter, the beautiful Snow Maiden (*Snegurochka*) dressed in a traditional sparkling blue-and-white outfit. That fairy couple showed up as a surprise at children's homes or parties with funny games, song, dances around the tree, and requests for small performances to win prizes.

When Americans ask me if there is anything that I miss in Russia, I think about those final weeks before the New Year—the holiday even more wonderful since it was totally secular and, therefore, shared equally by everyone: Christians and Jews, Muslims, Buddhist, Communists and atheists alike.

The Scientific Research Center traditionally had its party on the last weekend before the New Year. Our office building formerly housed apartments and therefore had no banquet hall, so parties had to be held in someone's home. That year the hostess was my immediate coworker, divorced Stella. She had only one room in a big communal apartment, but it did not seem to bother anyone. The advantages of Stella's place were its convenient location in the city center, the size of her room, and the fact that she was not married. Spouses were not welcomed at a party held for the sake of inner-office flirting.

I don't know why I decided to go. I had no friends in my company; many people openly disliked me. I loved to dance, but was convinced that no man would invite me. Perhaps I did not want to alienate my coworkers even more by acting openly anti-social. Maybe I was hoping that the pies I was planning to bake for the potluck supper would win me some respect from my female colleagues. Or did I have an intuition that something unusual would happen to me there?

I was impressed by the great job Stella had done. The one room where she lived with her two children had been successfully transformed into a dining room and a ballroom at the same time: the beds had been removed, the children sent over to the grandparents, and several tables placed together and covered with snow-white tablecloths, to form one long table that could seat thirty people. The freshly cut New Year tree was shining and glittering with lights and fine glass ornaments.

Arriving women went straight to the kitchen, to unwrap, arrange, or heat delicacies they had prepared. Men, traditionally responsible for drinks and fruit, waited for them in the room. After that initial separation, all guests congregated near the tree. Everyone was dressed up: men wore leather shoes, comfortable for dancing, dress shirts and ties. Women looked fabulously sexy in long dresses with open shoulders; they walked gracefully on high heels, laughing quietly—their voices changed, their movements became different. The air smelled lightly of perfume, fresh pine, and candles.

A few minutes later everyone sat down around the table, and the party started with a champagne toast. Two dozen plates and bowls with salads and hors d'oeuvres made their first round around the table. Russians do not understand the concept of a "buffet supper": the table is the center of any party, until the moment when people get up for dancing.

The only light in the room came from the candles and the tree lights. A record was playing soft romantic music. I was as dressed up as everyone else, my high-heel shoes matching my tight dress with wide skirt, my long hair down and curled. It was a real, beautiful New Year party—one of those parties that I missed so much while living with Lev Fedorov. And I felt profoundly lonely.

Luckily, book shelves lined one wall of the room. They covered all the space from the floor to the ceiling, just the way it was in my home in Akademgorodok. I was aimlessly browsing the hard leather covers, which mostly had familiar titles, when my eye caught a ten-volume collection by Leon Feuchtwanger. Michael often talked of Feuchtwanger, and especially praised *Josephus*, a historical novel about the war between Israel and Rome in the first century A.D., which resulted in the second fall of the Jerusalem Temple. Identical maroon hard-cover volumes were sitting in my parents' living room, but I had never gotten around to reading any of the novels. I felt a sudden inspiration, as if an invisible force pushed me toward the bookcase. It took me about five minutes to find the right volume among its twin brothers, but the moment I opened the first page I stopped feeling lonely: the book captured my imagination completely.

I was distracted from time to time by new guests coming in. Several people had worked in the company before I came there, and I did not know them. One of the newcomers, a young man about my age, was greeted especially enthusiastically. Men and women rushed over to welcome him; he was smiling, shaking hands and talking excitedly. For some unexplainable reason, I stopped reading for a few minutes and watched him.

I must have heard his name before, but I could not remember in what connection. He was tall, slim, athletic, and had the typical face of a Jewish intellectual, my favorite type. I had to remind myself that I had no reason to keep staring at him: he was the most popular person at the party; I was the least popular one. Several girls, very attractive and much younger than me, were openly seeking his attention. The new young man seemed to be everyone's friend, and I had been always suspicious of people who were too popular. Their social success was a sure guarantee that they would never need me. I felt closer to loners and outcasts like myself; we could understand each other, and help each other. The new guest was clearly way out of reach.

The supper was over, the music from the tape recorder sounded louder. We reached an intermission between food and dancing, maybe the most charming part of any party. The flickering candlelight made the poor room look mysterious and romantic. I was back into my book, so much involved in it that I felt almost happy. My recent loneliness was gone; I forgot who I was, where I was, and who were the people around me. I only regretted that candles did not give sufficient light for comfortable reading.

My dissociation was suddenly interrupted by someone's voice:

"May I ask what book are you so involved with?"

I looked up, and was astonished to see the new young man. My first instinct was to answer politely. My second one was to show him that I was not up to flirting, and that he could find himself another girl for superficial entertainment. I lifted the book for a few seconds, so he could see the cover, with the author's name engraved on it. As I mentioned earlier, all volumes in the collection had identical covers, with no way to tell which novels were inside.

"Show me one line, and I'll tell you which novel it is," he said.

Intrigued, I turned the book around. He glanced at the page for about thirty seconds, and then said (not asked, but stated):

"Josephus." That's a good one, but not my favorite. Do you like it?"

I nodded, still not ready to get into a conversation of light flirting.

"Now, may I ask you to put away your book, and dance with me?"

I could not resist. I went to dance with him.

His name was Vladimir.

Volodia.

10

Was it love at first sight? Or was it just another dream, a substance to fill the emptiness of my soul? Was Volodia a real hero, the one that Lev Fedorov was supposed to become but failed? Was he someone I had been waiting for my entire life, or was he created by my still idealistic imagination?

I did not know the answers to those questions, and probably did not want to know. All I knew was that the party had turned out to be totally different for me than I could have ever imagined. I did not care anymore what my coworkers thought about me. I stopped feeling inadequate and weird. The world started making sense again. It was filled with wonderful people, smiles, happy sounds, bright colors. There was hope in life—something that I thought I had lost forever...

Volodia and I danced most dances together, and it felt as if I had known him for years. He left me only twice during the evening, to dance with another woman. She was the wife of his close friend, and he apologized for leaving me alone. Like Volodia, Svetlana had worked at SRC before I came there. I studied her face and figure while she was dancing with Volodia. She was a few years older than me, not a perfect beauty, but attractive in her own way. She had a nice figure and a calm, intelligent face. I thought that she almost certainly was not married to an abusive man, or ever had her husband imprisoned. She was not a bit coquettish, but rather somewhat stern. Nevertheless, there were other men besides Volodia who wanted to dance with her. And when she was not dancing, she was always talking to a few people. She seemed to be a person I had always dreamed of being—but never could.

It was way after midnight when the party ended: the subway trains stopped running at one in the morning, so there was little choice. Volodia and I walked to the subway station together and parted underground, when each of us took a different train home.

At about two-thirty in the morning I was awakened by the phone ringing. It was Volodia, who wanted to make sure that I had made it home safely. I thanked him, feeling touched and shocked at the same time. I had been wearing my wedding ring at the party, and never mentioned to Volodia that my husband and I were separated. I would not dare to even imagine Lev's reaction if he had been woken up in the middle of the night by a strange man inquiring about his wife's safety. Perhaps Volodia, being a bachelor, had no experience with jealous spouses, but I was surprised that he was not afraid of waking up my family, or neighbors. After all, he had no way of knowing that I lived by myself.

Later, when I got to know Vladimir Sonovsky much better, I understood that he was not the kind of person who bothers himself with noticing such petty details as wedding rings, or worries about waking people up. In that case, however, his phone call did not do any harm. Grandma Galia slept far away from the telephone, and did not hear it ringing. As for me, if I did not go back to sleep right away, it was because of an unfamiliar feeling of happiness that was becoming more and more overwhelming, rather than because of interrupted sleep.

He called again the next evening, but our conversation was superficial, and he did not offer to meet; I was clearly losing him. And then, as a typical drowning person, I grabbed the last straw. The straw happened to be there very conveniently, and was large enough to serve as a small flotation device: I was about to have a housewarming party.

To my great relief, he accepted immediately. There did not seem to be any girlfriend in the picture, or any other reasons why we could not become friends, if not begin dating...

My first feeling when I hung up was that my life would never be the same again.

And then I started panicking.

It was the first time that I had invited my friends to see my new, just repaired, apartment. I expected only a few people, my closest and most trusted friends, all intellectuals with so-called "anti-Soviet" views, who read underground literature, learned the news from foreign radio stations, and knew by heart songs by Vladimir Vysotsky and Alexander Galich. That meant that most of the conversation would revolve around politics, with an emphasis on strong criticism of the Soviet regime. People would be saying things that could get them in serious trouble should they become known to the authorities. And everyone would feel safe, knowing that I could not possibly invite a guest unsympathetic with these views.

And I had no idea, what Volodia's political views were...

The fact that he had read all the novels of Feuchtwanger was in no way a guarantee that he held dissident views, although that made it more likely. He was obviously a Jew, which by itself increased the probability that he was one of "ours," but I still could not be certain. Nevertheless, it was too late: I could not cancel my invitation to Volodia, and neither did I have any way of warning my guests that they should keep their mouths shut.

I agonized over that problem for the next two days, but finally decided that there was no way that Volodia could be a KGB informer—after all, I had to trust my intuition. At the very worst, he would start arguing with my guests, expressing "pro-Soviet" views that none of us shared. It would create an awkward situation: my friends would feel uncomfortable; Volodia might be offended and would never want to see me again. But if his views were so different from mine and my friends, I would not want to see him either. I decided that the risk was worth taking—and there was nothing that I could do anyway, except just hope and pray for the best.

* * *

He was, indeed, *one of ours*—more than anyone could wish. It became clear during the first hour, when one of my guests quoted a line from a famous song, available only through *Magnitizdat* audiotapes:

> *In the fight heavy odds have opposed us,*
> *But the merciless huntsmen keep ranks.*
> *With the flags on their ropes they've enclosed us.*
> *They take aim and they fire at point blank.**

---

* *Vladimir Vysotsky*, translated by Kathryn Hamilton

It was a strongly anti-Soviet song, something that made you remember the quote by another famous dissident: "Samizdat: I write it myself, edit it myself, censor it myself, publish it myself, distribute it myself, and spend jail time for it myself." *

For a few seconds I got tense, not knowing how my new guest would react—but he simply continued the quote:

For a wolf cannot break with tradition.
With milk sucked from the she-wolfs dugs
The blind cubs learn the stern prohibition
Never, never to cross the red flags! **

Remember, earlier on I was talking about *the passwords?*

Similar interaction happened between me and Nina, back many years ago, when we, careless students, were raking leaves in the Summer Garden. That song of Vladimir Vysotsky was another one of our passwords.

And Volodia knew it.

11

Volodia and I spent the New Year night of 1986 together, at a big and merry party, with plenty of good food and wine, dancing, and singing to the guitar. "All is for the best in this best of all worlds," Aunt Olia repeated her favorite phrase, after I politely declined her invitation to spend the New Year Eve at a quiet gathering of her family and a few close friends. "Good thing you will be with people your age. Just don't rush with this young man, you don't know him that well yet... sometimes relationships can hurt, you know..."

I sure knew that relationships could hurt—and I was nowhere close to starting an affair with Vladimir Sonovsky. While awake, I was thinking about him more often than not. But the feeling was still too new, too fragile—I was far from the point of admitting to myself that I might be in love again... It all just happened too fast, too unexpectedly... I needed to let it sit.

---

* *Vladimir Bukovsky*
** *Vladimir Vysotsky*, translated by Kathryn Hamilton

In any case, the year started happily, and, according to the Russian tradition (or call it "superstition" if you wish), I expected it to remain so. I had a new apartment, new friends, and a wonderful new winter coat, my parents' present to me for the New Year. I was doing rather well at my new job, and rarely required help with writing computer programs. I finally stopped feeling like permanent misfit. Life was smiling at me, and I was looking forward to seeing my husband again. Our first date of the year was scheduled for early January, which seemed just like one more present to me from Her Majesty Life...

* * *

So, here I was, in Moscow again, walking along the narrow dark corridors of Butyrskaya Prison. The happiness that I was still feeling that morning waking up in Tanika's apartment had now disappeared, suppressed by the grimness of the place, replaced by anxiety bordering on fear... I couldn't help thinking of Lev's last letter warning me that the prison rules had changed, and this date would be very different from previous ones. How different? What did he mean?

Another turn. Another armored door with a uniformed guard. Guards never have faces that you could remember and later recognize. They never look at you as a person with a soul and a beating heart. They are machines that check papers and make sure you aren't violating any rules.

It seems to me that there are more doors and more guards than before, but maybe it is just my imagination? My new fur coat is very warm, suitable for the January weather outside—but inside this building I am feeling chills. There must be other people walking beside me—people who, like me, are hiding beneath their winter coats their grief, hopes, frustration, hatred, the joyful anticipation of a meeting with loved ones... I do not remember any of them; like the guards, they are just shadows, soulless beings with no names and no faces...

We have finally reach our destination. This, indeed, will be a *very different* date... Instead of a number of small rooms shared by two or three dating couples, we all are horded into one enormous, poorly lit cell. A long table in the middle separates those who came from outside from the ones kept inside. Two dozen prisoners are seated in a row behind the table. Dressed in similar dark-blue uniforms, they are silent and subdued, patiently waiting for their visitors to find them.

* * *

It took me a few minutes to find my husband among those identical figures. I was beginning to panic when I finally saw him. He was looking at me without smiling or making any attempt to attract my attention. I suddenly felt a hot wave of fear mixed with shame when I realized that my husband had never seen my new coat. It was a very fashionable coat made from finely processed sheep skin, with a fur lining and big fluffy collar and cuffs. Those sheepskin coats were fairly expensive and, being in high demand, not easy to find. The war with Afghanistan being at its peak, those coats, bought at village bazaars, were brought to Russia by a few lucky warriors who wanted to celebrate their survival by making some extra cash. My mom had bought it for me in one of the Novosibirsk second-hand shops—even though the coat was brand new. In my stupid woman's vanity, I wanted my husband to see me in my best; I had been imagining him affectionately taking the sheepskin off my shoulders, smelling soft, slightly perfumed fur, kissing my neck, telling me how beautiful I was... But in this long dark room with almost as many guards as prisoners, where Lev could not even hold my hand, let alone take my coat off, it seemed shamefully luxurious, totally out of place, almost a sign of betrayal. Lev continued looking at me heavily, without saying anything. I sat down on the other side of the table across from him. To the right and left of us other people were talking quietly, trying to separate their partners' voices from dozens of other quiet voices in the room. Lev and I were silent for a while, not knowing how to start a conversation. I hated myself for wasting the precious minutes of our short date, but my husband's grim silence made me depressed and almost scared, and nothing appropriate came to my mind.

He finally broke the silence, nodding at the coat that I had hung on the back of my chair:

"New?"

"My parents' present for the New Year. Mom found it in a secondhand store, although it is brand new. It must have been brought from Afghanistan..." I had to whisper in order not to interfere with the conversation of others, and it made my words sound like an apology. Lev nodded again, but his eyes softened.

"What's happening here?" I pointed at the table and the guards.

"New boss. Cleaning things up for the New Year..." He added a dirty curse, moving his lips almost silently. "It will pass. New broom sweeps well. I have at least another year here; it won't stay like this, you'll see..."

"A year?" A year was an eternity, but it had been less than two years since Lev's arrest, and he was sentenced to four years. Was there a hope for parole? My heart jumped with joy, but that feeling was brutally ruined by my husband's next phrase.

"Are they going to let you out early? You think you might be home in a year?"

"Yes, at least a year, don't worry. You still have plenty of time to enjoy it with your lover. Is he a good f-cker, by the way? I hope you've found someone better than an old man like me. And generous, too... I won't have the money to buy you coats like this..."

"Lev," I said, feeling dizzy and sick to my stomach, but still half-hoping that my husband was not serious. "I've just told you that it was my parents who paid for the coat, OK? And I do not have any lover, regardless of what you may think..."

His look was almost contemptuous. "Do you think I am a stupid little boy? I *know* that a woman your age *cannot* be without a man for so long. It is called biology, honey... I know something about life, don't you think so?" There was hidden hatred in his whisper, or maybe hidden pain—I could not tell.

"All right, if you know that it is all only biological, it would not be my fault, right? So, why are you talking about it with such anger?"

"Ah, so you do have a lover! Then why have you lied to me just now that you did not have one?"

"I did not lie." I suddenly felt very tired. I was not sure if I cared anymore what he was thinking. "But you've just told me that it would not be a big deal even if I did, because it is all biological..."

"So, you did betray me! You've picked the right moment, didn't you? When I am incarcerated, having lost everything, humiliated... Of course, you are young, you are beautiful. You are free... The old stupid husband is in jail—why not use the time? Got rid of the child, too: very convenient. Your supportive mama makes sure that the little girl does not interfere with her daughter's affairs..."

My mother? After all, I was getting angry, too. My mother certainly trusted me more than my husband did, but if she had as much as suspected that I might have a lover, she would not think about biology. She would not buy the theory that *a woman cannot...* She would curse and disown me forever. I would be far more afraid of my mother discovering my relationship with Stanislav Rozov than my husband. And Lev, who had known my mother for several years, could not see that? What was this man's heart made of, that he saw only garbage in people?

"Nadia has to live with my parents because there is no day care for her in Leningrad", I said wearily, without any hope of reasoning with him. "I wrote you all about that. What I did not write to you—mainly because I was afraid that you might misunderstand—is that if I were formally divorced, the waiting list for the day care would be several times shorter."

"Do you want a divorce, then?" His eyes were white with fury, but I sensed hidden fear behind it.

"No," I said firmly. "No, regardless of what you may think, I do not want a divorce. I don't know how you feel about me, but I intend to wait for your return—hopefully, only for one year, or two years if I need to—and give our marriage another chance. I've invested too damn much into this relationship, to give up that easily."

"Sure," said Lev mockingly (at least he did not sound angry any more), "as soon as you are divorced and free, your lover will have to marry you. And he probably doesn't want to. It is so much nicer to f-ck a married woman, especially if the husband is not around. Same pleasure, but no obligations. If you are divorced, he may actually decide to leave you—just in case you might become too possessive."

The conversation sounded even more ridiculous because we had to whisper. People around us were too absorbed in their own problems to pay attention to what we were saying, but louder voices would have disturbed them. During the second half hour, the majority of the visitors were preoccupied with trying to get some food from their purses, without attracting the guards' attention, and sneaking it across the table. Most couples succeeded, even though this time the "no-feeding" rule was enforced. Two women, caught in the process, were sent away before their hour ran out, and their husbands had to return to their cells immediately.

Nevertheless, the incident did not stop the others: there was some desperate stubbornness in the women's persistence. Everyone must have understood that a few pieces of sandwiches or fruit would not solve the prisoners' nutrition problem, but people, humiliated as they were, nevertheless had enough pride not to observe a rule they found unjustified. By violating one stupid regulation, they asserted their inner freedom, their right to decide at least something for themselves.

Unlike other prisoners, Lev did not seem to be interested in food.

"Don't bother," he said. "Take it back to your friends. I have everything here. Yes, including caviar. Where did you get it, Akademgorodok? Should have left it for my lady-bug... She likes caviar, doesn't she?"

I assured him that Nadia had enough of everything, including caviar. I wished I could have done something for him. I wished we had spent our short hour talking about him, rather than discussing my imaginable lover. I was also wondering if my husband was telling me another tall tale: how on earth could he be getting caviar in jail? He did not appear particularly malnourished, but he did look pale. Or, maybe, it was the dim light of the cell. I would never know...

When the hour was over, and prisoners and visitors got off their chairs preparing to leave, an inmate called my name and greeted me with a smile. I recognized Alexey. He seemed to me even thinner and paler than when I met him for the first time, but his smile was the same and his eyes were glowing with affection. He pointed to Rina, who was gently wiping her leaking mascara mixed with tears with a laced handkerchief.

"Talk to her, please," he said, while a guard was pushing him away from the table. "She is so upset, she needs support..."

Those two clearly had a much better date than we, I thought with bitterness. I was depressed enough not to want to talk to anyone, especially Rina. But I had no choice when she slowed down in the corridor, waiting for me to catch up. We walked out of the prison together.

"They had promised to let him come home by the New Year," sobbed Rina. "And now they are saying that the appeal courts are too swamped. It may be another two or three months before the judge gets around to reviewing Alesha's case..."

She was selfish, that bitch of a journalist. She dared to complain to me about two miserable months. I might have had two full years

to wait. Not that I was half as impatient as she was, especially after today's date, but she had no way of knowing that. She was wearing a gorgeous white rabbit coat that must have cost at least three
times more than my sheepskin, white leather boots with high heels
(almost certainly brought from abroad) and long diamond earrings.
Apparently, her man did not see her outfit as a sign of her betrayal or
infidelity...

* * *

I was in no mood for seeing anybody upon returning to Leningrad.
I told Volodia I would call him after I had caught up with my office
work. To Nina, I told the truth: I had a horrible meeting with my husband, and was too depressed to discuss it—while talking about anything else would be difficult for me right now. Not surprisingly, my
ability to write programs plummeted as well—so, for better or for
worse, I had to call Stanislav. I had been hoping to avoid telling him
about my last prison date, and concentrate on the program instead—
but of course it did not work out: words poured out of me as soon as
I walked into his apartment.

"And how many times have I told you that, no matter how modest
and how faithful you are, your husband will never believe in your faith-
fulness?" was Rozov's immediate response.

"Men like him judge everyone by themselves. Lev had been screwing
around during all the years of his first marriage. That is probably the
main reason why he and his wife eventually got divorced, regardless
of all the stories he was telling everyone about her 'awful character,'
'lack of mutual understanding,' etc. He then married two more times,
albeit briefly—and no one knows much about those women, or why it
never worked out... You yourself found out that he had a mistress when
he was already married to you. Your husband may be a good engineer,
but a very bad psychologist: he is completely incapable of imagining
that other people may be different from him. Besides—and it is probably the most important reason—if he allows himself to believe that
you, having had all these opportunities as a single woman (young and
beautiful in addition) never slept with anyone because of your commitment to him... he will have to admit your moral superiority. And that is
something that Lev Fedorov will never, never do..."

271

Rozov was crude, but my intuition told me that he was right. I had been a stupid naive girl, to have trusted Lev Fedorov for so long. Trusted and hoped that things would eventually work out between us, in spite of all my bitter experience. And what made me think that he would suddenly change? His very first letter from Butyrki, which his lawyer Svetlana Semenovna smuggled out in her underpants? But he had given similar promises before his imprisonment, and violated them right away. And then, that nighttime conversation with Rozov several months ago... I tried so hard to forget it, to erase it from my memory... but the bitter truth was still there—even if my mind refused to accept it...

Rozov poured himself another cup of freshly brewed hot tea and took a few sips with obvious pleasure.

"Actually, I am a little suspicious that he suddenly became so violently jealous. I don't think your new coat is an adequate explanation. He knows your parents have money, and that you are their only daughter. It looks as if he was deliberately searching for a reason to accuse you of infidelity. He would have found something else, if your new sheepskin had not served the purpose so conveniently..."

Rozov's face at that moment was the one of an artist who has gotten a sudden inspiration and is rushing to create a masterpiece before that inspiration is gone. I thought I understood what he meant, but wanted him to say it out loud.

"He could not possibly get a mistress in jail, could he?"

"Certainly, he could! And he would not be the first one, I assure you. It's not easy, and for the majority of inmates it's a luxury beyond their wildest dreams. But some men do get lucky. Your husband's position in Butyrki is clearly not an ordinary one, even if he exaggerates a little. And women like him—you know that better than anybody else. I am almost certain that he has started an affair since your previous date. That's where his jealousy comes from. And his hatred. While he is doing it himself, he cannot help imagining how, at this very moment, you may be doing the same thing with someone else..."

I thought that Rozov may or may not be right. After all, there could be many reasons for Lev's sudden jealousy. He had had inexplicable mood swings before—mood swings too sudden to have any reasonable explanation. There must have been a secret life going on deep inside Lev's head, independent of the reality of the outside world. His rapid changes from love to hatred, from trust to suspicion, were probably caused by sudden flashes of memory, associations, and god knows what other chemical processes in his brain. I knew that the next time I saw him in jail, he may very well be warm and loving, mistress or no mistress. Not that I would ever again trust his love, or his warmth...

"You don't understand my problem, Rozov," I said wearily. "And I don't feel that you're sympathetic enough. I was hoping that you would teach me how to love my husband again, in spite of everything that has happened. I *must* love in order to function. And I need *love,* not just sex. I need to be looking forward to something wonderful ahead. I've suddenly lost purpose in life. There is an enormous emptiness inside me, with nothing to fill it. Or is that too abstract a concept for such a resolute materialist as you?"

I knew I was being unfair to my friend. Rozov almost certainly understood me—but what could he do? He had said everything he could. He had also *done* everything he could, to help me. His response to my last phrase was more cynical than I was prepared to hear:

"You'll fall in love with someone else, don't worry..."

12

It was one of those dull, gray, windy and snowy evenings in March, when the whole world appears depressed because winter refuses to leave. Grandma Galia was in her room by herself, watching TV, as usual. I had just finished cleaning he kitchen after supper, when the phone ring made me startle.

A man's voice sounded familiar, but in the first few moments I could not remember where I had heard it before.

"Anna," the voice said formally, "how are you tonight?"

"Who..." I started, and suddenly felt chills down my back. That voice, so calm, so quiet, so confident, in my small neat apartment surrounded by a stormy night, sounded almost otherworldly.

"Lev..." I almost whispered. "How... You?.. Did they let you out?!"

"Not at all," said my husband's voice in the receiver. "I just wanted to see if this will work. My very personal telephone that no one knows about. Just wanted to check and see how you are doing..."

"Will I be able to call you back?" I asked, trying very hard to feel joy, but instead feeling cold, slippery fear.

"No, no way. I will disconnect this line as soon as I hang up. So that they don't discover it in the morning... There is no number for *this* phone. But Alexey will call you soon."

"Alexey? Who is Alexey?—it was all so sudden, I could not think straight.

"My former inmate, Alexey. The one whom you met in Butyrki. Alexey and Rina, remember?"

Of course, I remembered Rina. Her perfume, her makeup, and her white rabbit fur coat. And quiet, sad, intelligent Alexey—the direct opposite of my volatile husband.

"So, they did let Alexey out on parole?"

"Yes, finally. He and Rina are going to visit some relatives in Leningrad. Would you like to meet with them?"

It sounded as if Lev wanted me to meet Alexey and Rina, and so I said "Yes, of course". Alexey, in spite of his recent prison past, did not frighten me. And he probably could answer many of my questions. For example, how on earth my husband, even with all his privileges, could make a phone call from a jail cell to the outside world? And to many other questions, which Lev could not write about and probably would not tell the truth anyway...

* * *

"Oh, this is simple," said Alexey.

He, Rina and I were sitting in a cozy small kitchen in the apartment of Alexey's relatives. The owners were not home, and Rina made tea and served sandwiches and pastries, acting as naturally as if she were the hostess.

"Lev is responsible for the electrical and telephone communications inside the jail. The position is usually held by a free-hired engineer, but now they are saving lots of money by having Lev do the job for free. Lev has his little private office. Of course, he is not supposed to go there after hours, but prison officers often ask him to fix their personal electronic equipment, so he has to do that when his official work day is over. And he must do it in his workshop. The guards love Lev and allow him to do many things forbidden to other prisoners. Marina, the lieutenant, is formally his supervisor, but in fact she is below him. She adores him—as we all do—and lets him do practically everything..."

"So, you mean that Lev has a telephone in his office?"

"Oh, no, of course not! They would never allow that. But he can connect some wires, and create a temporary phone line; he is so skillful, you know... That's why the phone works only one-way."

"And what about that Marina? Does she know about that phone?"

"Probably not. It would be too risky. She is a cop, after all, no matter how fond she is of Lev. But we are lucky to have her. She is a fine woman, too young to be a lieutenant in prison; not as beautiful as you are, but..."

Alexey suddenly stopped, as if he had unwittingly said more than he was supposed to.

"Oh, she is helping Lev a great deal," Rina stepped in, apparently trying to save the situation. "For example, she mails his letters from the city; that means that Lev's letters do not have to go through the prison censorship. Thanks to her, he can maintain his outside connections—and not just for himself, but for many other inmates as well. But you certainly know that! You must have been receiving those letters, with no prison stamp on the envelope, and were wondering how they had been mailed..."

I looked at Alexey. His face was bright red, with drops of sweat on his forehead.

These two do not know how to lie, I thought. Otherwise, they would at least have agreed on what to say, before meeting me.

Rina, without realizing it, had betrayed my husband: the problem was that I had not received a single letter from him without a prison stamp on it. I had no idea what letters Marina was mailing from the city, but Lev had never, ever given her a letter to his wife. He may never have told her that he was married, and Alexey probably knew that.

Marina adores Lev... Well, poor woman.

"There is nothing there... nothing..." mumbled Alexey. "They are just friends, only friends, nothing more..."

"Just friends..." Little does he know his friend Lev Fedorov, not to understand that he has never had *just friends*. My husband is out to *use* people—men and women for different purposes. He likes to be liked, yes; even better, to be adored, to be worshipped. He may have no plans for using Alexey, but just enjoys his adoration. But being "a friend" with a woman? Well, he is a healthy man, after all, and he was without sex for too long to resist such temptation. But, regardless of his physical attraction to that lady lieutenant, making love to a prison officer would raise his self-esteem so much that he could not possibly have missed such a chance…

Strangely, I was not shocked, or even upset. I did not have time to figure out exactly what my feelings were, except that I had always known that such things did happen in prisons. I remembered a novel by Solzhenitsyn, in which a young female officer falls in love with a prisoner she is supposed to guard, and offers him her virgin body.

And then, Rozov. Damn cynical Rozov, he was right again…

Northern March sun shined shyly from a light-blue sky and the dirty snow was melting, creating a feeling of festivity, renewal and liberation, when I left Alexey and Rina's cozy apartment. It was located at the outskirts of the city, a good two or three bus stops to the nearest subway stations, but I decided to walk. I had no place to rush to, and wanted to be alone to gather my thoughts.

I was sure that everything Alexey had told me about Lev's position in Butyrki and his relationships with his fellow inmates was the truth. I could see my husband leading the "political hour," where he was supposed to present the latest news to other prisoners. According to Alexey, Lev slightly changed newspaper stories, just enough to make them hilariously funny. Alexey did a great job describing the inmates choking with laughter while Lev Fedorov, with the most serious expression on his face, reported the latest political news. Lev's stories deviated from the ones presented in newspapers so subtly that the guards on duty could not understand what was going on. Their confusion and frustration with the prisoners made the situation even funnier.

Several times the guards tried to accuse Lev of perverting the facts, but he always managed to get away. The guards were feeling that something was not quite right there, but were too dumb to pinpoint where exactly my husband was distorting the facts. Lev, as the only inmate with a PhD, continued to be responsible for the political information of the prisoners. And the prisoners continued to enjoy his presentations immensely, laughing heartily at the news, as well as at the dumb guards.

That quality of my husband should have caused respect, if not admiration. He turned out to be an amazingly strong individual, having managed to make the most out of his own imprisonment. He did not let himself fall into depression. He was using his time trying to make friends and useful connections.

As for his affair...the main problem I had with that was that he was apparently lying to the woman. Had he told her that he was married and intended to return to his wife after his term, it would have been an honest game. I would not perceive it as betrayal or even adultery. He was not sleeping with another woman because he preferred her to me; he was sleeping with her because he *could not* sleep with me. I was far from being so selfish as to require my husband, in addition to all inevitable sufferings associated with imprisonment, to endure abstinence. I would only be happy if he had an opportunity to make his servitude a little more tolerable. But I had a feeling that he was using that woman, the same way he was using other people, and that bothered me.

To me, Marina was not my husband's mistress, but another woman who had fallen prey to man's selfishness. She was still unaware that her beloved would betray her, which made her even more vulnerable. My strongest feeling after I parted with Alexey and Rina, was female solidarity. But the farther I walked from their house, the more I realized that there was something else.

For a while I could not figure out what it was. It certainly was not jealousy on my part, but then what?

I thought about my recent conversation with Rozov again. My husband's friend had explained it all perfectly clearly: Lev immediately attributed his own crime to me. He could not allow himself to feel guilty, so he made me guilty. I will never be able to forget the dirty scene that he made during our last date, the hatred in his eyes and the quiet fury of his voice. He had no information, and even less proof, that I had been unfaithful to him—but since he was doing it, I must have been guilty as well. All right, let's assume I was—so what? Why was I capable of understanding my husband's physical need for sexual relationships, while he refused to understand mine? Why he, at the age of fifty, could not be without a woman, and I, at twenty-seven, was supposed to live like a nun? At the very minimum, he should have allowed me what he was allowing himself. Especially after all the abuse that I had endured from him. Any other woman would simply have left him long ago. And I not only remained his wife, but spent so much time and money trying to get him out of the shit that he had gotten himself into.

All my trips to Moscow, begging his supervisors for help... All those humiliating visits to Kerimov... All my tears, sleepless nights, pain that I felt because *he* was hurting...

For the first time in my life I felt hatred toward my husband. The empty space that remained after my love for him was gone, was now filled with anger and contempt. "Yes, I will wait for you, and return to you, Mr. Fedorov. I promised it to you, I promised it to myself, I promised it to the entire world. I will keep this promise. But, damn it, you will never, ever own me again. You will never tell me how to live my life. You will never treat me like shit, and especially make me feel shitty about myself. You've lost your power over me, my dearest husband..."

I did not notice how I reached the subway station. I did not realize that my high leather boots had gotten all wet from walking in melting snow. I wanted to be home. I desperately wanted to call Volodia. To see him, to talk to him... To be close... I was tired, tired of being alone. It was more than the desire for sex, much more. It was a desire for closeness. For real, unconditional love, a love that has no fears, no restrictions, and is based on complete, absolute trust...

I did not think that I would be able to tell Volodia the full truth right away. Our relationship was still too new, too fragile, to subject it to such a shock. But maybe, I could find a way to tell him about meeting Lev's former cellmate and learning from him about my husband's affair...

Anyhow, I still had at least a few hours to think of what I would say to Volodia. The main thing was just to be together. Having him sitting on my couch. Making supper for him. Listening to him talking... I will figure out the rest later... Later...

Chapter Six

HEBREW

1

"JACOB HAS LEARNED BOTH HEBREW and Aramaic," said Volodia. I had no idea who that Jacob was, so the statement seemed a bit out of the blue.

"My childhood friend," explained Volodia. "Actually, my babyhood friend. Our mothers had been best friends long before we were born, and we were born just a few weeks apart. During our first year of life, Jacob and I must have seen each other almost every day—not that we had any choice in picking friends back then... Right now, he is much closer to my sister than to me. Nevertheless, if you really want to learn Hebrew, I can talk to him."

I did want to learn Hebrew, but my desire was more theoretical than practical. I had decided that I would do it someday, but that day belonged to a remote future. There were too many other things going on in my life that spring, to fit in Hebrew lessons. Nevertheless, I did not want Volodia to consider me one of those superficial ladies who talk for the sake of being entertaining, so I said:

"Oh, yes! Ask him, please!"

I was not at all happy when, during our next meeting, Volodia handed me a piece of paper with Jacob's phone number.

"Just don't mention the reason for your call over the phone," he warned me. "His phone is being tapped, and he is very cautious. Tell him that you are calling at my suggestion, and that you'd like to meet. He will set up a time. You'll discuss everything else in person."

What did I get myself into? Now I *had to* call Volodia's mysterious friend, but was procrastinating. Learning Hebrew was a serious commitment that I was not ready for. I could not imagine what I would say to that Jacob. How would I explain *why* I wanted to learn Hebrew? And if he agrees to teach me, where would I find the time?

"Did you talk to Jacob?" was Volodia's first question when he and I met next time. I had to lie that I had tried to call, but no one was home. When Volodia asked me the same question for the third time, I realized that I had no escape. I shouldn't have talked to him about wanting to learn Hebrew, that's all... Now it was too late. I swallowed my shyness, and called...

* * *

It was late evening at the end of April when I rang the doorbell of Jacob's apartment. A young woman who opened the door had oriental features, and was as pretty as a Chinese porcelain statuette. She showed me into the neatest and coziest living room that appeared to be the only room of the studio apartment. A young girl about Nadia's age, pretty as her mother and nicely dressed, was watching cartoons on TV. One of the walls was covered with book shelves from the floor to the ceiling—a very typical picture for an educated Russian home. I briefly scanned the spines: in addition to the standard collection of popular Russian, European and American classics, there were a number of books in Chinese, and at least two full shelves of books in Hebrew. I had only a few seconds for my observation, because Jacob himself emerged from the kitchen. I could barely contain my surprise: never in my life had I seen such a perfect male beauty—except maybe in movies. Jacob reminded me of Michael with his classical Biblical face, very rare in the modern world. He was, however, much taller and slimmer than Michael, and about ten years younger. There was an irresistible charm in the internationality of that family, with the Chinese wife and the Hebrew husband, their books in three languages and a trilingual five-year-old child.

The host invited me into the kitchen that traditionally for small Russian apartments served as a dining room and a study at the same time. The table was already set for tea. There was almost no food on the table, except sugar, lemon and a bowl with assorted cookies: our meeting was clearly a business one.

I took several small sips of hot and very strong tea, while Jacob silently studied my face.

"I only agreed to see you because Sonovsky asked me to," he said finally, without either friendliness or hostility, just stating the fact.

"I tried teaching Hebrew many times, but have long stopped any attempts. None of my students have learned enough to make teaching worthwhile for me. At this point, I am officially banned from teaching Hebrew: I've signed a promise at the KGB office that I would never teach; that was the condition for my current job."

"In that case, I don't understand why you agreed to see me?" I could not help feeling awkward.

"Because otherwise our friend Sonovsky would have bugged me to death," said my host without a trace of a smile on his biblical face. "He swore that you were *different*, and that you *must* learn Hebrew. I promised him that I would meet with you. I did not promise that I would teach. However, I did not make you come all the way here, just to tell you that. I *might* teach you, but I have to learn more about you first.

It is your turn to talk now: I'd like to hear why you want to learn Hebrew, and at what level. Do you want to be able to read the Bible? Teach at Jerusalem University? Emigrate to Israel?"

"There are two separate questions here." I hated feeling so tense, and tried to smile to relax, but it did not help.

"It is up to you which one you want to answer first." Jacob was sounding more like an investigator than a teacher. "Just keep in mind that it is late—so try to be brief, please..."

I took a deep breath. I still did not know how to answer the first question, but I knew that if I made a mistake there would be no second chance. I looked straight in Jacob's eyes.

"I grew up as a fully assimilated... actually, as a Russian child, with a Russian mother and a Jewish father. For many, many years I thought of myself as a Russian—culturally, mentally and, well, by passport. But then, due to various events in my life, I gradually started feeling my other, Jewish, part, stronger and stronger. At some point... well, since about a year ago, I do not know any more who I am: a Russian or a Jew. And I *need* to know that. I can't explain to you why I feel that I must know it, but I know I do... And I started thinking that knowing Hebrew—the language of my father's ancestors—might help me figure out *who I am*. If that does not help... then, I do not what else to do. But I want to give it a try.

Do I want to emigrate to Israel? As of today, I am not planning on it. However, things have been happening in my life that I never thought would happen, even less planned. I can't say 'No, I definitely will never emigrate to Israel.' I can say 'Probably, not. But you never know.' Reading the Bible in Hebrew? I would certainly love that! But I also want to learn modern, spoken Hebrew. I'd like to understand their songs... Sorry, that's the best answer I can give."

It seemed to me that Jacob's eyes had softened while I was speaking, but I was still anxious about his reply. He continued studying my face for a few more minutes, then said:

"Well, that was quite a comprehensive answer. You have to understand, though, that no one—save Sonovsky, since he arranged all of that—should know that I am teaching you. Not even your best friends. You will never mention our lessons over the phone: my phone is being tapped twenty-four-seven, and every word is recorded... I am busy enough, and will have to arrange our lessons in a working order. I will try very hard to stick to meeting you at least once a week, but I can't guarantee that. Sonovsky said that you work in SRC, right? It is close by, as far as I remember..."

"About fifteen minutes' walk, I think."

"And how flexible is your work schedule? I mean, can we meet during the day? Evenings are harder for me, you see?" he nodded toward the living room. "We are renting this apartment, and it is too small for three people."

"Early mornings are fine," I said. "I can always find an excuse for coming to work late. Except the days that are right after the night shift. I mean, after I have worked all night on the computer, I'd rather go home and sleep."

"So, we both will need to be flexible, then. By the way, you may know that I graduated from the same Library School as you, and Sonovsky, and half of your Research center. Almost everyone in your company knows who I am. It will be better if you do not even mention that you know me. Let's not tempt people to be curious. Sonovsky said I could trust you completely. Not that he is a great psychologist... But in this case, I suppose, he may be right...

Hearing that from a man like Jacob was a tremendous compliment. He felt that he could trust me—and he obviously had a lot at stake. And now he will tell Volodia his impressions of me...

"May I ask where you work?" I could not contain my curiosity any longer.

"I thought Sonovsky had told you. I am the director of the Hebrew collection in..." Jacob named one of the leading libraries in the Soviet Union. "They would much rather have a non-Jew for that position, but they couldn't find anyone with an adequate knowledge of Hebrew. By the way, five rubles an hour is not too much for you, is it? I have no financial interest in teaching; nevertheless, I am not quite ready to work for free." Five rubles an hour was the standard price for a private lesson of any kind, and I was almost surprised that Jacob did not charge more for a skill so rare and a job so risky.

While I was walking back from Jacob's house to the subway station, breathing the wet cool air of that late April evening, his words kept sounding in my head: "None of my students has ever learned enough to make teaching worthwhile for me..." I *must* be different; I must really *learn...* So that Jacob will never be able to say to Volodia that he wasted his time on me, that I was just like everyone else... Volodia must always remember that I am different, different, different... Different from any other woman he has ever met. And, most importantly, from anyone he will ever meet in the future...

2

"I did not have a chance to get a real textbook for you," said Jacob half-apologetically. "I am hoping to get one by our next lesson. For now, we are going to read *this...*"

He reached for his bookcase, took out a heavy volume with golden letters running across the familiar leather cover, and placed it on the table in front of me. I could not believe my eyes: it was the same pre-revolutionary edition of the Tanakh that I had borrowed from Nina's mother a year ago, with the parallel text in Hebrew and Russian. My heart started beating faster: I could not imagine that after a few lessons I would be able to read it in its original language. It would be one of my wildest dreams coming true...

Meanwhile, my teacher was quickly writing on a piece of white paper the letters of the Hebrew alphabet, with their transliteration. He wrote a column of consonants, then a column of vowels, and finally, samples of several syllables at the bottom of the sheet.

"The consonant is pronounced first, then the vowel underneath or above it. Now, try."

I had learned most of the letters by studying Michael's pictures, so I was able to read my first syllables fairly easily. Jacob seemed satisfied.

"Let's try the book now. Whatever signs you can't recognize, don't pay any attention to them. They are for a cantor, instructions for chanting. But you must be able to identify the vowels that I've just shown you. The very first word in the Bible is *brashit*. It has no adequate translation into Russian, or any other language that I know of. It is translated, quite inadequately, as "in the beginning." When... well, *if* you ever learn Hebrew, you will understand, or rather *sense*, the exact meaning of this word, and learn to appreciate the beauty of the language..."

I did not notice how the hour passed. I spent the first Hebrew lesson of my life reading the first page of the Bible, syllable by syllable, like a four-year-old who is just learning how to read. I had to consult Jacob's chart three times in order to pronounce one word, but by the end of the lesson we had finished the first paragraph.

It was early morning, and Jacob and I were sitting in his neat living room. His wife and daughter were gone for the day. The dining table, which we used as a desk, stood right near the large window, so the room looked like an extension of the outside world. Wet hundred-year-old trees with swelling buds rising against a silver-gray sky, cheerful squirrels hopping from branch to branch, and birds singing their first spring songs, were all part of the Creation that I was reading about...

* * *

I walked up familiar stairs to Michael's photo shop. It was located in an apartment that he was renting exclusively for that purpose, in a god-forsaken area of the city, the existence of which I had never heard before I met Michael. It was a few minutes after 8 PM, and the shop had just closed for the general public, while remaining open—although unofficially—for the owner's friends.

Michael opened the door after my first ring—smiling, smelling of photo chemicals, hands wet, shirtsleeves rolled up, his black curly beard disheveled—soft, warm, familiar, close, almost like my brother. He gave me a big bear hug and disappeared into the lab, which in some earlier times used to serve as a washing room. He yelled from there that he needed a few minutes to finish printing some pictures, and I should start making tea.

I looked around me. I thought I knew every single piece of furniture in the shop, every sign on the wall, every advertisement. Most often I came here right after work, since the computer center that SRC rented was only two subway stops away. Sometimes I made a special trip, although not as often recently as I used to …

How many times I came here with Nina and Boris, or just with Nina— but most often, by myself?.. I could come to Michael's studio feeling anxious, unhappy, lonely, mixed up, disappointed in life. When I left, I always felt better about myself and about the world. Things that had been confusing appeared clear; questions that seemed to have no answers turned simple; memories that had been tormenting me suddenly became unimportant. For me Michael was a great counselor, although he himself barely realized it. He must have enjoyed feeling responsible for my slow but steady conversion to Judaism and "Jewishness." He probably liked the fact that he was learning something new from me, getting a fresh look at many things—although he would be reluctant to admit that.

"I should come here more often," I thought. "If only for the sake of staying sane…"

Looking around the room, I saw a photograph of a page from an Israeli book on the table. It had a large picture, and a few lines of Hebrew text underneath. The text must have been written for *olim*, or new immigrants, since the letters had vowels and the sentences were short and simple. I took the photograph in my hand. I had been hoping to find something like that, and smiled, imagining Michael's reaction to what was about to happen. We hadn't seen each other for a while, just talked briefly on the phone, and Michael knew nothing about Jacob and our lessons.

He finally emerged from the lab, wiping his hands with an old white towel, and walked toward the refrigerator to take our supper out. He noticed me studying the Israeli photograph, and started explaining where it was from. "*Toda raba*," I said with a smile. "*Meanyen meod*,"* and read the entire text under the picture aloud, carefully pronouncing

---

* *Toda raba* means "Thank you very much," and *Meanyen meod* means "very interesting" in Hebrew.

Hebrew sounds. Michael stopped, and for a minute was staring at me in silent amazement.

"How..." he finally mumbled. "How do you know?.. I did not teach you *that!*"

"No," I said, enjoying his astonishment. "But other people did. Didn't I tell you that *I would learn* Hebrew?"

"You know what," said my friend a few seconds later, returning from his kitchenette with loaves of whole wheat bread, bacon and cheese, "I'll tell you something. When I finally die to the joy of my numerous enemies and go to Hell, there will be fewer coals in my fire, because of what I have done for you. You are my first and, almost certainly, the only pupil, who has gone farther than the teacher..."

3

"What is she doing? Studying her *Jewish language* again?"

"She is your daughter as much as mine. Go talk to her, if you wish..."

Oh well, they are going to start it again. I thought I was done with my parents for that night. I had endured a discussion with my mother that sounded more like a fight, just half an hour ago. It was after eleven o'clock, and I was not planning to stay up past midnight. I had decided to finish my lesson before going to bed, but my parents' constant interruptions did not let me concentrate.

My father entered the living room. Unlike my mother, he at least decided to be affectionate.

"Anechka, my girl, why are you doing this? If you have free time and are bored, learn something useful. Learn French, or German, or Japanese. Do you want me to find you a tutor?

"I have already learned German and French, papa, and there has been no use of either knowledge..."

"Nobody speaks Hebrew in the modern world, except one little country, and you will never go there..."

"Papa! I am never going to go to Japan, either! You and I have been through this at least ten times already—aren't you tired? And after all, I am twenty-eight years old, and have a right to spend my free time learning whatever I please, and be left alone by my parents!"

I say this louder than I should, and my mother hears my words from the kitchen. I was hoping that she had finished her lecturing for tonight, but I was wrong. My last words made her furious; she bursts into the living room, almost screaming:

"To be left alone? You dare to talk about being left alone? After we've been raising your child for two year! After all the money we've spent to support you! So, what are you doing here? You live in this house, eat the food I cook, expect us to continue sending you money after you leave, and want to be 'left alone'? No, my dear, it is a two-way street! You want anything from us, you be kind enough to listen to what we are telling you!"

It is better not to answer. I have learned by now that neither my mother nor my father will go so far as to take my books away from me, and they cannot possibly lecture me all night. But scenes like this happen every single evening. Nadia goes to sleep at 8:30 PM, so the time between nine and midnight is mine, to study Hebrew. Jacob suggested that I should try to cover as many lessons during the summer as I could, so I have decided that I may as well finish the textbook. It goes easier than I feared: I have mastered the art of using Hebrew-English dictionary (my only choice, since Hebrew-Russian dictionaries could be bought only in Israel), to be able to find all the unknown words; I understand almost all the grammar explanations, even though the textbook is entirely in Hebrew. I feel excited, happy, drinking the sounds of this new language like a thirsty person drinks water; I am infatuated, in love with it even more right now than I am in love with Volodia Sonovsky.

I mostly think of Volodia at night when I go to bed. I dream of us making love, and fall asleep happy. I wake up with his image, anxious about the possible development of our relationship in the fall, when I return to Leningrad. But during the day I get distracted. I spend most of my time with Nadia, taking her to the beach, reading to her, or arranging play dates with the children of my former playmates. Overall, I feel more cheerful than I was in Akademgorodok during the two previous summers: the image of my unjustly incarcerated husband suffering in jail does not haunt me anymore. I look forward to evenings, when Nadia falls asleep and I can go back to my Hebrew studies. I look forward to returning to Leningrad in September, to resume my studies with Jacob and, of course, to see Volodia. I know that

Lev will come back some time, maybe even before the next summer, and that is OK. But, while he is away, I am going to make the most of my life...

There is no logical explanation for my parents' reaction to my studies. They can't blame me for taking the time away from my daughter, since I do not open my textbook until Nadia is asleep. They say that my husband will never approve it—but where is it written that a woman at the end of the twentieth century must obey her husband in every little thing?

My mother scolds me for not reading books any more. She was always proud of me because I read a lot, and now I spend all my free time studying Hebrew, while there are so many wonderful books in the world that I have never read. If I fall behind, unable to keep up with the reading all intelligent people do, what will become of me?

And then in the fall, when I take Nadia with me to Leningrad (it has been decided that Nadia should finally live with her mother), am I going to continue these useless and time-consuming studies? With Nadia's grandma being far away, the poor girl will inevitably be neglected: I cannot possibly work full time and study a foreign language, while raising a four-year-old child alone...

Somewhere behind these arguments there is a much deeper issue. No one verbalizes it, but we all know what it is. I have no doubt that my parents would fully support me if I spent exactly the same amount of time studying, let's say, French, or even Japanese or Chinese. It is Hebrew that makes them mad: my mother has sensed correctly that it is a sign of my first rebellion. She clearly expressed her unhappiness with my interest in Jewish history when I visited in the winter. She opposed my reading novels of Feuchtwanger that I had taken from her own book shelf, on the grounds that I was "only reading about Jews" and therefore, limiting my interests. During my winter stay, my mother was still hoping that this sudden interest would soon pass; but learning Hebrew is going way too far. It is not something that I could have picked up from my parents; it cannot not possibly be a result of my mother's influence; therefore, it must be a rebellion. And that is what my strong authoritarian mother cannot accept.

"All intelligent Jews are assimilated. They are great people when they absorb the culture they live in. They contribute to the cultural development of the countries that have become their homes. But as soon as they limit themselves to being only "Jewish," they turn into nobody. Jews in Israel have not created anything—no great works of literature, no art, not even significant scientific discoveries. Israel is a big ghetto, and people who live there isolate themselves from the great world culture..."

I know intuitively that my mother is wrong, but cannot find words to argue with her. I wish I could tell her what was so easy to tell Jacob—that in my late twenties I don't know who I am, and that learning Hebrew is my last hope in helping figure it out... But my intuition tells me that such a confession to my mother would be a disaster—so I keep it all to myself. My mother used to be my closest friend when I was growing up. Ten years after I left her home, she turned into an enemy who will continue hurting me until I surrender.

Is it at least partially a religious conflict? As most Russian intellectuals, the only religion my parents recognize is Orthodox Christianity. (Officially all Soviet citizens are atheists, and for most people religion is no more than mere defiance of the government.) My mother encouraged me to read the Bible for years, but to her "the Bible" is the New Testament only. She says she is scared that I may become a member of that "sect," as she calls Judaism, into which "Michael and others" are trying to draw me. "You have no mind and no will of your own! You need to follow somebody—and like all weak people pick up the ones who dress in bright colors and sound sweet, but have no real values behind their empty words!" Is this reference to Michael? Or is it a scream of pain that I suddenly stopped following *her*?

"Lev will never forgive you for this!" is my parents' final pronouncement. "You will end up alone, and you will leave your child without a father!"

"What is the point of having a husband who can leave me just because I'm studying a foreign language? If he cannot accept that little independence, I do not want him myself!"

"You know very well that it is not just 'studying a foreign language'! This is an *ideology* that neither Lev, nor anyone I know, will ever accept! As for your 'I don't want him'—you do not even understand what you are talking about! Are you planning to join the crowd of single women who are running around frantically looking for husbands and ready to sleep with anyone in hope that the guy might marry them? Are you going to become one of them?! And what will happen to your daughter, have you thought about that?! You have never been a responsible mother, and I know you will step over her... You think you will be always surrounded by male friends like you are now? They all are there only because you are married, and therefore 'safe'! Wait until you are divorced, and all your men will see you as a potential threat! They will all disappear before you know it!"

These arguments are taking us long way from my learning Hebrew. My mother's last statement is a blow below the belt, although she herself is almost certainly unaware of it. Unknowingly, she says the same thing as Lev said during our date back in winter.

I don't need either of them to add to my already existing anxiety: Volodia Sonovsky might be interested in me only as long as I am someone else's wife. And—most importantly—as long as he doesn't understand that I love him. He may be infatuated with me, like a young page is infatuated with a queen. He adores her and worships her, as long as she is beyond his reach, beyond hope. But God forbid if the queen becomes a maid and falls into the page's arms—she loses all her charm instantly...

...In spite of my parents screaming at me persistently every evening whenever they saw me studying Hebrew, by the end of my two months' summer vacation, I finished the last lesson of the textbook.

4

"Listen, maybe you should try to *disappear* for a while? I have a feeling that the main problem is that you are always there, any time he wants you..."

"Where can I go? With work and especially with the child?"

"Well, maybe not really disappear, but somehow pretend that you are not there? Not answer the phone for a week, or something like that?"

Nina and I were sitting in her room, while our daughters were playing in another part of her huge apartment. My friend's idea that I should be less available for Volodia seemed worth trying—but I could not imagine having enough character to hear the phone ringing and not pick it up even for one day, not to mention a whole week. And then, what about Grandma Galia? Even if I somehow manage to force myself not to answer the phone, she certainly will.

"Can't you talk to her? She is a woman after all. She should be able to understand you..."

Grandma Galia? Understand me? She was one of those people who seemed incapable of understanding anything that did not match their personal experience. As most women of her generation, she had spent her entire life having slept with one and only one man: her husband. When he left her after many years of what everyone perceived to be a very happy marriage (presumably, because she could not have children), she stayed faithful to his memory. She never remarried or even had an affair, even though, according to our relatives, quite a few men were interested. Naturally, she considered her behavior the only appropriate path, and anyone who might act, or even think of acting, differently, was by definition an immoral person. Having sex with a man who was not my husband would be terrible enough even if I were not married. Now I was committing a double crime, and Grandma Galia stopped talking to me after the first night Volodia stayed over.

"Every time I try to say anything to her, she turns away in disgust, or plainly calls me a whore. No, she won't understand," I said.

"But something must be done about it, right?" insisted Nina. "You simply can't go on like this. I have never seen you this miserable. Ever. Not even after Lev had just been arrested. We somehow have to make Volodia feel that he might lose you."

"Do you really think that might help?"

"Men are scoundrels. Selfish bastards. We must accept it, and work from there."

"But what does it have to do with..."

"They want what they cannot get, and, as soon as they get it, they become bored. Unless, of course, we can make them feel that we might disappear; then they're more likely to make efforts to keep us."

"Do you think *all* men are like that?"

"My Turkey certainly is ("Turkey" was the code name she and I had given to Boris). He disappears for months in a row without any warning, because he is sure that I will be there when he finally feels like showing up. But as soon as he senses that I might disappear too, he starts making movements to be around."

"But your husband is not the same way, is he?"

"I don't know... I never could understand him... Before the wedding, he was much more in love than I was; he seemed constantly nervous that someone else might marry me before he does. I think that was the main reason he finally got around to proposing to me."

"But what is he doing now? He seems to be married to his programs, and he never spends any time with you. Is it because he is confident that you will always be there?

"Almost certainly, yes. And the funny thing is, he's right..."

"But if you just pretend that you are having an affair? Do you think he would start paying more attention to you?"

"I can't *pretend* I am having an affair," sighed Nina sadly. "I *am* having one... And I would rather not tempt my fate by letting my husband suspect it. After all, he does not deserve to be hurt..."

As usual, Leonid walked me and Nadia to the subway station. It was only about eight-thirty in the evening, but the world was dark, rainy and windy, dim street light making empty streets look even lonelier. My daughter was overexcited and tired at the same time, so she whined and complained all the way. Leonid, who had interrupted his work for what he considered to be his male duty, was walking slowly, adjusting to Nadia's pace, but kept silent, apparently absorbed in thoughts about his computer programs. I thought that Nina deserved a livelier husband, but that part of her life was at least stable. That stability gave her strength to tolerate Boris's inconsistent behavior. And she lived with a mother who understood and supported her, even if she did not know everything about her life. And she never, ever had to come home to a dark, empty apartment...

Nadia fell asleep in the subway, her head on my lap—pale, thin, tired, and a very lonely child. Her presence was supposed to make me feel less alone, but somehow it had almost the opposite effect. My life—or whatever was left of it—was over the moment I picked up my daughter from daycare: she was incapable of entertaining herself even for a few minutes, demanded constant attention, acted cranky and teary in one moment, too loud and mischievous the next. She would scream at me and call me names, or even hit me—just to become clingy a minute later, holding on to me for dear life, as if I could suddenly disappear. Her pediatrician recommended that she see a child psychiatrist—but at the daycare she was a non-problem little girl, always well-behaved and reasonably social; I could not stop thinking that it was me who was a bad mother, and putting my child on medication would not fix that...

In a minute, I would have to wake her up: we were approaching our subway station. After a brief walk through the marble hall where mosaic walls and crystal chandeliers create a perpetual feeling of festivity, we'll emerge into a cold wet darkness. I will see my house right in front of me, barely two hundred yards away—and two windows on the fourth floor will be dark and empty, like the eyes of a blind man...

5

"If he is there now," I thought, walking up the wide marble staircase of my subway station, "if I see the light in my window... It will almost certainly not happen, but *if*... Well, then everything Nina and I were talking about all evening is irrelevant. I will not do that... At least, not now... But if he is not there... If he can go through the entire weekend without seeing me... then Nina is right, and I must, I must do something about it..."

My four-year-old girl, still half asleep, was pulling my hand.

"You're walking too fa-a-st, ma-aa," she whined.

"I want us to get home faster, so you can go to bed, honey."

"I lied," I thought. "I am impatient to get on the ground, so I can look at the damn window... I am still hoping that there might be light... That *he* might be there..."

I made myself slow down. I needed all my will power not to look up at my window after we got out. I kept looking down at my feet. "He is not, not, not there," I kept repeating to myself. "I must not be disappointed. The room is dark, just as I left it. He has not come. I will have to do what Nina and I have decided..."

But I did look up—just before turning around the corner, to enter the building. My heart sank, then jumped all the way up into my throat, so that for a few seconds I could not breathe. I felt hot, then cold, then hot again. There was light in *that* window.

"I may have looked at the wrong window," I warned myself. Such a thing had happened once already, and I could not forget my terrible disappointment after I realized my mistake. I took a deep breath, and looked up again. There could be no doubt: it was the fourth floor, the second window from the corner of the building, with emerald-green curtains; it was my room.

"I must have forgotten to turn off the light when I was leaving..." I just could not afford another disappointment, right after my heart almost jumped out from happiness. I was walking up the stairs slowly, not so much because of Nadia, but to give myself time to calm down. If I walk into the apartment like I am now, Volodia will certainly hear my heart beat, and see me breathing as if I had run a marathon... That must not happen... I shall be calm... I shall be casual...

But my desperate need for love, mixed with the anticipation of happiness, was stronger than all reasoning. In a few minutes I may be in Volodia's arms... It was almost too good to be true, but yet it might be true...

When my daughter and I reached the third floor, I could hear the sound of a typewriter from an apartment above. It was Volodia. In my room. Typing that book. Waiting for me...

* * *

I did not remember who had given me the book. My parents, perhaps? It was a *samizdat,* "published" on somebody's home typewriter, and not even the first copy. It was a memoir by Eugenia Ginsburg, a young literature professor and the wife of a prominent Soviet official, who was arrested in the nineteen thirties in the wake of Stalin's first "cleaning" of the Russian *intelligentsia.* (The term is explained beautifully in Wikipedia). The author survived over twenty years of prisons and labor camps, and, after her release following Stalin's death, wrote an autobiography that eventually made her famous. (It was translated into English as *Journey into the whirlwind,* and published in the USA multiple times). It is a powerful story of Stalin's punitive machine aimed at exterminating intellectuals in Russia as a social class; a woman's story of physical and moral suffering; a narrative of human degradation, the crushing of beliefs and ideals, and the struggle for survival, courage, and friendship that sustained people

294

in situations in which survival seemed impossible. I swallowed three or four hundred pages of the book in a few evenings, with chills of horror, tears of anger, and shame for my countrymen who had forgotten such a recent period of their history. Volodia, who had heard about the book but had never had a chance to read it, finished it in two nights and asked my permission to give it to his friends. The book was still circulating somewhere in Leningrad, when he summarized his friends' opinion:

"We need more copies. Memoirs like these will never get published in this country. (Volodia was wrong: the book was published in Russia during Perestroika, and had several more editions thereafter—but who could have predicted that in the beginning of 1987?). I have huge respect for people who spend their time typing them. I wish I could do the same: distributing this kind of knowledge is the duty of every honest Russian…"

"Do you want to type it together?" I asked, hardly believing what I was offering.

"Can you get a typewriter?"

I thought that I probably could, and called Aunt Olia. She said I could borrow hers, but not more than for two weeks: she would need it shortly, to meet the deadline for an article she had to send to some mathematical journal. Two weeks went by quickly, and Volodia and I had barely finished the first few chapters. Volodia had not planned on spending money on a typewriter; neither did he find working on the book in his own house to be safe. He fully trusted his sister and her husband, but they had too many visitors, some of whom could accidentally wonder into his room. I had not been planning on buying a typewriter either, but could not imagine dropping the work after we had just started.

"I'll buy a typewriter," I said.

A typewriter was bulky and heavy, so it was Volodia who went to the store and bought one—with my money. The pretty orange machine was installed on the desk in my room, and Volodia and I started taking turns typing the book, page by page, chapter by chapter. It went very slowly, but I was enjoying the mere process of doing it together with Volodia…

When our dating turned serious in September, I felt as if I had finally found the man of my dream—never mind I had been mistaken about

Lev Fedorov. Wasn't one mistake enough? Subconsciously, I knew that I could not afford another one. On the conscious level, however, I could not find any faults in Volodia, or in our relationship. We saw each other almost daily; on the days he could not come, he always called. He used to tell me his schedule, day by day, hour by hour. He spent hours talking about his childhood, his friends, and stories from his life that he thought had the biggest impact on him. After making love, we used to lie awake, discussing all kinds of issues from international events, domestic politics, or Volodia's writings (because, as a son of a well-known journalist, he considered himself a writer), to social justice and the inadequate position of women in our society. We would fall asleep in each other's arms, and wake up a few hours later totally refreshed.

"There have been only two other women in my life whom I ever respected as much as I respect you," said Volodia on numerous occasions. "All the other women I see around me are just *females*: they speak about cooking, children, and clothes. Oh! Women in my office speak about cosmetics... and about underwear... Like where to buy fashionable bras!—imagine? Or they discuss their husbands. You are a *person*, not a *female*. You are more beautiful, more gentle, more sexy than most of the women I've ever met, but you are intelligent, you have broad interests. I can discuss everything with you, as if you were a male friend..."

Of course, I wanted to know who the other two women were; I complimented myself for having guessed correctly even before Volodia named them. The first one was his twin sister, a college professor of English language and literature; the other one was Svetlana, the woman Volodia danced with at the SRC party, where he and I first met. Since Svetlana was the wife of Volodia's best friend, I did not perceive her as a rival. And although the only times Volodia said to me "I love you" were in bed in the midst of the highest passion, I had no doubt that it was only a matter of time before he said these words calmly and consciously.

But he never said them.

Moreover, it seemed as if the more often we met, the less involved he became. Having a little girl hanging around certainly did not help—notwithstanding Volodia's endless proclamations of his fascination with young children. Maybe, Nina was right, and I just needed to show him that I could disappear, too—so he at least stopped taking me for granted?

* * *

"Ah! Finally!—said Volodia, walking out of the room. He was wearing that old gray sweater that I loved so much, and had this half-smile that I wanted to kiss a thousand times. "I was just about to leave..."

"What do you mean 'about to leave'?" It made so little sense, that I did not even get upset. "You knew I could not come home much later than nine: it is a work day tomorrow, and Nadia needs to go to bed..."

"Anya, I need to be some place at ten," said Volodia, without any smile at all. "It is..." he looked at his watch. "It's almost nine-fifteen. I actually should have left by now."

"I finished here," He pointed to the mark on the page. "You can continue from here on. I really need to run now. I am already late; I wish you had come home earlier. I'll call you tomorrow..."

I felt like a person thrown from the top of a green and sunny mountain into a deep dark cave. No, it could not be true... After I had just been so happy...

"When am I going to see you?" I asked, trying not to show my despair.

"I don't know, Anya. Tomorrow I have a football game and a tennis lesson right after that. I will call you in between... Around seven o'clock, I guess. I need to meet my professor on Wednesday, so Tuesday I am definitely preparing for that: I still have not written the thesis that he wants. Maybe, Thursday. Hopefully, I will know by tomorrow night. But, if not, I'll call you on Wednesday again. Do you have lots of homework in your Hebrew? Why? I thought you might be able to do some typing meanwhile: it would be nice to do at least one chapter per week. Anyway, see you. Good night."

He kissed me casually and briefly, and ran downstairs. I could hear his steps, moving farther and farther away. I tried not to look out of the window, to see him disappear into the cave of the subway station. I looked, anyway...

The clock in the living room was ticking obnoxiously loudly. Nadia was sound asleep in her room. My great aunt was either asleep or watching TV in her room, I could not tell. She never talked to me, anyway. It was not ten o'clock yet, too early to go to sleep. I opened my Hebrew notebook and tried to study, but could not concentrate. I finally went over to the living room, moved the bureau away from the wall, and unplugged the telephone. Then I moved the furniture back, and stuck the phone cord underneath its back leg, so no one could pull it and find out that the phone was unplugged. Having done that, I swallowed two tranquilizer pills and went to bed...

6

It didn't take my grandaunt more than a day to notice that the phone was not working. I was wondering if she would break her vow of silence to inquire about it—and of cause, she did. Not that she sounded friendly or sympathetic in any way when I told her that I must have forgotten to pay the monthly phone bill, and now it would take at least a few days to get the phone back working...

Monday night was fantastic. I could go on with my chores, play with my daughter, make progress with my Hebrew studying—I was almost my old self again: I did not have to wait for Volodia to call me. Moreover, I couldn't help feeling some satisfaction thinking of him dialing my number again and again, and hearing the phone ringing in vain... Whatever his feelings for me, that had never happened before. It was all well worth listening to Grandma Galia's grumbling...

* * *

It was Thursday evening, and I was at the end of my English class, when he came.

The two hours a week when I taught English to the neighborhood preschoolers were the best in my life. I did not depend on Volodia or anyone else having called or not called me; I was not thinking about my work, Grandma Galia's contempt, or my grim future with Lev Fedorov. I was happy, creative, fully absorbed in playing games in English with five-to-six-year-old boys and girls. Those one-hour classes—one on Thursday night and another one on Sunday morning—were my best coping strategy, my pain relief. All my anguish and anxieties disappeared as if they had never existed. If only I could teach forever, I would have been a much happier, much more self-confident person. But as soon as the kids started putting on their boots and coats, the anesthesia disappeared instantly, and all the pain returned, fresh and burning as ever.

It did not happen that Thursday, because just when I was about to say, "That's it for today," I heard a key turning in the front door. Had I been at home alone with Nadia, I might have gotten scared, but the presence of eight children somehow made it sound more funny than spooky. I could hear the intruder's hand trembling while he was trying to turn the key in the lock. When I opened the door, Volodia was there, pale and shaking like I had never seen him before.

"Anya! Oh, my god, you are all right!" He paid almost no attention to the surprised kids, or to Nadia who happily ran to greet him. I called several times every day! Where were you? I thought something terrible had happened…

I felt almost ashamed. Nina's plan worked beautifully, but I had no idea that Volodia would be that worried. I knew that he called Nina on Wednesday, only to hear that she had not spoken to me since Sunday night. It was just another part of our conspiracy: I would call Nina from a pay phone every evening, but the answer she gave to Volodia was the one she and I had agreed upon.

"My phone wasn't working," I said. "Apparently, I forgot to pay last month's bill for long-distance calls, so they disconnected the service. It's ok; I paid yesterday, so it should be back on tomorrow."

"Why didn't you call me?" insisted Volodia. "Didn't you understand that I was worried?"

"Call you? But you're never home!" I tried to play a woman-who-does-not-care, but it was very much not my role, and I started feeling false.

"You could have left a message with my mother!"

I thought that I had left messages with his mother many times before, but she always had that *when-are-you-going-to-leave-my-son-alone* tone. After a while, I decided to avoid such contacts with her as much as possible. Of course, I did not say that.

"Sorry! I could not imagine that you might worry that much. I certainly would have called if I had known…"

Whether I had done a bad thing or not, Volodia was there. He was passionate, tender and loving as I had not seen him for a long time. He absolutely had to be some place that very evening, but he promised to come back tomorrow. He also suggested spending most of the coming weekend with me and Nadia—something that had not happened for a long time.

In brief, Nina's and my little deception would have turned out to be a success, if only... if only I could continue showing Volodia at least some coldness, or indifference. I should have told him that I was busy on Saturday, that I had already made other plans. I should have been "not at home" when he called me, at least once in a while. But I could not lie any more—and pretending that I did not love him was beyond me.

On Saturday night when we were in bed together, I almost broke down. I never confessed about the trick with the phone, but I tried to tell Volodia once again how much he was hurting me. I begged him to give me at least some stability. I even hinted—for the first time—that my relationship with my husband had not been happy and that I was waiting for his return from prison out of mere duty. But, the more I revealed my soul, the colder and more distant Volodia was turning.

He left around one in the morning, to catch the last subway train home. Obviously, he did not want to begin his Sunday waking up in the apartment with me and Nadia. He left with the promise *to call* (but not *to come*) on Monday. I had to live through Sunday without seeing him, or even knowing where he was. I had to survive Monday, when the time was moving slower and slower, the closer it got to seven o'clock; and at about six it seemed to stop completely. The clock kept ticking, but the hands did not move; the air became painfully thick, so thick I could barely breathe. My daughter was saying something to me, and I heard the sound of her voice, but could not understand a word. By a quarter to seven I was nauseous and dizzy, and the entire universe froze...

It all started over again. This time at least I knew what I was doing wrong. I could have won Volodia back, if only ... if only I could pretend that I did not love him.

* * *

"I would sympathize with you... if there were no people who suffer more, much more than you do," said Volodia.

I thought that he was referring to my imprisoned husband. Or, maybe, to all the poor, hungry, and oppressed people around the world. Victims of Stalin's terror. Or the Holocaust. I feared his next phrase, feared his contempt, like one fears to be hit. He was silent for a while, but his face was expressing greater and greater pain.

"Me... I suffer so much more than you do..."

"You?!.."

"Anya..." he was almost choking. "I've never told you, have I? I love a woman... Have loved her for a long time...She will never be mine... She is... the wife of my close friend... I will never even sleep with her. Never... Anya, do you understand? I have never, ever slept with the woman I love! And never will... And I see her almost every week... Do you understand how much *I* suffer?"

I looked at him in astonishment. His words should have hurt me, but I do not remember the pain—just amazement. I thought of his passion in bed with me only a couple of months ago, his hot whisper: "Anya... Anechka... I love you so much... I love your name... It is the same as my mother's name, do you know?"

Damn it, he was not loving *another woman* at that moment!

I must have said something, although I do not remember what. Almost certainly something stupid. I was making one mistake after another, first trying to make Volodia feel sorry for me, then arguing that his situation was much better than mine. I couldn't imagine him seriously thinking that he was unhappier than me. He was male, with no family obligations, young, handsome, wealthy, healthy, with dozens of friends and probably at least as many women who wanted to sleep with him. I thought about his football games, his tennis lessons, his huge room full of rare books and expensive records, his twin sister who was his best friend, their house full of interesting people, his intelligent and understanding mama who was his cook, his maid, and his secretary, and who, respecting his manhood, never interfered with his personal life.

"I should have stopped our relationship long ago..."

"We *started* it only a few months ago—so when did you have time to stop it?" I wanted to say.

"I have been wasting time with you here, don't you understand?!"

"*You are one of the three women in the world whom I respect...* How could anyone *waste time* with someone he respects that much?"

"I need to create my own family. I want to have my own child, after all! I am thirty-one; I cannot go on forever sleeping around. I need to look for a wife..."

"Hold on!" I said. "There is a contradiction here: you've just said that you would never be able to marry the woman you love. So, how can you go out looking for a wife? Are you planning to marry someone you don't love?"

"Anya!" he was getting angry. "I may regret having shared that with you. It is none of your business after all whom I love, and whom I shall marry. What is clear here, is that I will not marry you! And I do want to get married, and especially have my own children. I am tired of caring for my niece and then being lectured by her parents that I do everything wrong! I need my own family—and with you I am wasting time!"

"I don't believe you," I said. "Thirty-one is not the age when a man becomes desperate. Not in this society. And I do not believe that, even if we break up right now, you will find a woman who suits you any time soon. You are not a guy who can marry without love, and as you just said, your heart is taken... Listen, I offer you a bet: I am convinced that you will not be married, or even engaged, a year after you and I have completely broken up. You may not even have a mistress whom you respect. I'll pay you a hundred rubles if I turn out to be wrong, and visa-versa—deal?"

"Anya, I am not going to take any money from you!" He sounded annoyed. "It is not your money anyway, it's Nadia's. And I am not going to make any bets on an issue that is so important to me! I must go now. As I said, I have to be somewhere at eight. I will call you... No, tomorrow I have two tennis lessons in a row, and then I have to finish reading that book... I may not be able to call tomorrow, so I better not promise. I will call you on Tuesday. Yes, Tuesday at seven. Try to make some progress with the typing; I would like to have this book finished. I may be able to come on Wednesday during the day, and type for an hour or two..."

He left.

It was not even seven-thirty. Too early to be alone on Sunday night. Too late to go visit anybody, considering that Nadia needed to be in bed in about an hour.

"Wednesday during the day..." If I find a way to come home early, he might still be here... I might be able to see him, even if only for half an hour... But what for? What have our dates brought me lately, except pain, humiliation, and more pain? The only time I wasn't hurting was when Volodia and I were in bed together. But even that may have been ruined now, by that one phrase: *I have never slept with a woman I loved...*

I thought at that moment that he was referring to the fact that he did not love me. Painful truth, but not particularly new. Now I realized that he meant "*the* woman he loved", not "*a* woman he loved..." No grammatical distinction in Russian. You have to guess...

I was surprised how little jealousy I felt. I was hurt, hurt badly, ashamed of myself, humiliated, but not really jealous. I had no doubt I knew who that woman was. Too many hints: "the wife of my close friend", "I see her almost every week" and, of course, one of the three women he had ever met in his life that he respected as a *person*, not just a *female*. One was me. Another one was his twin sister. And the third one, Svetlana, Ivan's wife.

There had been numerous occasions when it was quite appropriate to introduce me to that couple. They had parties where I would have fit in one hundred percent. From Volodia's description, they resembled my mother's parties in Akademgorodok. A few people from our SRC were frequent guests there, but Volodia always managed to find an excuse for not bringing me over.

"I don't want Svetlana and Ivan to ever see me with any woman," he said once.

"Why?" I thought back then, but preferred not to think about the answer...

Now I knew it.

Knew it? Volodia had loved Svetlana "for a long time"? I remembered that New Year party a little over a year ago, when I first met him. Svetlana was there,and without her husband. Volodia could have danced every single dance with her, but he barely danced one or two. He preferred to dance with me! I remembered how he was looking at me that evening... A man does not look at a woman like that when the one he loves is in the same room...

Nevertheless, he almost certainly did not lie to me. His love may have been in his head more than in his heart, but once having decided that Svetlana was the one and only woman for him, he must have believed in it. And thinking of his own hopeless love allowed him to suffer and to pity himself for his suffering! And he expected me to have empathy?..

I wanted to tell him that he would probably never choose *to love* Svetlana if she were single and available, but I would not be able to prove or disprove it. Unlike me, Svetlana seemed to be married very happily. Volodia could dream about her forever, without the slightest risk of ever being disappointed...

7

Sometime in the early 1980s, the major Leningrad newspaper discussed a local political court case. According to the article in *Leningradskaya Pravda* ("Truth of Leningrad," in a rough translation), *Traitors of our motherland, bourgeois elements that had sold their souls to Western imperialists, were poisoning the minds of the Soviet people with their mendacious, dirty writings.* The newspaper called for severe punishment of the guilty. *Soviet people do not need these rotten vegetables in their garden; they are not going to buy the dissidents' "revelations" that slander their country*—and so on.

Such a tone was neither new nor unusual. Proletarians found it totally appropriate. Intelligentsia spit and vomited, but could not do anything, except quietly provide some moral support to the subjects of the article, if the latter happened to be among their acquaintances. At least ten percent of Leningrad citizens kept *samizdat* in their homes and could easily have such an article written about them. The majority, however, were never discovered. People continued to read, write and distribute *samizdat*, and the KGB continued to pretend that it was doing its work. The few unfortunate ones who got caught became scapegoats. Their court cases, widely publicized, did not discourage anybody from doing the same, but warned people to be careful.

The main character of the above-mentioned article was someone called N*, arrested for possessing and allegedly distributing *anti-Soviet literature.* Interrogated by the KGB and apparently trying to reduce his inevitable prison term, N* gave away the names of all his friends and acquaintances who had ever borrowed books from him. All the people mentioned by N* were, in turn, interrogated and their homes searched. Two of his friends were arrested. N* himself was sentenced to three years of imprisonment; others received different forms of lighter punishment.

One of N*'s friends who was interrogated repeatedly and barely avoided arrest, was Sasha Radzinsky, a young professor of Library Science at the Institute of Culture, from which Nina and I had recently graduated. Like Aunt Olia, Sasha lost his job overnight, together with the right to ever teach young people again. After having been unemployed for a while, he was offered a modest position of research assistant at the Scientific Research Center of the very college where he had recently been a respected professor.

I did not know Sasha's story when I first met him at SRC. Tall, very thin, slightly slouchy, he impressed people as a very educated and intellectual young man, and I could only wonder what he was doing in our god-forsaken company, on a salary only slightly higher than mine. I saw Sasha regularly once a week, when he stopped at our office to get a new detective story from Stella. I soon noticed that Stella was proud of that superficial friendship and treated Sasha's visits as a great honor, which did not surprise me. What puzzled me was that this intellectual with a PhD expressed so much interest in detective novels, a literature more appropriate for a teenager or a middle-aged housewife. Several times, having run into Sasha in an empty corridor or on the staircase, I was about to ask if he ever read more serious books, but never dared to open my mouth. Like the majority of my co-workers, Sasha clearly disliked me, and his dry "hi" did not encourage any conversation.

I thought of asking Volodia about Sasha, but kept forgetting, until one day Volodia mentioned N*'s story and the scandal related to it as something I was expected to know about. When I said that I had never heard of the case, Volodia was astonished. Hadn't I heard about it from Sasha? I had to admit that Sasha and I practically never talked.

"You ought to talk to him!" said Volodia. "Sasha Radzinsky is one of the most intelligent, honest, honorable people in Leningrad... well, probably in the whole of Russia. He is also a friend of mine. Not a close friend, unfortunately, but I would be honored to be his close friend. You shouldn't worry that he might misunderstand your story. Just tell him all about your husband; he will have complete empathy with your desire to be private and reserved about it..."

In spite of Volodia's encouragement, I still did not dare to talk to Sasha until the day I gave my supervisors notice of resignation. Not that

I had been unhappy in SRC, rather the opposite—but, in my newly-acquired vanity of a computer programmer, I decided that it was time for me to move on, and find a more challenging job with a higher salary. (Later it turned out to be the most stupid decision I made while living in Leningrad—but at that moment I was feeling rather good about my own bravery.)

Knowing that I would soon leave SRC forever, made me realize that I had to act now—or never; after all, there was nothing to lose. Next time when I ran into Sasha on the staircase, I told him that I would like to talk to him in private. He looked surprised, but promised to find a few minutes and let me know.

The following day, I met Sasha in his office during the lunch break, when everyone else was out. I do not remember exactly what I said. I must have mentioned Volodia as a "reference;" I definitely told the story of my husband's unjust imprisonment. While I was talking, Sasha's face expressed not just understanding, but compassion.

"You are a courageous woman," he said, "and I wish I somehow had known all of that before. I have to admit that I did consider you arrogant and lofty, which obviously has nothing to do with reality. I agree that you did not have any choice: you could not allow your husband's story to become known at SRC. Yes, you could have come up with some plausible lies or not wear your wedding ring. But I respect you hugely for the choice you've made."

Sasha happened to live in the same area of the city as I, just one subway stop away. At the end of our conversation, we exchanged home phone numbers and agreed that we would talk again, in a more relaxed environment.

Sasha had come over for tea three or four times, before he asked what was going on with me.

"Every time I see you, you look more and more depressed," he said. "I cannot explain it by your worrying about your husband, since that has been going on for three years. You seem to be upset about something new. I am asking not to be nosy, but because I want to find out if I can somehow help you..."

I tried to smile.

"I was not planning to talk about it, but since you are so perceptive I will admit that something very bad is happening with me right now.

I am embarrassed to say that it has almost nothing to do with my imprisoned husband, but rather with my relationship with another man. And I would gladly accept help: I cannot stand being alone on weekends, and would be extremely grateful if you could sometimes spend evenings with me..."

It was amazingly easy to talk to Sasha like that. It was easy to tell him what I could never say to Volodia: that my relationship with Lev Fedorov had been far from happy, and that my husband and I had all but broken up a few months before his arrest. I had not gotten into the details, but said enough to feel confident that Sasha would not condemn me for having an affair. I still was not ready to mention Volodia's name, but was not surprised when, only a few weeks after that conversation, Sasha guessed it correctly.

"I am surprised that Sonovsky could hurt a woman. He has always seemed like a very decent man to me, honest and with high moral principles. But I can see that you are hurt, so he must have done something wrong. I just wonder what..."

I wished I could answer Sasha's question, but did not know how. I wanted to quote Volodia's "*I should have stopped our relationship long time ago... I have been wasting time with you here, don't you understand?*"—but I was not ready for that. Sasha was a very good listener, but I did not feel comfortable going through all the painful details of my recent past, and neither did I want to reveal my humiliation.

Sasha repeated his question, in slightly different words, several times, without me being able to answer. He ended up admitting that the reason did not really matter: I was hurt and extremely depressed, and that's what was important. In order to help me, Sasha did even more than I had asked for: he took me out every single weekend, instead of "sometimes".

He usually called on Fridays, to tell me what evening would be good for him, and we both decided where we would like to go. Usually we went to a movie, since movies started late, and I could put Nadia to bed before leaving the house. Sometimes we went to a classical music concert at the Philharmonic. Those evenings were the best, but unfortunately the concerts started as early as 7:30 PM. I had to leave my daughter with Grandma Galia, and Grandma Galia was a lousy babysitter: in fact, she hardly paid any attention to Nadia at all. I did not feel great about leaving them together, but being able to go out on the weekends was critical for my psychological survival. Luckily, my brave five-year-old did not mind going to bed on her own.

There was not a trace of romance in my relationship with Sasha, and that was the beauty of it. We were becoming more and more comfortable with each other, able to discuss personal issues easier and easier. I soon learned that Sasha had been deeply in love with a divorced woman with two children, but, being on the KGB's "black list" and not having a reliable income, did not dare to propose to her. She finally emigrated to America, and from her rare letters he got an impression that she was missing him as much as he was missing her. Sasha wondered whether he may have made a mistake, and suffered from his inability to reverse the time and try again. Having, like myself, a Jewish father and a Russian mother, Sasha nevertheless had rejected the idea of emigration long ago. He would not have had a problem receiving a refugee status from almost any Western European country, not just the U.S.A, but he could not see himself outside Russia.

"Some of us have to stay here," he said with his gentle quiet smile. "If all the intellectuals leave, what will remain of our country?"

"Don't you have friends who are refuseniks? What are you going to do when they all emigrate?"

"I have almost no close friends who are *not* refuseniks," he answered sadly. "And I do hope that one day they will all leave. What I am going to do then? I guess I will start looking for people who *stayed.* Maybe, I'll ask some beautiful young woman to take me out once a week, to help fight depression..."

＊ ＊ ＊

Fifteen years later, planning just another short visit to Leningrad (which is now called St. Petersburg), I am thinking of Sasha. He is the one who has always come to meet me at the airport; it was Sasha who helped my mother carry Nadia's heavy suitcase when, at the age of thirteen, my daughter flew to Russia on her own for the first time. His several-pages-long letters in small, fast handwriting, where I could see his soul in every word, have long been replaced by impersonal electronic mail. I hate communicating this way, but E-mail rarely gets lost—and it does not go through censors. Both Sasha and I become nervous when we don't hear from each other for more than a month, and when we meet there is nothing that we can't talk about.

Sasha is now a senior librarian in the Saltykov-Shedrin Public Library, the *Saltykovka* of my youth. He is invited to conferences all over the country, and occasionally travels abroad. He also is a part-time professor in the Leningrad University, a school much more respected than our poor Institute of Culture (although it has been renamed since, to sound more important). He regularly publishes literary reviews and has edited several books. Sasha is quiet about his literary success, but from time to time I hear his name from other people. He occasionally runs into Sonovsky at parties and meetings, but, for whatever reason, Sasha does not like him any longer.

Sasha is now a confirmed bachelor. Since he and I met, there was at least one more time when he was almost ready to marry, but, like with his first love, he procrastinated too long with his proposal. When he finally pulled his courage together, the woman he loved had just applied for emigration from the Soviet Union. He smiles sadly when we talk about it.

"Maybe, I am just too slow in making important decisions. I keep asking and asking myself: "Are you sure?"—and by the time I get rid of all doubts, it appears to be too late..."

"Or maybe, you are just one of those men who are so afraid of marriage that they keep finding excuses. I suspect that you would have escaped through the window five minutes before your own wedding, like that character from Gogol—remember?"

"That is something that we will never be able to check," he smiles again. "Unfortunately, I'm not convinced that you are wrong. Now I wish that it all had worked out differently, but..."

8

It was the worst possible time to start a new job.

Why had I decided to leave SRC, in any case? I was doing reasonably well there, and the absence of friends did not bother me anymore. Everything was familiar and predictable; I even managed to adjust my family schedule to night shifts, although they still presented the main disadvantage. But other than that? Was it my wandering soul that constantly sought changes?

I was still reasonably confident in my relationship with Volodia as well as in my programming skills, when a friend of a friend mentioned that his company was desperately looking for a computer programmer in PL-1. After I said I might be interested, the man called the hiring supervisor himself, to arrange an interview for me. How could the department head not see through all my boasting about my "programming experience," I don't know—but I was offered the job on the spot. Volodia praised me a lot for the courage and initiative: having worked in SRC himself, he considered it a professional dead end. After that, it seemed impossible for me to reject the job offer. Feeling anxious and scared, I accepted.

I regretted my decision the very first day I started the new job. It was a human factory, with strict discipline, and no flexibility in hours or a chance to leave early. Twenty people shared the same office, and there was only one outside phone line for everyone. The programs that I was supposed to write were of a different kind than the ones I was familiar with. The operating system was new. My boss made me read piles of documentation that did not make any sense and put me to sleep.

The job had no overnight shifts, that was a definite advantage. But I was so unaccustomed to coming to the office at a precise time, that I was late more often than not—and got severe reprimands for that.

My new boss appeared to have a lot of patience, and, under different circumstances, I might have learned a few new skills pretty fast. Unfortunately, while my relationship with Volodia deteriorated, I was having more and more trouble concentrating on my work. At first very bad days alternated with bearable days, and sometimes even good days. My success in acquiring new knowledge at work mirrored events at home almost precisely. Then the good days disappeared, and bearable days became more and more rare. At first, I was crying in the office once or twice a week, then every other day, then every day.

In many other countries I would have been fired on the spot—and therefore left, with my young child and imprisoned husband, without any income. Russians are generally more sympathetic, and I may have been lucky with that particular crowd. There were at least two women in my department who liked me and tried to act as my counselors. My immediate supervisor, without attempting to get into the specifics of my personal life, made it clear that he understood that I was going through a rough time. "Don't worry, I know that you will learn. If you need to take it easy now, that's what you should do," said that kind man. In order to keep me occupied, he found some simple clerical work for me, which did not require any special training. I was still paid as a programmer, and expected to catch up and start doing programming at some point, but there was no pressure. Nevertheless, I was losing respect for myself as a professional, which did not help my morale.

I was trapped in a vicious circle. Failure in the new job made me feel even worse about myself, and increased my already severe depression. And depression made it even harder for me to concentrate on my work. In the office I suffered from being surrounded by strangers, and longed for a moment when I could finally hide in my small apartment, like a turtle in her shell. Then, as soon as I was at home alone with Nadia, I felt as trapped as an animal in a cage. I needed to go out, to be with other people—preferably not just with anybody, but with close friends. But it was very hard to go out with Nadia who needed to be in bed early. In addition, she always misbehaved in other people's houses, unless there were other children to play with. Even Nina began to find excuses not to invite me over with my daughter: apparently, her own little girl had plenty of playdates with better behaved kids...

The most serious problem, however, was within me: the worse my relationship with Volodia became, the less I was capable of talking about anything else besides him. I had turned into a very difficult guest, and my social life continued deteriorating just like my love life. The only person who stayed faithful to me during those horrific weeks, was my new friend Sasha Radzinsky. Sometimes I thought that it had been worth quitting SRC, just for the sake of getting to know Sasha.

I could not enjoy anything. I slept with a triple dose of tranquilizers (generously prescribed by my dad's wonderful cousin, Marik's mom, who was a practicing doctor), and forced myself to swallow a few bites of some food once or twice a day. I felt weak from hunger, constant anxiety, and almost certainly anemia—but could not force myself to eat. Seeing my daughter was painful, and her demands for my attention almost intolerable. Teaching English to the neighborhood kids and learning Hebrew with Jacob provided some distraction, but the relief was very limited and short-lived.

Only in Volodia's presence did the pain subside. I could talk about political events in the world, about my Hebrew lessons, even books and movies—although not with the passion and intelligence of former days. I could even smile. Surprisingly, we still saw each other, although rarely more than once a week. Volodia usually came to use my typewriter, or to pick up the chapters that I had typed. Sometimes he stayed over for supper (and those were the only times I could eat without repulsion)—but never later. He never hugged me, or showed any kind of affection. And he never visited on weekends.

Once, when Volodia seemed warmer and closer than usual, I broke down and attempted talking about our relationship. I tried to tell him that living in constant pain was impairing every aspect of my life, and begged for some clarity and stability. But he interrupted me almost rudely:

"That's enough, Anya. You've said all of that before. *I'm tired of hearing about your feelings. It's boring after all—don't you understand?*"

The following two weeks, when Volodia did not come at all, were the darkest and the most horrible, even compared to the anguish of the previous few months. That was the second time in my life when I began thinking about suicide. At the end of the two weeks, he showed up on a very short notice, and—the most unbelievable thing of all— we even made love... But emotional relief caused by that miracle was very temporary: the former romance never truly resumed; at the same time, he would not disappear from my life either.

Thinking back of those days, I see myself standing near my bedroom window, looking outside at the entrance to the subway station. I was either waiting for Volodia to appear—and those were the happiest moments of my life—or remembering how happy I was only two days earlier when I *knew* that he would appear in a few minutes... It was some kind of craziness, that grabbed and held me like a mental disorder. I kept attributing the problems that were all inside me, to the circumstances of my life, which I was desperately trying to change or at least control—without any hope of success...

The world outside was still cold, with snow changing to sleet, then to rain, then to sleet again, but the days became longer. It was already light when I dropped Nadia at the day care in the mornings; it was not quite dark yet when I picked her up after work. Spring was returning to the North, shy and unsure of itself, but the changes were already visible: wind became gentler, air smelled different, there was hope in the birds' cries. Meanwhile, I was sliding downhill, faster and faster, not knowing what I could grab on to keep myself afloat...

And that was when Lev Fedorov called.

9

This time Lev was not calling from prison, but from his own apartment in Moscow. Or, to be more precise, his son's apartment, since legally he had no right to be there without Dmitry's consent. Not that the Lion had any doubt that his offspring would do anything he says...

My husband sounded more matter-of-fact than excited. It was not the way you imagine a man who has just returned after three years of unjust imprisonment would talk. Yes, he had been released on parole, cutting his term eleven months short. No, he could not leave Moscow until he has received his passport—and passport required *propiska*... So, that it where his son Dmitry came into play... In any case, I could visit him meanwhile, if I wanted...

The call came on Thursday evening. The next night, having dropped off my daughter at Nina's house, I was on the fast train to Moscow. I thought that it would be better for both Lev and me to meet for the first time without the presence of our five-year-old. The moment that I had been waiting for during three long years was finally approaching—and yet I felt more scared than happy. My first meeting with my husband would determine a lot about our future relationship. I had to be careful not to make any mistakes. I was anxious about how Lev would behave, anxious and curious at the same time.

I forgot to bring tranquilizers, but finally fell asleep on the top bunk of a second-class car. The train arrived at the capital at quarter past six in the morning, but I could not help feeling disappointed that Lev was

RAISA BOROVSKY   ◆   SIBERIAN SUMMER

not at the station to meet me. He could have made it if he had taken the first subway train, but he chose not to bother. I thought that he was probably as nervous about the moment of our first meeting as I was, and had no desire to hurry. Never mind, I knew the way to his apartment well enough...

* * *

In late spring of 1987, I started looking for a job in Moscow. My husband had come back, and was legally restored in his former apartment. Over three years ago he was arrested on his way to pick up Nadia and me from Leningrad. He finally made it there—and was as impatient for the three of us to finally live together as a family as I was in the spring of 1984.

This time nothing was preventing me from moving, except that the dream came true too late. I wished those three years had not happened; I thought I could give up anything to turn the clock back, to become that former naive girl madly in love with her husband. But no matter what I did or where I went, I had to carry an enormous load with me, a load so heavy that it made me bend down like an old woman.

One positive difference from the former days was that I did not have an option to live in Moscow as a housewife, financially dependent on my husband. I had to work—and work right away. Two unemployed spouses would look too suspicious to the authorities, especially when the husband had just been released from prison. No matter how eager I was to leave Leningrad, I could not quit my current job until I had a firm job offer in Moscow.

Indispensable Professor Shlomov, a friend of our family friend Yurivanych, who had helped me several times before, promised to recommend me to his colleagues in the capital. The timing was not great, though: it was almost summer, and many people were away on vacations. Shlomov must have made a dozen phone calls, in order to arrange three interviews for me. I was happy to use them as an excuse to spend a few days in Moscow. My Leningrad employer, knowing that I would be leaving the company, did not object to short-term unpaid leaves.

Nadia had gone to Akademgorodok for the summer, so Lev and I had all the time for ourselves. We spent a week in the same apartment where I had first visited him six years and a century ago: clean, neat, with barely any furniture, shiny hardwood floors, sunny and bright, with large windows facing lushly green yards—a dream home waiting for a happy family. Even Aunt Katia was there no more; her former room, empty after the authorities had confiscated her piano and the antique china cabinet, was waiting for me to fill it with new furniture, new friends, and new life.

On Saturday at the end of that week, we were hanging around the house and visiting nearby furniture stores. We talked about our future family life, although the discussion was somewhat one-way: Lev was telling me how he saw it, and I was listening, making very few comments. Lev hated Moscow even more than before his imprisonment; besides, there was no way he could ever regain his former status as a department head, no matter which organization he would apply to. It seemed that the time to fulfill his old dream and move to the countryside had finally come.

He realized that authorities might become suspicious of him if he lived in a village unemployed, so it would be better to get a formal job. The only job Lev could see himself doing was a forester. When I expressed doubt that the salary of a forester would be sufficient to sustain the family of three, he brushed me off with laughter: "There are many ways for a man with brains to make lots of money out there. Don't worry, honey, I won't let you starve..." I figured out that the old game was not over, but knew all too well that any objections on my side would be pointless...

There were several openings for forester positions in the Moscow region, but a recent prisoner released on parole and with no relevant experience needed very good connections to get the job. Lev was working hard to pull all the old strings and to establish new connections, and therefore was busy.

On Sunday morning of my second visit to Moscow, Lev left the house for what he had described as an important business appointment. I brought a chair out to the balcony and sat down with a book. By early afternoon, I was expecting Lev to return any minute; the phone rang, but it was not my husband. The voice belonged to a young woman, and that woman was either close to tears, or had been crying for a long time.

"Is Lev Alexandrovich home? When is he coming back? Is he OK? This is Marina—he must have told you about me... He was supposed to come over last night, and I was waiting for him all evening, but he did not even call. I thought something bad might have happened to him... Would you please tell him to call me at home as soon as he returns? I must talk to him... I'll be home all evening—so maybe he can come over tonight..."

"Yes," I said to Marina, "I'll make sure he will call you today. I'm sorry about yesterday: he had an unexpected appointment, but I completely agree that he should have called you. I've heard many good things about you, and I hate to hear you so upset."

"Oh, thank you, Elena! I'm glad you understand. Please, tell him I will not leave the house today, until he has called me..."

"Elena..." That explained it: poor Marina mistook me for Lev's daughter. No wonder, we were almost the same age, and Marina had never heard my voice. Neither did she know that Lev was still married, and especially that he had spent the last night in bed with his wife making plans for their future life together, precisely at the same time he was supposed to be in bed with her...

My main feeling when I hung up had nothing to do with jealousy: it was anger. I felt more than just empathy with Marina: it was the strongest female solidarity mixed with fury against her perpetrator. No man should ever be allowed to treat a woman like that, even if she works as a prison officer... Lev Fedorov was not just using Marina in Butyrki: he lied to her then, and he continued lying to her for almost two months after his release. He had been promising her a relationship that he had no intention of having. He almost certainly continued sleeping with her, but somehow that did not bother me as much as his betrayal of a woman who loved him and trusted him.

Was it possible that he kept her "in reserve," in case I decided not to move in with him? It didn't take me more than a couple of minutes to realize that it could not possibly be the case: had my husband been interested in keeping Marina, he would have called her the night before, with some plausible lies. Instead, he simply did not show up; he did not give a shit about her, or her feelings. He must have been visiting her and sleeping with her when he had nothing better to do. Saturday night was not one of those times, so he simply forgot about her existence.

"I'll call her some time tonight," said my husband casually. "I promised to find somebody who could get new parts for her car…"

Lev came home in a very good mood: his meeting must have been successful. He clearly did not want to be disturbed by thinking about his rejected mistress.

"She said that she would not leave the house until you call. Whatever the reason for her anxiety, I don't care, and I'm not interested in your explanations. But I would appreciate it if you call her right now—and please, apologize for not showing up yesterday!"

"May I have lunch first?" Lev started feeling uneasy. After all, he could not talk to her in my presence.

"Lunch is not ready yet. I will cook something fast after you have talked to Marina. Meanwhile, I am going to close this door, and go out on the balcony. And you can stay in Aunt Katia's room, and close your door. That way you will have complete privacy… unless you talk too loud."

I thought for a few seconds, and added:

"And no, you're not eating lunch when another person is crying because of you. I don't care what lie you tell her, but make sure she feels better after your phone call, and doesn't spend the rest of her day in tears…"

Having said that, I took my book and went back to the balcony, after honestly closing all the doors between me and Lev. However, I could not concentrate on my reading any more, and finally got tired on sitting on a hard chair. In about half an hour I came back into the living room and lay down on the sofa. Lev must have left the door to Aunt Katia's room open, because I could hear him still talking. Individual words were mostly indistinguishable, but the tone was very clear: it was the typical voice of a man lying to his mistress when he knows that his wife may be overhearing the conversation. A voice, very difficult to describe or define, but instantly recognizable by anyone who has ever heard it: as sweet as if someone put sugar in it, with occasional high-pitched notes that adults use talking to very young children. I put a pillow over my head trying not to hear it. I wished I could go out to the hallway and slam the door of the late aunt's room. Why on earth did Lev leave it open, when I specifically asked him to be as private as he possibly could?

The phone conversation must have lasted for about an hour. I was getting hungry and annoyed, when Lev finally came into the living room.

"Over and done," he said smiling. "She will not bother us again."

"She didn't bother *me*," I said, "but I am curious to know what she was so upset about."

"What was she upset about?" repeated my husband with a light laugh. "I promised her that I would marry her, and that fool believed it! Now, what are we having for lunch?"

10

The first time Lev came to Leningrad to visit me, I did something very bold. With my husband's prior consent, I had arranged to have a little party celebrating his return and at the same time introduce him to my friends. I had invited Volodia and Sasha Radzinsky, but also Svetlana and Ivan, whom I had finally met through Sasha. Nina and Leonid were the only guests Lev had known before his imprisonment; they brought along a couple of our mutual friends, who considered themselves hard-core dissidents.

I was impressed by how naturally and easily Lev talked about the prison, its grim everyday life, its written and unwritten laws, his work there, the people he had met. He sounded as if he was making a well-prepared presentation rather than confessing a painful personal experience. I was wondering how many of his stories were made up, but no one else seemed to have any doubts that his every word was the truth. My guests listened with profound interest and respect. Afterwards, I served a light meal with wine, to brighten the atmosphere—and it worked out beautifully.

I was trying not to look at Volodia, but each time I did, he was eying me with the expression I had not seen him have for many months. Nina later whispered in my ear that Sonovsky had been looking at me with open admiration, and seemed to be more interested in my brief remarks than in Lev's stories. He paid almost no attention to

Svetlana, who was noticeably pregnant and therefore, probably, too "female" for him…

The party certainly distracted me, but then the pain returned with full force… If only I could feel close to Lev, trust him, confess in him, cry on his shoulder… But, as soon as the guests left, he turned cold, dry, and formal. He was not abusive or rude (at least not yet), and sex with him caused no repulsion. It did not cause any excitement, either—but I knew it could be worse…

Could it be better? I had been dreaming for so long that Lev and I might, after all, be happy together, that his love and understanding would help me to forget Volodia Sonovsky… Now that dream seemed to be crashing just like all others: the more time I spent with my husband, the more strongly I missed Sonovsky. There were too many things that I could not discuss with Lev, and I was mentally talking to Volodia about them, imagining not only his responses but the tone of his voice and the expression on his face. Several times a day I found myself standing in front of the window, looking at the entrance to the damn subway station. I was not expecting Volodia anymore, but memories of the days when I could watch him emerging from the subway and walking toward my house, made me almost happy…

"I will go crazy if I don't do something about it immediately," I thought. "I have to run away, leave this apartment, this city, leave everything that could remind me of *him*. I need to abandon my present personality, become another woman, married, enjoying my work, devoting myself to my daughter, maybe even having another child. Lev does not have to be close to me, understanding, or loving; he just needs to be around. But oh—if only he could change, become another person, I might be able to fall in love with him again…"

In my mind I knew that such an outcome would be too good to be true, but there was still a tiny part of my heart that was hoping for a miracle…

* * *

"Lev, come on, I haven't slept with anyone since you came back!"

My husband's face scared me. Had I made a mistake? But I did not want to lie to him! After all, he could not possibly think that I had lived like a nun for over three years! Hadn't Lev's best friend Rozov said numerous times that Lev would never believe that I could have stayed faithful to him—even if somehow I had?..

"So... you did it?! You bitch, f-ng whore! After I have trusted you so much!!"

Trusted me so much? He must have forgotten the disgusting scene he made during one of our prison dates when he saw me wearing a new winter coat, not to mention all those letters that had turned me away from him long before I met Volodia...

"But listen!" It was too late to correct my mistake, so I tried to reason with him. "You did it too, and I have not said anything..."

"I did it? I?"

"What about Marina? You even promised to marry her, and that is by far a bigger betrayal than honestly sleeping with someone who knows that you are married..."

He looked as if he was about to hit me, but contained himself.

"I've never slept with Marina! Bitch, you judge everybody by yourself, don't you? Marina was my supervisor in jail—in jail, can you understand that? I had to please her if I wanted to survive! She was hoping that I would get a divorce; I told her that I loved my wife and was planning to return to her. Now I understand that I was a stupid and naive boy!"

That was not what I had learned from Alexey and Rina, never mind Marina's hysterical phone call only two weeks ago. Strange relationship with a supervisor, in jail or not in jail. Lev never bothered to learn how to lie without contradicting himself. But I could not win by showing him his mistakes; it would only make him angrier... Why hadn't I just lied? I didn't like lying, and I did not think he would believe me in any case. But it looked like lies were all he wanted. I should have played his game...

That morning started badly already. It was Lev's third of fourth visit to Leningrad. Nadia had been delivered to Akademgorodok to spend the sumer with her grandparents; Lev and I were planning to join her there briefly, before I start my new job in Moscow.

My husband and I spent about an hour in bed, after he arrived from Moscow at about seven o'clock in the morning. I thought that it was the best time he and I had spent together since his return, and I was more relaxed than usual. But after breakfast, Lev started searching the house for proofs of my infidelity. Who, for example, had hung the new window-shades in my bedroom windows? The shades were not here during his previous visit, and I could not possibly have done it myself, so there must have been a man in the house!

Yes, there had been a man in the house. An employee of the housing management, who hung the damn shades for five rubles, having spent a little more than ten minutes on it. I could have asked Rozov to do that, but Rozov was out of town, and my small bedroom was getting unbearably hot when the summer sun started shining right in the window.

That explanation, true as it was, did not satisfy my husband. What about all the other things in the apartment that had been done by men's hands? All housing management employees? I must have had a hell of a lot of money, if I had to pay for everything! And why on earth would a beautiful young woman living alone want to pay money to men, when it is so easy to offer another kind of payment? Enjoy yourself a little bit, too... How much had Volodia done here? Or Michael? Or what other f-er of mine?

"Michael surely has done quite a few things in my apartment. I helped him with his English, and he helped me with fixing things around the house. He is my friend, and friends in Russia help each other, don't you know that?"—I was trying not to get defensive, and subconsciously chose an offensive tone, which may have been a fatal mistake.

"Other stuff, like the new frosted glass in the living room and kitchen doors, was done by the paid workers. That is a professional carpentry job; besides, only the workers employed by the housing management could get hold of frosted glass; it is not sold in regular stores.

"Mostly it was Rozov who was helping me to get settled. Rozov and Aunt Olia, you can ask both of them... As for Volodia, you don't have to worry: he can't pound a nail in the wall for the life of his. Volodia did spend a lot of time here, mainly because we were typing the book together. Why is it coming up again right now?"

"What are those contraceptives in the bathroom? They have been recently used, and you did not even bother to hide them, so I could not see..."

"Of course, they have been recently used, damn it! You and I have been together a number of times during the last two months. And, if you were using your brains instead of I-do-not-know-what, you would realize that I would have found a way to get rid of those contraceptives if I did not want you to see them!"

But no logic could satisfy—and even less calm—my husband, who had already gotten on his high horse. That's when I said that damn phrase that seemed to have ruined whatever relationship we might have still had: "Come on, Lev, I have not slept with anybody since you came back!"

Lev and I were taking a stroll on the boulevard outside my apartment complex. It was a beautiful sunny day; the temperature was about seventy degrees, but a light wind from the Gulf of Finland made it feel cooler. The boulevard was practically empty, so we were able to talk more easily than in the apartment with Grandma Galia in the next room, although I suspected that Lev would not mind if the entire city of Leningrad could hear us. Our gloomy conversation created a strange dissonance with nature, which seemed to be celebrating the return of life after the endless northern winter.

"I must have been deceived by this beautiful sunny day, or by Lev's warmth earlier this morning," I thought with despair. "Why, why, why on earth didn't I just continue lying to him? What if I have ruined everything now, just when I was about to climb out of that shitty hole I had dug myself into?"

"Listen, Lev," I said as softly as I could. "I understand that you have a reason to be hurt. I deserve your anger, but I am really and truly sorry. It was not a big deal, after all, just a casual lay... I needed sex—physically, that's all! I did not love him, and I wasn't planning to have any serious relationship. I shouldn't have done it, but I was weak... Can't you forgive me?"

"How many of them have been here? How often?" His face was still scary.

"One. One time."

"When? Who was he?"

"Over a year ago. A guy I used to know in college. We ran into each other totally by accident in a coffee shop. Talked for a while, then had a cup of coffee. He took my phone number, and then he called a few days later and asked me out for a movie. It was a grim rainy weekend, and

I had no plans for that night, so I went. He saw me home afterward... Listen, I really was very lonely... without you. I wanted to be with you, don't you understand! But you were nowhere, and, after all, I am young, I need—don't you understand?—I need sex! Sex just for sex, for a simple physical pleasure! I thought, I'll just do it once... He was a clean kid, and I knew I wouldn't get anything from him... Just forgive me, OK?"

"You said it only happened once? Why didn't he come again? Didn't like you?"

"I have no idea! I did not want any relationship with him. He called once or twice afterwards, but I said that I was busy. He didn't insist. It must have been totally casual for him too. I tried to forget it... I don't ever want to think about him again! Especially since you're back... Why are you forcing me to remember?"

I do not remember how long that ridiculous dialog lasted. I knew that by the time the Rozovs were supposed to come for dinner, Lev and I had returned home together, holding hands like a loving couple. When Stanislav arrived with his wife, Lev was roasting a duck in the oven, looking as if he had been cooking all day. During our little dinner party, he was at his best: witty, confident, smiling, making jokes that made others crack with laughter—in short, the same Lev Fedorov I had fallen in love with six years ago...

11

When I woke up the next morning, Lev was already dressed and had finished his breakfast. He was clearly in one of his grim moods; there could be many explanations for that, but I decided not to provoke him by asking questions. There were errands I had to run and people I had to see before departing for Moscow tomorrow, so I was hoping for a busy day and therefore little interaction with my husband. As the morning progressed, Lev became more and more cheerful. He started talking about our trip to Akademgorodok, and how happy Nadia would be to finally have both her parents together. I attributed his earlier bad mood to a lack of proper sleep or a hangover, and got more or less relaxed. And that's when Lev struck.

"And how did that young f-er do *it* to you?"

The question came totally out of the blue. I felt sick to my stomach, and the bright sunny day instantly turned gray.

"I thought we had discussed everything yesterday. Do you really want to keep coming back to that?"

"You lied to me yesterday. I pretended that I believed you, so as not to spoil our dinner with *my* friends... Now I am surprised that you have never invited *him* over.. When? That night, you bitch, when you forced me to make a show for your so-called "friends..." Reliving all the horrors I had been threw... While you were so obviously having a great time... So, are you seeing him tonight?"

At least he was not talking about Volodia. My heart stopped pounding, and the light partially returned to the room. But my god—when, when is it going to be over?

"I told you that I hadn't seen the guy after that one night. I don't even know his phone number."

"You haven't seen *that* guy—but what about the other one?"

Lev's tone changed, so that I could barely recognize his voice. His face was getting darker and darker, until it became scary, like a blue sky that suddenly turns black before a heavy thunderstorm.

"This will never be over," I thought, feeling dizzy and nauseous. "And I will never get out of the house this morning..."

"You are imagining things that have never happened. I do not understand who you are talking about."

"Don't take me for a fool! While you were sleeping this morning, looking so innocent... You are lucky, bitch, that too many people know that I am here... I would have killed you otherwise, strangled you in your sleep while you were dreaming about your f-er... I would be in Moscow tonight, and my friends would confirm that I had spent the entire weekend with them..."

"I was looking at your photographs. You did not even bother to hide them, did you? Were you that sure that I would believe every lie you tell me? You were having a good time here, while I was suffering in the dungeon! Who is that f-er you're hugging?! Who?!"

"I don't know whom you are talking about. Show me the photograph." My mind was racing: no, it could not be Volodia; I did not have any pictures with him. Michael? No, Michael took many pictures of me, but together? He would never have allowed any pictures that could compromise *him*...

Lev almost threw the photograph at my face, and I sighed with relief. I saw Boris's boiler room, where Boris and I, probably half-drunk,
were hugging each other and laughing. It was Nina who had taken the
picture, with her own hands. Nina, Boris's mistress, the woman madly
in love with him.

How could anyone who knew me at all, suspect me of having an
affair with my best friend's boyfriend?! If there was an absolute taboo
in my life, it was having any romantic relationships with my girlfriends' men, regardless of who they were: their husbands, fiancées,
or lovers. My friend's boyfriend was not a man for me. He turned into
some genderless creature that I could respect, like as a friend, or even
admire—but could never imagine as my romantic partner.

As for Boris, I did not even particularly like him. I could never understand what Nina had found in him, besides his movie-star-like
appearance. To me, he was just a selfish bastard, responsible for my
friend's unhappiness. Me and Boris having an affair? The idea was too
ridiculous; there should have been no problem explaining that even to
such a jealous idiot as Lev Fedorov...

But there *was* a problem. As soon as I opened my mouth, I realized
that I had no right to betray Nina by revealing the secret that only she
and I knew. In my husband's eyes, Nina was a happily married woman
with a child. Admitting that my best friend was unfaithful to her husband would have just persuaded Lev that I was doing exactly the same
thing. Besides, no one could predict what volatile Lev would do with
such information. If he decided that telling Leonid about his wife's affair could fuel his revenge, nothing would stop him...

I must have spent over an hour trying to persuade my husband that
Boris was a married man, a close friend of Nina and Leonid, and that his
boiler room, due to its privacy and convenient location near the Winter
Palace, had been our favorite meeting place—all in vain. We went around
and around the same cursed circle that seemed to get us nowhere, but
then Lev suddenly gave up. Did he grow tired of playing Othello, or simply decided to take a break? In either case, we finally left the house, each
one for our own errands, having agreed to meet at home for supper.

We did not have supper that night, however. Instead, Lev launched
a new round of interrogation about Boris—all over again, as if we had
not talked it through in the morning. From Boris, he switched back

to "that other f-er—*how did he do it?*" It went on and on and on, like an endless ride on a merry-go-round, and no matter what I said, the conversation came down to the same burning question: "*How were you spreading your legs for him?*"

And finally, I lost it.

"Leave me alone, will you?! I am not asking you how Marina spread her legs for you, or whoever else had been there before you got arrested!"

A heavy blow knocked me off the chair. The sunny room instantly turned dark. All I could see, was Lev's face over mine, deformed with fury, with red eyes, the horrible face of the man I once used to worship. I was lying on the floor, while blows from Lev's heavy fists came down on me so fast that I could barely keep on breathing.

We were not alone in the apartment; my grandaunt was in the next room, probably watching her TV as usual. Should I scream? Only a thin wall separated us, but even if the Grandma hears me (which is not very likely with the TV on), it would take her a good five minutes to get here on her bad legs. And it is very possible that she may decide not to interfere at all, considering me guilty of adultery and therefore deserving punishment.

No, I am not going to give Lev the pleasure of hearing me screaming... Neither will I ask for his mercy. He can kill me, but he won't own me... Only I wish he would stop, I can't breathe any more, I am losing consciousness...

I did not lose consciousness. Lev stopped. His face was still the same scary face of a man capable of murder, and his voice was not any better, when he hissed:

"How many were there? I want names—of all of them, and you must tell me details of *how* you were sleeping with them!"

"Do you really think you're going to get anything out of me this way?" I was finally able to catch my breath. "I told you the truth, and you can beat me all you want, you will not hear anything new."

"Do you realize," he almost whispered, and that made his words even scarier "do you realize that one useful thing I learned in Butyrki, was *how to beat so there will be no bruises, or any traces on your pretty face*? I can make you a cripple for the rest of your f-ng life, and no doctor, no expert will ever find anything!"

"Why don't you get out of my house? With luck, you may still catch a train to Moscow tonight. You do not want me, I don't want you..." I made an attempt to get up, but prematurely.

"I am not finished with you, bitch." He knocked me back on the floor. "Before I leave, I need to make sure that no one will ever want to f-ck you again..."

He beat me some more, but without former fury. Then he left the apartment.

I looked at myself in the mirror. My husband was right: not a single bruise. My body felt as if it had been broken into thousand pieces and then hastily glued back together—but there was no sign of the beating.

He said that he had learned in Butyrki how to beat without leaving marks... Well, he had, indeed. He must have had a good practice, not just theoretical instructions. Little did we know about that world, even after all the stories that I had heard during the last three years... Neither was Eugenia Ginsburg's book of any help here...

Lev did not mention anything about that part of his prison life while he was talking to my friends. He presented himself an innocent victim of our screwed up legal system, who managed to be strong enough to make the most out of his unjust incarceration. He created the image we all wanted to see. A hero who suffered innocently. One more example of the numerous failures of the socialism. He gave my friends the drink that they were thirsty for...

I wondered how they would have reacted if he had told them about the "friends" who had taught him to beat to half-death without leaving any bruises... And, most importantly, on whom he had practiced.

They probably would not have believed him. Neither would I...

Because I did not want to know...

* * *

Lev returned at about one-thirty in the morning, to apologize. He said that he had walked all the way to the Moscow Train Station (that I had trouble believing), only to find out that all overnight trains to Moscow had been sold out (which did not surprise me at all). He said that he was terrified of what he had done: the old head trauma that he had received in his youth must have acted up; he had not been aware of what he was doing. It did not really matter, whether I slept with anyone during his absence: what mattered was that I had waited for him. I could not possibly leave him now, after he and I had been through so much together...

I did not believe that Lev's guilty mood would not change back to jealousy and hatred, without giving me any warning. But now I also knew that, no matter how furious he might get, it would pass. Like the capricious Leningrad weather: you can never trust a sunny day, but a sudden storm eventually stops and gives way to the blue sky, although no one knows for how long...

I was sure I could avoid being beaten again; I just had to be careful not to say certain things. It wouldn't be too difficult to do. My husband could not hurt me any longer, no matter how much he would like to: I did not love him.

Chapter Seven

PERESTROIKA

1

AND THERE WAS MORNING, AND there was evening… And more mornings, and more evenings… There were days that resembled nightmares, and nights that brought relief from pain because they were filled with dreams that could never become true.

At least in Moscow I could sleep without tranquilizers. Lev seemed not to believe that I was asleep, and used to show up in my room every night about an hour after I had gone to bed, hoping to find me waiting for him. But I never was, and he finally switched to making love during the day, which I hated even more than being awakened from a deep sleep. Unfortunately, confirming Nina's bitter wisdom, the less I wanted him, the more my husband wanted me.

I had moved into Aunt Katia's former room. Her spirit did not visit me—or maybe I was too insensitive to notice it. The room was almost empty—thanks to the government, which had confiscated most of the furniture in the house. I had to buy a simple bookcase, which was now filled with my Hebrew textbooks, my notebooks, and a couple of jewelry boxes. In the same bookcase, I kept the bottle of expensive French perfume in a shiny blue container, the one that Lev had given me on the day he learned that I was pregnant, and that I had never used up.

I did not get the impression that we were poor, even though for a while Lev did not work at all, and when he found employment, his salary was symbolic. Just like earlier in our relationship, he never discussed finances with me. My parents offered us some help, but Lev proudly turned it down. I knew that the three thousand rubles left after confiscation of the property would last us for a while, but I was not sure that Lev was using that money at all. He must have had some other source of income that he never discussed. Once he mentioned "a loan from a friend", then called it "gratitude from somebody whom he had helped". Money was just another part of my husband's dark personal life that I wanted to know nothing about.

He disappeared for a few hours almost every day, always giving me some explanation of where he was. I knew that his explanations were all false and did not bother to remember, or even listen. However, I could not avoid answering the phone and occasionally overhearing my husband's conversations, and, depressed as I was, some of them triggered my curiosity. The callers were all males, most of them sounded as if Lev had met them during his imprisonment. Names of the prison officers were often mentioned, and once Lev swore to me that he had just had coffee with the head of Butyrki, a highly-ranked officer and an influential political figure. Somehow that time I was not sure that he was lying, and for a minute I wished that I could learn more, but instantly remembered that asking questions would do no good.

2

I remember my first two years in Moscow as a sequence of fragments, and I am not even sure that I can now put them in a chronological order. Some memories are brighter than others, but all of them feel unreal—a weird dream, a movie seen many years ago or a story that happened to someone else...

One of the strangest and scariest episodes must have happened early during my first Moscow summer. It was a cool, drizzly weekend that felt more like fall. Lev was looking for a forester's job. Someone told him about a position in a remote village many hours drive from Moscow, which Lev nevertheless considered worth checking out. He seemed mildly annoyed when I said I wanted to go with him, but did not object directly. We set off early Saturday morning, picked up by one of my husband's new friends, in an old four-wheel drive van with no seatbelts and a tarpaulin top (the kind of vehicle that was widely used on muddy country roads but looked out of place in Moscow).

Before we left the city, another man joined us. We continued driving for a few hours, as fast as the vehicle allowed. My husband and his two friends were talking quietly, while I was looking out of the window at the scenery of a middle-Russia countryside, so dear to the heart of any Russian. There was something incredibly soothing in a low gray sky, lush wet grass bursting with snow-white daisies with tiny yellow suns in their middles, peasants' log cabins still dark from last night's rain, dirt roads running through the fields and woods and disappearing in the mysterious worlds that we could only dream about on the boring asphalt we were traveling on.

We finally stopped for lunch in one of the small villages along the way. In a log hut with a fenced front yard people were expecting us. The owner was either a friend or a relative of one of the men in the car, and he was to join us in our later journey. We were shown into a big room furnished traditionally for Russian village houses, with a wooden dining table in the middle and a big white Russian stove in the corner. The stone walls of the stove still kept warmth from the fire that had burned inside it earlier. Through a small window I could see several hens walking thoughtfully in the yard, followed by a snobbish rooster who tried to pretend that he had no interest in them. A gray striped cat gracefully strolled on the fence, then jumped off and disappeared into the outside world. A dog barked lazily, the moo-moo of a cow echoed, and everything was quiet again.

The lady of the house, a middle-aged woman in sloppy cotton pants and a blouse that had long lost its color, set the table. There were big bowls of traditional home-made coleslaw, pickled cucumbers and to-matoes, a smaller jar of marinated mushrooms (last year's crop), boiled eggs, milk still warm from the cow, and cheeses. The smell of hot ov-en-baked potatoes and fresh warm bread reminded me that I had not eaten anything since early morning, but the men seemed to be in no rush for food. They remained in another room, discussing something behind the closed door. The woman, after having waited for a few min-utes, entered that room, but returned shortly.

"Men's business," she said, looking somewhere over my head. "They'll be here shortly; we shall wait." She attempted small talk with me that I could barely keep up with; she did not suggest starting to eat without the men, which made me think that they were coming right away. But ten or fifteen minutes went by, and the food was getting cold, so I decided to see what was going on.

They stopped talking instantly as soon as I entered the room. The opened window let in fresh cool air from outside, but there was something sinister in the men's sudden silence. My husband broke it suddenly, by getting off his chair:

"The food is getting cold, and the ladies are waiting," he said with pretend cheerfulness.

The three other men followed without objection. Lev was clearly the boss.

The situation repeated after lunch, when the men disappeared again with their tea cups, closing the door behind them. That time Lev told me explicitly that my interruption would not be appreciated. The owner's wife walked in and out of that other room, bringing the men hot water for tea, jam, or cookies, and often remained there for a few minutes. The secrets that were kept from me were obviously not secrets for her. Some time later, another person showed up. Was he a neighbor? A relative? Another former inmate? He was a middle-aged man in a hunter's raincoat and dirty boots, and he clearly had been expected. He passed through the front room without as much as saying "hi" to me, and tightly closed the door behind himself.

I played with a kitten, flipped over old illustrated magazines and scolded myself for not bringing a book. I tried taking a walk outside, but the neighborhood dogs did not seem particularly friendly, and a cow pointed her long horns at me, so I returned to the house. After a while, the door to the mysterious room suddenly swung open, and I heard Lev's voice cheerfully discussing picking cranberries in the fall. The newcomer apparently knew the right marshes with excellent cranberries.

"About two hours walk from the last point you can drive to, and the marshes are sprawling—you have to know what you're doing. But it's worth every minute of it. You have to get there by seven in the morning, so you may want to spend the night here. Let me know if you decide to come, and I'll arrange it for you."

"Interested?" asked Lev, turning to me. "You pick cranberries in November, and the nights can be very cold. You may prefer to stay in Moscow."

"I'll go, if you go," I said. "You know how much I love the outdoors."

I had never been to a real marsh, but had heard that they could be breathtakingly beautiful. Besides, I had done my share of lonely weekends.

There was no cranberry picking in the fall. Neither did I see Lev's strange travel mates any more.

That day continued, with us driving farther and farther, until the flat Moscow suburban landscape turned hilly. There were now four men in the car, with my husband and the car owner taking turns driving. I had no idea where we were going, but did not dare to ask.

By the end of the day the drizzle stopped, the wind tore the clouds apart and the evening sun showed up in a pale blue sky. We were now off the paved road, driving among hills and fields, with dirt beneath us, sun and wind above us, flowers, grass, birds, trees and mosquitoes around us. It was fairly late in the evening when we reached a tiny village in a valley, and Lev announced that we were spending the night there.

I was surprised that such a tiny off-the-road place could house the office of the forester, but Lev said that the size of the village did not matter. The village lay within the jurisdiction of Lev's future forestry, and that's where he wanted to live—provided that he got the job.

No one seemed to expect us, or even knew who we were. We wandered around the village, Lev and I separately from Lev's three fellow travelers. It took my husband only a few minutes to find accommodation for us.

"I am the new forester," he said to a very old peasant woman. "Would you mind if my wife and I spend the night in your house?"

The woman's face lit up. She was happy, honored, glowing with the desire to please us. She showed us into a very neat small room, apologizing profusely that the floors had not been washed properly: her grandchildren had just been visiting and left yesterday, so she could not sweep the floors for three days. It was a popular Russian superstition that I was well familiar with: cleaning the floors after guests have just left, meant sweeping their steps away, to make sure they will never come back. Not something you want to do to your own grandchildren.

Our travel mates must have found accommodation in a similar ways, possibly in another village. I do not remember seeing them that evening. Lev and I had supper in our hostess's dining room (which served at the same time as a kitchen and a living room). We must have brought some food with us, but the old lady was going out of her way to offer us whatever meager supplies she had. I remember warm milk from her own cow, a sweet creamy drink with a distinctive smell that I've almost forgotten during the years of living in America, but will miss forever.

I slept hard on a narrow bed that I shared with my husband, but when I woke up shortly after sunrise, he was gone. There was no latrine on the property (an unusual fact that I attributed to negligence and carelessness, rather than to poverty), so I had to use the bushes that grew in abundance behind the house. Our landlady was already up, milking her cow. Lev was nowhere to be seen. I walked a little through the village, admiring its almost unreal beauty—like theater scenery— and trying to imagine what life was like here in winter, with deep snow covering the ground, or in late autumn when cold winds have shaken the last leaves off the trees and rain has turned roads into rivers of mud. How depressing life must be, especially when one does not have an outhouse, and the only creatures to share your loneliness are your cat, chickens, and a cow.

Lev was not there when I returned to the cottage. The old woman offered me some warm milk and bread, and lit a small kerosene stove to boil water for tea. My husband must have been very busy, she said, to start working that early. She was hoping he would like their village and make it his residence. The previous forester lived in a big village a few miles away, so they practically never saw him. All her neighbors were excited that the new forester had chosen to be closer to people. Their village was a wonderful place; everyone lived like one big family. She was sure I would love it, too.

I was sure I would love it, if only... It should have been four times closer to Moscow, in order for Lev to work here and still have a family. The distance did not seem to bother him, though. Or his strange friends.

By the way, where the hell were all of them? I had not seen anyone since we parted the night before, nor had I seen their car while strolling through the village in the morning. I began to wonder if they had abandoned me here. I did not seriously think Lev would do that: there seemed to be no point in it, but I felt rather uncomfortable. I could not bear listening to the old woman praising my husband as a new forester, when he was not even sure that he would take the job. There is something grossly immoral in deceiving children and old people, and I suffered from having to take part in that deceit.

Lev returned around ten o'clock in the morning, only to announce that we were leaving instantly. The job was not what he had thought, and it was too far from Moscow anyway. The men were waiting in the car at the other end of the village.

It felt almost like an escape, and I asked what the rush was. Didn't we want to spend some time in the area, to drive around a bit to look at scenery? Maybe, find a lake or a river to swim? No, said Lev, there was nothing to see here. Villages and dirt roads, like everywhere else. We had a long drive, and his friends had other commitments for that day.

"We need to thank our hostess," I said. "At least, pay her for the meals."

"It was regular Russian hospitality, nothing to pay for," replied my husband.

I disagreed: how could we accept her hospitality like that, when the woman was so much poorer than we were? Besides, she had offered it to *the forester,* not to some Lev Fedorov.

Lev agreed reluctantly. The woman was nowhere in the vicinity, though.

"We'll see her when we walk to the car. Let's go."

"Why don't we leave some money for her on the table?" I asked. "Just in case we don't see her."

"We will see her," said Lev. "Besides, I gave her ten rubles yesterday."

He almost dragged me out of the house, and a few minutes later we were driving away from the village. Although I looked very hard for our hostess, we did not see her. And I knew that Lev had not given her any money.

* * *

The surprising thing is that I got scared only later. At that moment the strange adventure had distracted me from thoughts about Volodia and, therefore, provided some kind of relief for my soul's pain. But later, contemplating it in the comfort and safety of my Moscow apartment, I realized how close I had been to the dark world of criminals—the world that my friends had only seen in movies and that for them existed in a different universe.

3

I had to be honest with myself: if my husband had ever been an innocent victim of a screwed-up legal system, he had since turned into a serious criminal. I would have understood it earlier, if only I had not been trying so hard to push the truth away. His success in saving his son from the army should have served as a red flag. Then there was the way he beat me up in Leningrad and his frequent and unexplained absences since he had been released from prison. He obviously had money that he did not want to explain. And now that strange "job interview" in a god-forsaken place at seven o'clock in the morning. What kind of job interview requires the presence of three men?

I thought about Lev's "friends'" secret talks behind closed doors. The doors were closed for me and for me only. I was not supposed to hear what the men were talking about. I remembered how their faces had looked when I entered the room, and suddenly felt scared. What if they thought that I had overheard their discussion? They would not have hesitated to get rid of me, unless Lev stopped them. But would he stop them? I was reasonably confident that, at that point of his life, my husband wanted me—not loved, but *wanted*, crudely and primitively, as a male wants a female. Would that attachment be strong enough to save my life, if he felt I jeopardized his business interests? What if he suspected that I might report him, and that he would end up in prison again, this time for a much longer term? No one could give a logical answer to that question, but my intuition told me that, had Lev or his friends suspected that I might know too much, my life would not be worth a ruble...

Well, then he must never suspect me. No more questions about where the money comes from. No showing interest in his absences. It may be OK to occasionally pretend that I am jealous and worried that my husband might be having an affair, but I must be careful not to over-play it.

I had a chance to test my determination to stop questioning my husband's actions just a couple of months later, when he bought a car. Technically, it was a used car, but with low mileage and in excellent condition, so Lev had to pay more than the official price. The car's owner, a policeman, met us on his day off (I remember it being a weekday because Nadia was in the daycare) in a small town of suburban Moscow. In an empty office with walls that desperately needed painting, Lev paid seven thousand rubles in cash to a clerk, while I signed papers that made me the sole owner of a car that I could not even drive. A few minutes later, in a shady grove behind the office, Lev counted three more thousand rubles to our seller, to match the market price for an almost-new *moskwitch*.

We drove back to Moscow in our own car. Before we could return home, we had to go through the exhausting process of registration, obtaining a license plate etc. That was also a world that I had never been to—although it was not necessarily the world of criminals. But it was the world of men with big money, the men who not only knew how to drive, but were able to repair their cars and, most importantly, knew the right people to get hold of parts. I remember a huge building with numerous queues, which without my husband I would have never been able to navigate, as a nightmare. Apart from the clerks, I was the only woman there, and men in leather jackets cast strange glances at me.

Our last stop was at the local notary office, where I signed POA allowing my husband Lev Fedorov to drive *my* car. It was after six PM when we arrived at Nadia's day care. All other kids had been picked up long ago, and Nadia, watched by an annoyed caretaker, looked very unhappy. She cheered up, however, and almost jumped with joy when she saw "papa's new car"—bright red like the dress of her new doll.

In the beginning, both Lev and I worried that authorities might get suspicious about the money for the car. Officially, however, no one had the right to question me—and so we were never questioned. Lev continued enjoying his new *moskwitch*, buying fuel and parts under-the-table, and seemed quite confident that things would work out this time. Within the next few months, I had to go to the notary office several more times, to sign permissions for various "friends" of my husband (most of whom I had never met) to drive "my" car. There was no talk about me getting a driver's license, and I did not insist. There was no reason why

I couldn't go to driving school, except that I wanted to share as little with my husband as possible. Even occasionally driving the car that he considered *his* would have been too stressful for both of us.

Another big purchase happened in early winter. Money-wise it was not as grand as the car, but in some way more important. Lev and I bought our very own "cooperative" apartment, in exchange for our big government-owned one. This transaction—or, more precisely, the law that allowed it—requires some explanation.

The big apartment where we had lived with Aunt Katia before Lev's imprisonment belonged to the City of Moscow. The government had not confiscated it while Lev was serving his term, only thanks to my stepson Dmitry. Dmitry, if you remember, was registered in the apartment with his father, i.e. had his *propiska* at the same address. After Lev's return, his son continued living with his mother and, being fearful of his father, did not bother us. Lev, however, was very aware that as soon as Dmitry got married, his mother's place would be too small, and he would claim his legal rights to one-third of his dad's apartment. We would then need to exchange the one apartment for two, and do that very fast, almost certainly at a big loss for us.

After a number of sleepless nights, I came up with an idea for solving the problem. I was afraid that my husband would not even want to consider it, but he appeared interested. I proposed a "family exchange" with Lev's ex-wife, who legally owned her apartment—the same way one owns a condo in the US. Her place was much smaller than ours, but still quite nice. It was also closer to the subway and that made me desire the exchange even more. The issue involved Lev's adult daughter Elena, a recently married young woman who, although living with her husband, had her *propiska* (registration) with her mother. The fact that Elena's and Dmitry's mother's apartment was a so-called cooperative meant that we would have to pay the current owner its full price, regardless of the fact that we were giving her a better place. (Now, if you are confused, don't worry: unless you lived in the Soviet Union and are familiar with its bureaucracy, you probably won't get the details—and they really don't matter.)

The official cost of our would-be apartment was only three thousand rubles (still an astronomic amount for most working Russians, but much cheaper than a car). We would also have to pay a similar amount of money to Elena for giving up any right to her mother's place. That made six thousand rubles altogether. My father, with all his scientific degrees and two highly-paid jobs, would have had to work for a year to make that much money (of course, whatever he made, was spent instantly, and my parents rarely were able to save more than a few hundred rubles).

The transaction required the active consent of four adults: my husband Lev, his ex-wife, his son, and his daughter. At first, I treated my own proposal just as one other crazy dream. Strangely, it all worked out. The new apartment, like the car, was in my name. Lev handed me three thousand rubles cash, which I deposited in the local bank, into the account of the apartment cooperative. Lev's and my passports made a brief journey to the local militia office, where our new address was stamped on the proper pages. Nadia had to go to a new daycare—a change that she took rather indifferently.

The only serious disadvantage of the exchange was that I had lost my own room, and now had to share the bed with my husband...

4

Our new place consisted of two rooms and a kitchen with the separate entrance, which was big enough to serve as a small dining room. It was located in a safe and very green neighborhood, with many little shops around and within five minutes walk from a subway station and therefore only twenty minutes from the city center. Although much smaller than Lev's previous apartment, it was an improvement compared to my Leningrad "khruschevka" where I lived with Grandma Galia. And when I thought of the semi-slum communal apartment that I had once shared with Klava, Praskovya, and their men, I felt that I had moved to a paradise.

Most of the time, Nadia and I had the whole place to ourselves. Lev had finally found his dream forester's job, which required spending most of his time in the village. It was a nearby village, a little over an hour's drive from the capital. My husband showed up in Moscow about once a week (usually without any warning) and stayed for one or two nights. He often had some business in the city and was absent during the day.

Having started the job on short notice, Lev had to arrange room and board with a local peasant's family. Of course, it was a very temporary solution: my husband did not become a forester to live in somebody else's house. He was by nature a master, a landlord: he needed his own space, his own privacy and, most importantly, power. The blueprint of his future house was ready on the day he accepted the job. During my first visit to his new place, he proudly showed me the site he had picked out for the construction: about half-a-mile from the village, on the bank of a fast and clean river, the forest beginning only a couple of hundred yards away.

"I'll install a water pump here, and we'll have running water inside, like in a city. You will not have to fetch water from a well any more..."

That "you will not have to" suddenly felt warm, almost close. And I admired the confidence with which my husband spoke: water pumps were not routinely sold in Russian stores; one had to have really good connections to obtain one from a construction company. But what was impossible for Lev Fedorov?

If only he could stop being a jealous violent bastard... He knew so well how to be witty, gentle, loving! If only he could always be that way, if only I could trust that he would not change, I would eventually be able to forget damn Sonovsky. I could probably even be happy one day...

Sometimes, when Lev did not have enough money to give me, he took off for the night in his new car, driving hitchhiking passengers around the city, and returning in the morning with a significant amount of cash. He obviously did not pay taxes off that money, but nevertheless it was honest income and the only aspect of my husband's life that I did not feel nervous about. The rest of it, in spite of him having official employment, was as shady as ever.

The forester's salary of ninety rubles a month would barely have lasted us for one week. I made twice as much at my new job, but with two separate households we were still spending way above our income. Lev, however, did not seem a bit concerned about money.

* * *

My new job was as different from my husband's as one job can differ from another. Three interviews arranged by the indispensable Professor Shlomov resulted in two-and-a-half offers. (I almost certainly would have received the third offer, in the Library of the Academy of Science, but the position was too senior and required tons of additional papers that I was not sufficiently motivated to obtain.)

The offer I had accepted seemed to me like a dream job, probably even more than Lev's one was for him. Again, I was a computer programmer—this time in the automation department of the Tretyakov Gallery, one of Russia's largest and the most famous art museums, located in the part of the old city beloved by Muscovites and by tourists alike.

The automation department was new to the museum, and consisted of just a few employees; all of that reminded me of my first job in Saltykovka, which left only good memories. Just like my first place of employment was supposed to automate the big scientific library, this department had to automate the large art museum. But unlike the poor library that could not afford its own computers, the Tretyakov Gallery had a contract with the Italian firm *Olivetti;* our department, therefore, enjoyed the world's latest computer models. During my first interview, I was fascinated by clear images of familiar paintings on the computer screen. Pictures could be enlarged, altered, and viewed in fragments, which was then (remember, we are talking about 1980s) only a little short of a miracle. I felt like a child about to receive an expensive toy that she had never dared to dream about.

The job offer was followed by two months of anxious uncertainty: the appointment had to be approved by the KGB. My would-be boss reassured me that it was a mere formality, and no one in her memory had ever been turned down. But I was far less confident. I did not dare to say at the interview that my husband had just been released from jail on parole and was under open police supervision. I bit my lips when, every time I called the Gallery, Natasha, my future immediate supervisor, expressed surprise that the KGB was taking so long to issue a formal document. "They must be swamped after summer vacations," she reassured me again and again. "It will be just fine, don't worry..." And, in spite of my anxiety, it indeed ended up being fine: the KGB apparently did not find Lev Fedorov to be a threat to society any more.

* * *

Tretyakovka (a loving nickname that Russians gave to their favorite art museum) disappointed me in the beginning. There was not as much work for me as I had expected. I was hired to be a liaison between museum workers and the system designers, and a trainer of the first. But the system was not ready yet, so my bosses considered training to be premature. And my programming skills appeared to be insufficient to participate in the system development.

For an office, we all shared one huge room that was originally designed as an exhibit hall, with ceilings the height of a two-story apartment building, a glass wall, and its own internal balcony, complete with cozy arm chairs and a coffee table. I hope it is needleless to add that the coffee table and arm chairs were used daily, together with electric tea pot and a set of fine china cups...

I worked in Tretyakovka for over two years, and spent more time with my coworkers than with anyone else in Moscow, so I might as well describe at least some of them.

My immediate supervisor, Natasha, was a stunning woman of about forty-two, with the body of a Barbie-doll. She was a bit shorter than medium height, which she corrected by never wearing heels lower than two and a half inches, whether they were light summer shoes or elegant tall winter boots. She carried her head and walked like a queen. Her movements when she sat on a couch, poured tea, or lifted a tiny porcelain cup of coffee to her slightly painted lips, were as full of grace as the movements of a ballet dancer.

In addition to this irresistible charm, all Natasha's clothes were masterpieces of art. She designed and hand-made all her own dresses and overcoats, and being an art major, treated everything she did as an art. The embroidery on the blouses and the laces on her knitted dresses would have done honor to any craft show or even museum.

Natasha's conversations were as pleasant as her appearance. She talked to her bosses with the dignity of an equal partner, and to her subordinates as if they were her close friends. She seemed to know everything about art, whether it was Russian art, European, or Asian, but she never sounded arrogant. She was an excellent business administrator, and that, as much as I understood, was her primary job in our department.

Another senior specialist was Grigori Ilych, lovingly called Garik. He was the chief programmer, and together with Natasha was responsible for hiring me. Garik was a cheerful kid in his fifties, with a silky silverfish gray beard and sparkling blue eyes that always seemed ready to laugh. He was robust, but with no extra fat and graceful as a cat walking on the roof. In addition to being an excellent programmer, Garik spoke several European languages, including fluent Italian, which automatically made him the main person the *Olivetti* people talked to.

Garik's popularity drove our department head Perlov crazy. He did not show it openly just yet, and it took me a long time to understand that there were strong underwater currents in the blue lagoon of our almost ideal department. These currents eventually broke the surface, and turned the tropical paradise into a stormy northern sea. They threw me ashore—but the timing must have been good, because instead of smashing my head against a hard rock, I landed on cold flat sand, and survived once again. But that was still two years away...

5

A seemingly insignificant episode of my first year in Moscow must have occurred in early September, when we were still living in Lev's old apartment. I woke up in the middle of the night from a nightmare; I had dreamed that I was trying to read a Hebrew text, but could not: the letters, once so familiar, were numb and silent. I was looking at the page as I did when I first opened Nina's family Bible: the letters were mere pictures; I could not sound them out. I tried to think of a few Hebrew words, but my memory went blank. I woke up in cold sweat in my big empty room at about 2:30 in the morning, only to realize that I had not seen a Hebrew text for over two months.

I turned the light on, and reached for my new bookcase. My nightmare continued in reality, while I desperately searched for a Hebrew book and could not find any. For a minute I thought that my lessons with Jacob had been just a dream, that the Hebrew textbooks existed only in my imagination, and that I had awakened to a bitter reality. And then I saw a book in Hebrew.

I opened it in the middle with trembling fingers and, my heart pounding, began to read in whisper. A silly text about a family on vacation in Israel had the power of a prayer. I became happier and happier with every single phrase I read: the Hebrew text flowed as easily and naturally as if it were Russian or English. I understood every word and could explain every grammatical rule. Nevertheless, I fell asleep anxious, thanking the Dream Fairy for the warning.

Next evening, after Nadia had gone to bed, I dug out the piece of paper with phone numbers that Jacob gave me when we parted. I studied the list, trying to figure out which one of my teacher's friends would be the easiest to call to. I finally dialed a number, feeling grateful that Lev was away in the village. Had my husband been at home, it would have been hard to justify calling a man, especially a man I didn't know.

Semyon was easy to talk to. Yes, he remembered his friend Jacob telling him about me. He had promised Jacob that he would give me lessons, and he was not planning to back away from his words. Unfortunately, he had just received the long-awaited permission to emigrate to Israel, so he would be leaving within two or three months. He would teach me some Hebrew meanwhile—once or twice a week, at our mutual convenience. He was not interested in money. He was sure that I would find someone to teach me Hebrew after he left: Moscow was a big city.

We met about ten times before he emigrated. Semyon was a single young man, quiet and pleasant, but there was not a sparkle of a romance or even friendship in our strictly business relationship. As he promised during our first phone conversation, he did not charge me for the lessons. He scanned the textbooks that I had brought from Leningrad, asked which one Jacob had been using, and shook his head.

"You've completed the basics. This book is boring and obsolete. And this one is too simple—you can easily finish it by yourself. I think you need to listen now, rather than to read. I have a tape—nice lively dialogues, but no text to accompany it, unfortunately. Well—we'll create the text. We Jews have to be creative if we want to survive, don't we?"

Semyon had not given any promises to the KGB about not teaching Hebrew, and he loved to teach. He did not mind discussing Hebrew grammar on the phone, and encouraged me to call him with questions at any time. He copied a tape for me. It contained a few *dusihim*, which in Hebrew means "dialogues." While preparing for a lesson, I listened to one of the dialogues several times, and then tried to write down the text. Semyon checked what I had written, corrected my mistakes and filled in the gaps. He then briefly explained the new grammar and translated the words that I did not know. I came to our next meeting knowing the old dialogue by heart. We would spend a few minutes practicing new grammar, and then move on to the next lesson.

My biggest frustration was that in two months we went over only ten of the fifty-two dialogues in the course. The two hours that I spent every night preparing for my next class were the best time in my life. The classes themselves brought less joy than they should have: I was always anxious about Nadia being at home alone—even though by the time I left the house she was fast asleep.

My first instinct was to keep my lessons a secret from my husband. He had not approved of my learning Hebrew before, and I could not predict his reaction to my visiting the home of a single man. But soon I was overwhelmed by another anxiety: what if Lev shows up unexpectedly and finds his daughter asleep alone and his wife gone until eleven at night? I finally decided to tell him. To my surprise, my husband took the news much easier than I had feared: he warned me grimly that I would get into trouble, but did not object explicitly.

* * *

One of the names on Jacob's list of Hebrew teachers was Michael Chelnov.

"He is the best Hebrew teacher in Moscow," said Semyon. "Unfortunately, he is also the busiest one. And an extraordinary person as well. I would be honored to have him as my teacher. You'll be lucky if he accepts you. I am sure Jacob talked to him, but it was a while ago, so he might have forgotten. I will definitely see Micha before I leave; I'll talk to him on your behalf. If he does not find the time to teach you himself, he will recommend someone. "

Micha, as I soon learned, was the nickname Michael Chelnov was known by among his friends and students. Unlike Jacob and Semyon, who were approximately my age, Chelnov was a man in his forties with a married daughter. He had a PhD in either history or ethnography and worked as a senior researcher in a respected institute. Hebrew was just one of a number of languages in which Chelnov was fluent. He was a walking encyclopedia on everything that concerned Jews, from the history of the people to Jewish religious traditions. Like the overwhelming majority of Soviet Jews, Chelnov's family was secular. Nevertheless, it was in his house that I experienced my first Passover Seder.

"I *have* to teach you," said Micha when I first called him. "After two people whom I highly respect have asked me, I simply have no choice. But I can't promise individual lessons: I may not be able to find the time. I can promise to find a group where you fit in, though; I have several groups, from intermediate to advanced, and am periodically forming new ones. I'll meet you once in private, to evaluate your level. We'll then decide where you fit in.

I tried one of Micha's groups, then another. He was a good teacher, and his lessons lively and interactive. Unfortunately, I was not a group person, and Chelnov eventually realized it. He finally agreed on private lessons, but they were irregular: he had a very busy life, and my flexibility was severely limited by having a preschooler at home. Luckily, he lived close by, and the commute to his place did not take long.

Chelnov was the second person I met in Moscow who owned two apartments. (Natasha, my boss from Tretyakovka, was the first one). The fact was rather remarkable, considering that so many Russian families crowded in one or two rooms, and were happy if their place were not "communal." The small apartment that was two subway stops away from my house was the one that Chelnov used for lessons, and later for meetings concerning emerging Jewish life in Moscow. The bigger one, where he lived with his wife and a young son, was located at the other end of Moscow. I would not bother my reader with this information if it were not relevant to the later story.

6

There was not too much work for me to do in the office, so Garik and Natasha did not mind when I pulled out my Hebrew books and spent an hour or two studying. They only suggested that I keep my notes away from the department head Perlov, because he could not be trusted.

Their warning surprised me: I liked my department head. He was what Russians call *intellectual*: well read, always on top of the world's political events, knowing everything about the arts. His speech, rich in vocabulary and highly grammatical, resembled the writings of the Russian classics. He was also handsome, a tall middle-aged gentleman with a neatly trimmed beard, always dressed up like a model for men's clothing. Perlov was what Americans would call "cool." But his friendliness was also of an American kind, somewhat superficial, too polished, too polite, and without the warmth and intimacy that I saw in Natasha and Garik.

Natasha was more my friend than a supervisor: I could cry in front of her, or share my family problems with her without worrying about how it might affect my job. Often, when she saw me weeping at my desk, she would come over silently and quietly put her hands on my shoulders. Garik could be occasionally grouchy or act annoyed, but he was always a *buddy*.

Unlike them, Perlov kept a distance. Was he also a "pro-Soviet" (i.e. believing that the Soviet system was the best of all economic and political systems)? I never heard him making any political statements one way or the other, but it would not have surprised me if he was not "one of us," especially considering his high position. If so, it would be wiser to keep my Hebrew studies secret from him: from the point of view of the authorities, learning Hebrew was not quite as disloyal as reading *samizdat*, but still close to state treason.

* * *

Our informal tea breaks continued with their usual regularity. The core of the group were Natasha and Garik (the two busiest people in the department, who nevertheless never neglected socializing), Aleftina, a very stylish woman in her mid-thirties who proudly considered herself Natasha's personal friend, and me. I did not have too much respect for Aleftina: she was sweet, but superficial, too interested in clothing and makeup and trying too hard to create an impression that everything was super-great in her personal life (which I knew was far from true).

Aleftina was indispensable in buying Turkish coffee and cream-filled pastries in our always crowded staff cafeteria, without waiting in line. (She had a talent for always knowing the right people, and Tretyakovka's barmen were among her useful friends.) It was Aleftina who hinted to me that Garik and Natasha were much more than just colleagues. I had suspected that for a while, so I had little doubt that she was correct. Nevertheless, I did not like gossip.

Another member of our informal coffee group was a young man hired a few months after me, by Perlov unilaterally, without consulting Natasha or Garik. He was a programmer and, according to Garik, "knew what he was doing", but I could not help disliking him. He was too confident, too self-important. He dressed in a somewhat showy manner—very expensively and exclusively in imported clothing—and worst of all, was a member of the Communist Party. That last circumstance automatically excluded him from our intimate inner circle, although that exclusion was very subtle and would not have been obvious to an outsider. He was a pleasant companion, although his communication was very superficial: he was a master of small talk, but never told us anything significant.

Perlov joined our mini-parties occasionally, but his presence made people tense. Luckily, most of the time he was away at meetings or art shows. Our breaks became more exciting but less intimate when our partners from Olivetti came to work in Moscow. Perlov then tried to be around more often, but in the presence of the foreign colleagues it became even more obvious that it was not him who was running the department, but Garik and Natasha. Our boss was smart enough to understand that everyone saw it, and was getting ready for war.

After the young communist, Perlov hired himself two more allies: a quiet girl straight from college, known as the daughter of his best friend; and an elderly gentleman with vague professional skills but an old personal friend of his. After a few weeks of working together with the gentleman, Garik christened him "Vermin." He almost certainly never said it to his face, but was not too discreet about the name either, and I am sure that the man knew it.

For a while, everyone kept pretending that things were fine. The sky seemed blue as usual, but thunder rumbled in the air and the storm was just a few miles away. And one day the lightning struck. I think it started with Perlov's announcement of some new disciplinary measures, although I was not paying much attention until I heard Garik screaming:

"This is all you are capable of! Keep going to your meetings and art shows—and leave the department to those who know how to do the job!"

Natasha was standing next to Garik, trying to calm him down. I could not hear what she was saying, but she was obviously on her friend's side. Perlov's face turned white as paper; he looked as if he were about to slap Garik in the face—but of course he could not do that. The Vermin turned away from his desk and was observing the scene, ready to rush to his master's help as soon as he was needed. The young communist and the college girl, on the other hand, stayed glued to their computers as if they were deaf, and probably wished they could have fallen through the ground. Aleftina decided to go to the bathroom and gracefully sailed out of the room, her high heels confidently knocking on the parquet floor.

The scene lasted for not more than a few minutes. Perlov and Garik exchanged several angry phrases, but in lower voices so their words could not be heard by others. Then Perlov resolutely turned around and marched out of the room, with the Vermin trotting behind him like an obedient dog.

"It's OK, guys, please, continue working," said Natasha's calm voice. Then she and Garik ascended to the balcony and sat on the couch at the coffee table, so they could discuss the situation in private.

The rest of the day went on as usual. Perlov never came back, but we were so used to him being absent that we barely noticed it.

For the next few days, Perlov and Garik openly ignored each other. Natasha acted as an interpreter, communicating work issues between the two men. There were no more disciplinary orders coming from our department head, nor any other instructions. He and the Vermin pretended not to notice when the others were having tea; during our breaks they either continued working, or left the room. Life went on, until one fine morning Perlov called a departmental meeting.

I knew that nothing good could come out of that, but what happened exceeded my worst fears.

"As the head of this department," slowly said Perlov the Prosecutor, "it is my duty to let everybody know that last week Grigory Ilych applied for the emigration from the Soviet Union. Now we all have to decide..."

Having dropped the bomb, Perlov looked like a conqueror who had just won a battle. After a few seconds of absolute silence, Garik's mocking voice said:

"Too late, Perlov. People who need to know your astonishing news, already know it—and not from you. I hate to break it to you, but you are not getting the pleasure of *deciding* anything here—as you seem to be incapable of making any meaningful decisions. I will continue working in this department regardless of how much you hate it, until it is time for me to pack and leave for the airport. Until then, you better mind your business and abstain from harassing anyone..."

That day I left work early. I needed time to be alone before I could see anyone, even my daughter. I spend the afternoon in my lonely living room, crying. The only part of my life that seemed positive and stable collapsed with a crash. The little island that provided at least some escape, my job, was sinking under water. It would not disappear right away, but its time was ticking; when that last refuge is gone, what will become of me?..

7

Hebrew lessons are my most consistent memory from the first year in Moscow. The rest is in fragments. My husband's weekly visits, Nadia's joy at his arrival, and my subdued fear of what he might say or do this time. Long days in Tretyakovka, and even longer dark winter nights at home, empty and lonely when Lev was away, tense and stressed when he was in.

I never knew what to expect of him. He could be cheerful and gentle and loving one minute, warm and cozy, and suddenly out of the blue say to Nadia something like "Don't listen to mama! Our mama is stupid, isn't she?" Or "Mama was enjoying herself while I was away; tonight, she has to stay home and be bored."

I remember the three of us riding in Lev's car, when an automobile of an unusual bright-blue color pulled in front of us, and five-year-old Nadia cheerfully commented:

"Oh! Look! This car is just the same color as mama's new jacket! Mama needs to have that car, to match her jacket—wouldn't it be cool?"

"Mama should ask that guy in the car to be her fucker," answered Lev grimly. "Then she could have his bright blue car."

"What is 'fucker'?" asked Nadia curiously.

"All these men friends that your mama is seeing when I am away are called 'fuckers', honey..."

I bit my lips. My number one rule was: never argue with my husband when he is driving, especially with the kid in the car. He was almost certainty deliberately provoking me. Any response from me would have set off an explosion. He did not really want to know that except for my co-workers and my Hebrew teacher, I was not seeing anyone—regardless of whether he was home or not. Anger was burning inside him, a constant anger that I could not explain or understand and that he cultivated by making up stories about his wife. Probably, about other people as well. I just should not care. I must not care...

But it was hard not to care. There was Nadia. My daughter. Who, like all women whom Lev Fedorov wanted to charm, adored him.

Nadia stopped noticing me as soon as her beloved papa walked in the door. She followed him around like a shadow. She laughed at his jokes. She obeyed him like a machine. Unfortunately, he used that influence to get her do things that I did not allow: crawl into his bed in the mornings and do god-knows-what under the blanket (accompanied by happy giggles), eat dessert before dinner, play indoors when it was time to go outside, use words that I did not want her to know. Worst of all, he kept telling her bad things about me. I did not want to say to her that her father was an evil man and she should not listen to him, so I was helpless.

As time went on, she became more and more difficult, resisting any discipline and challenging my authority in every little thing. She would get hysterical as soon as something was not exactly her way, screaming at me one minute and rushing to hug me and apologize a minute later. Occasionally she could be calm and playful, even affectionate, a charming little girl—but I never knew when she might throw a temper tantrum. Like her father, she was unpredictable. Surprisingly, Nadia's tantrums and mood swings occurred only at home: her preschool teachers had no complaints about her behavior and were surprised when I asked about it. She was one of the most pleasant children in the class, bright and well behaved, although not as social as they would like her to be.

* * *

I hated that day. I wanted to have it undone. To go back to the beginning and start all over. I had screamed at Nadia again. That time she had not done anything terrible—just didn't stop her drawing right away when I told her to get ready for bed. I could have found a better way of dealing with my frustration... After all, it was not about Nadia at all... Not this time, at least.

I hated myself. I wished I were someone else. I wished I had a different life. Different husband, different daughter. Definitely, different self. Or at least that I could start that evening all over...

Nadia was becoming more and more difficult: rude, stubborn, disobedient. Neighbors—and even Tanika—told me she was spoiled, although I had no idea when I could have possibly spoiled her. It must have been her character, her damn character that she inherited from her father. And I screamed at her when I felt helpless (I wished I could scream at *him*...).

Sometimes she cried and said she was sorry, but other times she screamed back and announced that she hated me and did not want to be my daughter anymore—and then did not talk to me for hours. I realized very well that screaming and punishing did not do any good; I should have stopped long ago and found other ways of communicating with my child. Or take her away from here, from her father's poisonous influence, to run to the other side of the planet where she would never see him... But there was no place for me to go, and therefore Nadia had to stay where she was...

* * *

It was nine o'clock in the evening. I was lying on the sofa in the living room—the bed unmade, the lights turned off—and crying, and crying, and crying. My Hebrew notes lay next to me on the floor, but I couldn't study any more. After all, my parents may have been right: what was the point of that knowledge? Where would I ever use it? What did I know about the country where that language was spoken? I might just as well be learning the language of Martians...

"Because you think that it makes you special," said a scornful voice inside me. "You are afraid that Sonovsky will despise you if you drop it..."

"It fills my lonely evenings," I said to that voice angrily. "It helps me meet people. I need to see somebody except Lev Fedorov, don't I?"

"People? What people? Chelnov is not your real friend; he is very nice—but would he care if you die tomorrow? And where is Jacob? You've known him for almost three years, but can you pick up the phone and call him when you feel shitty? Nope! You wanted Jacob as a friend, to show Sonovsky that you had a life besides him! For the same reason that you started studying Hebrew, my darling..."

"But if I stop learning Hebrew, what will I have left? My job is about to disappear, I do not have a profession that I can be proud of. I am a totally inadequate mother. And even if I had the greatest relationship with my daughter, she is asleep by 8 o'clock in the evening... I hate and despise my husband. I hardly have friends in this city. Most weekends, I have no place to go. My weekends are so empty that I am almost happy when my husband comes home. Studying Hebrew is the only straw that helps me keep my head above the water..."

"But how long can you continue to do it?" asked the voice again. "Your life is useless—don't you see it? Just end it... Let the straw go— and sink..."

* * *

Maybe, I should, indeed, just end it? Fill the bathtub with warm water, and cut my wrist?... The pain will be brief, and I don't have to look at the blood flowing. They say it is an easy death. Lying in the bathtub and falling asleep. Just make sure the hot water keeps coming...

Fall asleep and forget the pain. Forget Volodia. Forget humiliation. Let Nadia scream at her dear papa. Maybe, she'll learn how to behave after he's beaten her up a couple of times. I can't do *that* when she is home, though. She'll have to be at school. Then one evening I will not show up to pick her up from preschool. All other kids will be gone, and my daughter will be waiting, and waiting, and waiting. The teacher will get annoyed and then angry, because she will want to go home. She will have Nadia put on her warm outside clothes, ready to push her out of the door as soon as her mom arrives. But mom will never come. Nadia will be hot and uncomfortable in a warm room in her winter coat.

Then she'll start getting hungry. And then scared. She will decide that her mom has abandoned her, just the way papa had told her she would. Ran off with some guy...

My face was wet with tears. No, not that way. I may have had no patience with my daughter, but I will not abandon her like that. I shall wait till school vacation, when she is in the village with Lev. He will bring her home at the end of the week, and find her mother dead. She will see me, too. Then she will know that I had not run away from her... Maybe, when she grows up she will understand what her beloved father had done to me... she may learn how to hate him for taking her mother away...

"No," said the same wicked voice inside me, "don't lie. Your daughter's father is not the reason why you want to kill yourself. It is *another man*. He may not be any more deserving of love than your husband, but you would run to him the moment he beckons you. The problem is, you know that he never will..."

My voice was wrong. In spite of all logic, there was still a tiny part of me that believed that Volodia might one day want me back. Maybe not forever, maybe just for a short time... Somehow that second time I will have to act with dignity, and leave him, leave him myself, before he has a chance to do that to me. Pretend that I do not love him. How could I ever do that? I did not know—but I did not have to decide right then, either. I had all the time in the world to dream... So, after all, it must have been those dreams that kept me alive—not love for my daughter...

Volodia did write to me. The letters were real. They were not love letters, but those of a friend—written to someone whom the author respected and whose opinion he valued. He talked about *Perestroika*—the new period in our country's history that none of us could have imagined just two years ago. He told me about books he and his friends were reading and discussing—stories and novels that only recently would have been confined to samizdat, but now were published in popular literary magazines. He was not particularly personal in his letters, and never asked any questions about me. But I lived in expectation of them, and the weeks that passed from one letter to another were as empty and dark as moonless nights in a desert. I always responded, not right away but soon enough so that he could still remember what he had written. And I never wrote first.

8

"I am sorry, I don't know when I can see you next time," said Chelnov. "You don't want to know details about my life, but believe me: my schedule is crazy. I've forgotten when I last had an evening with my family. I am trying to organize a Holocaust Memorial Day, among other things... We need to start talking about the genocide, not only about our glorious victory over the Nazis... I am dropping other students, too—so please don't take it personally. For a while, I will continue teaching one group of advanced students, maybe two. But even that is likely to stop very soon. You haven't shown any interest in group lessons, and you may have been right: you are doing quite well on your own."

"Could you... recommend someone else?" I thought my voice was trembling. (Not that... anything else, but not that...) "Or... can I come to your group lessons?"

"There is no room in either one of my groups. You are my old student, and I would try to fit you in, but frankly I am not sure how well it would work for you. In some way you are too advanced for them... You know what? I have a better suggestion for you. Why don't you try teaching yourself?"

"Teaching? What do you mean?"

"What I mean is that you know more than enough Hebrew to teach absolute beginners. Besides, the best way to learn anything is to teach it, don't you know? Listen: I am being perfectly serious: I receive a deluge of phone calls from people who know no Hebrew at all and beg me to teach them. Since I don't teach beginners, I've been referring them to my friends. But during the last year my friends have been leaving at the rate of several people per month. I still have a few teachers left, but they will not stay in this country for much longer, either. The result of what they call *Perestroika*. If this political situation continues, there will be more and more Jews wanting to learn Hebrew—most of them, unfortunately, for the practical reason of immigrating to Israel, rather than for using it here. And fewer and fewer teachers will remain.

People like you should take over. You have no experience—well, you'll learn. I did not have any experience either when I started teaching twenty years ago..."

Chelnov was mistaken: I did have some experience in teaching Hebrew, and that experience was quite awful. It happened last spring, when an acquaintance of mine (someone I must have met through Chelnov) told me that one of his friends was looking for a young woman to teach Hebrew to his eleven-year-old daughter. The family lived in the same area of Moscow as I—actually, only one subway stop away. Would I be interested in trying?

I thought I could handle an eleven-year-old, so I gave her parents a call. I was surprised to learn that the girl was not a beginner, and that the father spoke fluent Hebrew, but he thought that she could benefit from learning from a young woman rather than from her own father. He also had a younger daughter whom he was teaching himself.

Being very unsure of myself as a teacher, I asked for three rubles an hour—a symbolic price for a private lesson. The father accepted the price as "reasonable"—but I regretted later not having asked for more money: two extra rubles for a lesson would not have made a difference in my budget, but my employer might have respected me more. In any case, we agreed on what we agreed, and the following week I started teaching the girl.

The two hours a week that I spent in her parents' house was time I hated and dreaded. The family lived in a large modern apartment—almost too large for four people—that was so tidy, so orderly and so empty that I felt more like an intruder in some sanctuary, afraid to touch anything, rather than a visitor to a human home. In a big cold living room with huge windows, the girl and I sat together at a large square table, studying, while her father placed himself in an armchair three yards away from us, observing not only what my student and I said, but the tones of our voices and the expressions on our faces. He found it quite appropriate to correct my mistakes (that I inevitably made in such a tense atmosphere) in his daughter's presence, and concluded every lesson with a review of my work and suggestions (that were obviously obligatory) for the next class.

During the two or three months that I visited that awful house, I never had a chance to talk to my student's mother. Several times

I ran into her in the hallway, or saw her in the kitchen through the open door. She was a slim and pale woman who could have been pretty if her face did not have a subdued, unsmiling expression. In her own house, she looked more like a shadow than a living being. She never said anything more than "hi" to me, never invited me to stay over for a cup of tea.

I would have dropped those depressing lessons after the first week or two, if I had not become attached to the girl. She did not dare to say anything personal to me in her father's despotic presence, but through her obedient silence I could sense a desperate desire for human connection and for the warmth that was so obviously absent in her home.

We managed to talk only once, and a few words said in a hasty whisper fully confirmed my perception of the grim family that the poor children had to live in. We were in the middle of a lesson, when our tyrant supervisor was suddenly called to the telephone, thus leaving us alone in the room. My student and I had just been reading a text about Passover, so I asked her in Russian about the Passover celebration in her own family.

"I hate it!" she said with a childish spontaneity. "My sister and I both hate it. There are never any guests in our house, just the four of us, and father reads this endless prayer, and we can't eat until he is finished. Then we all eat in silence, and can't play that evening, or even watch TV..."

"Do you have any friends at school?" I asked.

"Yes, I have a few..." she was very unsure when she answered. "But they never come here. I invited my best friend once, but she did not like our house. And then we only eat kosher food, and she said it tasted gross, so she had to leave early to go home for supper... And when my sister brought two girls over, my father was really upset about the mess they created in the house, so mom asked her never to do it again."

"Do your friends ever invite you to their houses?" I asked, anticipating the sad answer.

"They used to—but not any longer. Father does not let us go, because their families don't keep kosher. Even if we went, we would not be able to eat anything there, so they stopped inviting us..."

At that moment our supervisor reentered the room. We instantly stopped talking, feeling scared and embarrassed as if we were thieves caught in the process of stealing. Awkwardly, we tried to continue reviewing the text from the same place we had left it a few minutes ago, but the father interrupted us:

"I think you were at this paragraph when I left. What have you been doing all that time?"

After that incident, I kept working as his daughter's tutor for about a week or two, until he politely asked me to discontinue.

"I came to the conclusion that I better teach my daughter myself," he said with the usual lack of expression on his handsome face. I wondered if anyone had ever asked the girl...

I tried to summarize that story in a few words, but Chelnov dismissed my worries with a smile:

"So what? This time you will be teaching adults, not eleven-year-olds. And you'll be working in your own house where you're comfortable. Just don't invite their parents to supervise you!"

The next evening, I called the number Chelnov had given me, to receive names and contact information of beginner students looking for a Hebrew teacher.

* * *

My first group of Hebrew students consisted of four young people in their twenties, two guys and two girls, and I enjoyed teaching them as much as I had hated the lessons in the family of my orthodox neighbor. We met in my living room for two hours, with a tea break in the middle. I couldn't start teaching until after Nadia had fallen asleep, but the late hours did not seem to bother my young pupils, and often they stayed for a while after the lesson was formally over, just to chat. I soon learned a great deal about their personal lives. Surprisingly, only one of the girls was studing Hebrew for the purpose of potential emigration to Israel. The others did not have that intention at all.

One of the young men was majoring in Arabic studies in Moscow University. He was not only ethnically "pure" Russian; he was a Russian who must have received security clearance from the KGB. A friend whom my student highly respected told him that in order to be a serious Middle Eastern scholar, he had to know Hebrew as well as Arabic. Since Moscow University did not offer any classes in Hebrew, the boy had no choice but to turn to private lessons. Unlike my teacher Jacob, that twenty-year-old kid was a son of Perestroika and belonged to a new, less fearful generation.

The second male in my group, a handsome serious guy in his late twenties, appeared to have similar reasons for learning Hebrew as I had explained to Jacob: a Jew by nationality, brought up in Russian culture, he was desperately searching for his Jewish roots and identity.

The girl who was not planning to emigrate to Israel, had a very orthodox brother who insisted that any self-respecting Jew needed to speak Hebrew; she also loved foreign languages, and didn't mind adding modern Hebrew to the Latin and Greek she had majored in in college.

For our first textbook, I picked the *Dusihim,* the audio course I myself had started with Semyon just a little over a year ago. Unlike me, my students did not have to handwrite the dialogues in the notebooks. One of Chelnov's numerous acquaintances managed to make Xerox copies of an Israeli edition of the book (almost certainly by using his office Xerox machine illegally), so I finally saw a real printed text of the course, in addition to the tape with the same dialogues.

Chelnov and I had almost finished the book, and I had enough knowledge and motivation to complete the few remaining lessons by myself. Reviewing my favorite course gave me great pleasure, and I felt that I was doing a good job presenting material to my students. All four of them clearly enjoyed our meetings, and learned fast. As for me, for two evenings a week my loneliness and depression were gone.

A few weeks after I started teaching, I made an amazing discovery.

For the two-hour lesson, my students paid three rubles each. (Chelnov charged five, but I did not dare to name the same price as my famous teacher). That meant for me receiving twelve rubles per evening. Multiplied by eight times a month, that unreported income was equal to about 60% of my take-home pay from the full-time job in Tretyakovka. Money was the last thing I thought about when I started teaching Hebrew, but that sudden move to a different financial level caused a feeling of a strange and unfamiliar excitement.

9

Meanwhile, amazing things were happening in the country.

As part of the economic restructuring announced by the Gorbachev's[5] government, the first semi-private businesses appeared in major cities. They were known as "cooperatives," and were strictly controlled by authorities. In the absence of clear rules and regulations, that control could easily turn into a nightmare, so brave entrepreneurs had to rely on personal connections and friendly relationships with local authorities much more than on the written law. Nevertheless, cooperatives gave people opportunities for business initiative unimaginable only a couple of years ago.

Ogonek, a popular weekly journal, suddenly turned from a boring and loyalist illustrated magazine for housewives, into a herald of *Perestroika* and *Glasnost.*[6] It published highly critical articles on the Soviet economy, gave unfavorable reviews of our social institutions and even dared to praise life in the capitalist West. Leading literary journals competed with each other in revisiting our recent history starting with the Revolution and the Civil War, depicted Stalin as a monster, and published more and more memoirs of gulag survivors. The book by Eugenia Ginsburg, which Volodia and I had typed on a home typewriter for many months, appeared in bookstores, illustrated and in hard cover.

The feature film *Repentance* by a famous Georgian director Tengiz Abuladze, a bitter satire on Stalinist repressions and the corrupt post-Stalinist Soviet bureaucracy, was playing in major movie theaters all over the country.

In Tallinn, thousands of people went out in the streets in a peaceful demonstration demanding Estonia's independence from the Soviet Union. Their example was followed by Latvians and Lithuanians. The police did not interfere, and no arrests were made during or after the demonstrations.

Sprouts of Jewish life, previously unknown in the Soviet Union, started appearing first shyly and carefully, but gradually getting bigger and stronger, spreading from the center to remote corners of our huge country.

After decades of the total absence of diplomatic relationship with Israel, in the summer of 1998 the Israeli Consulate was reopened in

Moscow. That event coincided with the birth of one of the first Jewish babies of Perestroika, the Society of Friendship and Cultural Connections with Israel (abbreviated, from its Russian name, as ODIKSI). It was an illegitimate baby, unwanted but nevertheless accepted: the government had nothing to do with its conception or birth, but did not persecute it either. ODIKSI published its own monthly newsmagazine and a year after its creation in Moscow had branches in forty cities around the country.

It was followed by the Center of Jewish Culture that appeared on Taganskaya Square, in the cultural heart of Moscow. As a result, lectures on Jewish history and Judaism, concerts of Jewish music and even meetings of solidarity with Israel became more and more common. The Refuseniks' movement emerged from the underground; the problem, still very far from being solved, at least became known and openly spoken about. For the first time in history, an International Symposium on Free Emigration took place in Moscow, and the question of Jewish emigration from the Soviet Union was an important part of the agenda. The bravest or the most desperate refuseniks dared to go out on demonstrations against authorities who denied them permission to leave the country.

Following the foundation of the Israeli Consulate, the first private Israeli citizens were allowed in the country on tourist visas. Emigrants to Israel who for many years were as good as dead for their Soviet relatives and friends, finally had a chance to come back for a short visit. At the same time, OVIRs started reluctantly issuing visas to Soviet citizens, allowing "guest visits" to Israel—a two-way ticket previously unheard of in our country.

With the growth of political freedom, the economy became shakier. Inflation was rising, slowly but steadily, and so was the crime rate. The amount of consumer goods available for sale was shrinking, and newly organized cooperative shops, small and very expensive, could not fill the gap created by empty department stores. The lines in supermarkets and grocery stores even in Moscow, which had always been an oasis in a desert of inadequate government food supplies, became longer and longer, and it took more and more time and effort for women to fill their refrigerators and feed their families.

* * *

In Leningrad, Boris received the long-awaited *permission*. I called Nina several times trying to find out how she felt, but she kept saying that "it was for the best". However, she was sick last summer, and having only long-distance phone calls for communication, I could not figure out what was wrong with her. My heart sank when I realized that Boris's exit visa almost certainly meant that Michael would receive one shortly. I had to go to Leningrad as soon as possible: there were too many friends there whom I had not seen for too long. But I could not imagine how to make Lev Fedorov let me go: for him, the mere name of the city was associated with my infidelity and "betrayal" during his years of incarceration, and caused outbursts of fury and violence.

10

"We must do something about it," said my boss Natasha. "After all, you cannot live all your life as a prisoner to that man! Who does he think he is? You should be able to go to Leningrad if you need to...to any place, after all! Now, try to relax a little bit and get some work done. I promise you we'll figure something out!"

I thought that Natasha better figure something out fast. I absolutely had to go to Leningrad, Lev or no Lev. I had called Nina over the weekend, but her mother said that she was in the hospital, and refused to explain what the matter was. She swore that "it was nothing serious," but could not tell me when she was expecting her daughter to return home. A week or two of hospital stay was not unusual in Russia: that was the time required for routine testing. But during medical testing, patients knew exactly when they were going to be discharged; the uncertainty in Rachel Naumovna's voice scared me.

It had been almost a year and a half since I had left Leningrad. It is amazing how long a person can survive without seeing one's closest friends. "'Survive' is the right word," I thought bitterly. "Existence amidst constant pain and depression, with almost no hope that things will ever change, could hardly be called "living". The few brighter moments—visiting Akademgorodok with Lev for the first time, a couple of birthday parties of my childhood friends now living in Moscow, my first Passover Seder last spring—made little difference. Teaching Hebrew was my only definite achievement, and the one thing in my life I looked forward to. Going to Leningrad, even for just a few days, would be a breakthrough.

Not to see Volodia, no... He will probably be busy, and I may not see him at all. Meeting him somewhere in town for a cup of coffee would not make any difference. But I had to see Nina. And Michael. And Sasha Radzinsky. And Aunt Olia. Aunt Olia was the only Leningrad friend I had seen since I left that city: she came to Moscow on business regularly, and usually stayed at my place—unless she knew that Lev would be at home. (In those rare cases she stayed with some acquaintances of hers, but she always spent at least one evening with me, no matter how busy her schedule was.)

In Leningrad, I would stay at Aunt Olia's house. I could barely stand Arkady, her husband, but it would not matter. He would get annoyed at my presence, but that would not matter either: he hated all his wife's friends, but they stayed over anyway. Aunt Olia was too strong and too proud a woman to allow her husband's bad character to rule her life. As for my own apartment, we had to rent half of it to some college girls, in exchange for taking care of aging Grandma Galia. I would visit her briefly, but there was no place for me to sleep over—not that I would want to stay there, in any case...

For a few minutes I was happy: merely dreaming about a trip to Leningrad made it feel real—almost more real than my everyday life in Moscow. Maybe it was my dreams, even more than the Hebrew lessons, that kept me from total despair? In the most depressing moments of my life, when there seemed to be nothing to live for and no hope, I always turned to dreams. Images created by my imagination came alive, so alive that for a while they completely replaced the real world around me.

Dreams had no boundaries. I had lived many secret lives, happy and exciting, parallel to the boring one other people could see. Those lives were hidden from everybody so well that even Lev Fedorov did not have the power to ruin them...

Natasha woke me up to reality.

"Would you be able to pay for your train ticket to Leningrad if I sent you there on a business trip?"

"Of course! Money is not a problem, but..."

"Wait a minute, let me finish. Perlov will be out of the office for the next two weeks, so I am officially in charge of the department. I can send you to the Russian Museum for two days. I have a friend there, and I've just talked to her on the phone; you'll bring her some of our materials, and she will show you around and give you some of theirs. It will be a two to three-hour assignment. You'll write a report when you return... you know how to write reports, I don't need to teach you. Unfortunately, the task is not important enough to justify having your tickets paid, but you said it was not a problem. I assume you do not need a hotel. That's settled, then: you can leave on a Wednesday over-night train for a Thursday appointment, and return some time over the following weekend: tell Lev there were no train tickets available before Sunday, or something like that. Good plan?"

It was certainly a great plan, and my kind supervisor seemed al-most as enthusiastic as I was. (Two women plotting against one guy are likely to get excited—never mind that one of them is a subordinate to the other...) But how could I persuade Lev to stay at home for four nights watching our daughter? There was absolutely nothing to do in the village in winter, but my husband was not a man who could toler-ate anyone, least of all his own wife, telling him how to organize his time. And, of course, Natasha's excellent plan did not solve the prob-lem of Lev's jealousy.

"You mean, he is not going to let you go on a business trip?" Nata-sha could not believe what she heard.

"He almost certainly will not let me," I said. "Especially if I can't persuade him that the trip is critical for my work. And I am not good at lying..."

"Well," said Natasha after a short silence, "I'm pretty sure I could persuade him... more successfully than you. If only we could arrange somehow that I talk to him..."

Now it was my turn to come up with a plan—and I did.

It all worked out as in a movie—so smoothly that I could hardly believe it. The next time Lev came home, I asked him to let me go to the Central Children's Department Store, to look for a spring jacket for

Nadia. The round trip to the store would take close to two hours, plus the time I'd spend there looking for the right item. Lev was in a good mood and agreed to watch Nadia for the evening, without showing any displeasure. In the subway station, I called Natasha from a pay phone and told her that it was her time to act.

A few minutes later, she called my house and asked for me. Lev, who had met Natasha a few times and, like all men, was charmed by her, was very friendly.

"I am terribly sorry to bother you at home, especially since you must have just arrived from the village and are very tired," she said in her soft deep voice. "But there is an urgent matter, and I did not want to wait till tomorrow. I wanted to ask Anna if there was any way she could go to Leningrad as soon as possible. I don't want to call her back late at night; maybe you could give her the message?"

Natasha then elaborated on the matter, explaining exactly what needed to be done in Leningrad; as a businesswoman, she had no problem inventing details of meetings, reports and office intrigues. Lev, who must have missed his former professional life, fell into the trap like a child.

"I would go myself," she added, "but I am replacing Perlov while he is gone, and absolutely cannot leave the department, not even for a day. And Anna is the only person whom I trust and who is capable of performing the assignment at the same time. I don't know if she'll be able to find anyone to watch Nadia while you are in the village..."

It does not take a great psychologist to guess my husband's reaction. Eager to make a good impression on that charming professional woman, he immediately volunteered to stay home through the weekend and watch his daughter while I was in Leningrad. It didn't take Lev and Natasha fifteen minutes to agree that I should leave for Leningrad tomorrow night, not to lose precious time.

I managed to play my part of the game by expressing surprise and even mild displeasure when, upon my return home, I heard Lev's report about the deal he had made with my boss without consulting me. But twenty-four hours later, I was on the fast train to Leningrad, lying on a comfortable bunk in a first-class compartment, with my heart pounding so fast and loud that I was afraid it would keep my travel mates awake...

11

Nina was discharged from the hospital the day before I arrived in Leningrad. A month earlier, she had nearly died while having a premature baby. The doctors in the local district hospital saved her by performing an emergency C-section. Her son, born at twenty-six weeks, seemed to have little chance of survival, but a month later he was not only still alive, but had a pretty good prognosis.

"I had very high blood pressure all the way through the pregnancy," said Nina with a faint smile. "My doctor wanted to keep me in the hospital until the end... but I did not think I would be able to tolerate it for that long... At first, I was convinced I would miscarry before... you know... Then I was praying to carry him for at least seven months. That appeared to be too optimistic: I could barely make it to six... But he will be all right... I gained a great deal of respect for our medicine during that month: the doctors went out of their way to save him... well, both of us..."

Nina had noticeably lost weight (that seemed almost unimaginable, considering how slim she had always been), but other than that, she did not change at all. Same hairstyle, with her long red hair stuck high up on the crown of her head; large round earrings matching the dress, high heels, gracious walk. The right amount of makeup on her thin, perfect face. The incision was still hurting her, but she was not planning to give in, not to pain, nor to sickness. I asked about Leonid. Nina shrugged her shoulders.

"He wanted us to have another child, but I could not understand what he felt when the baby was born. He did not seem particularly upset or worried when he visited me in the hospital... Even though I easily could have died..."

Nina and her husband had a great relationship—as always. Except that he was back in his closet working on his computer programs. But when her baby son came home, it would not matter anymore...

Boris called twice from Vienna, and several times from Rome. Yes, she told him she was pregnant. No, she did not think it was his baby. She would not have done it deliberately, in any case. She told him "no" when he asked the question. After all, what mattered was what she believed in. She was learning to live without Boris in her life. It would be better if he stopped calling her, but she could not tell him that. He was still in Italy, awaiting the permission of the American Immigration Service to enter the U.S., which — in his case, at least — looked like a mere formality.

* * *

"Julie is a medical miracle. My sister had miscarried three times before she was able to have her. She had to stay in bed for almost four months, and still she only could carry Julie until twenty-seven weeks. In any other country Julie would have just died. But not in the U.S... American medicine works wonders. The doctors not only saved my niece's life, but they also made sure she developed properly after birth. She is seven years old now — and look at her: a beautiful, healthy girl, at the top of her class. All thanks to our medicine..."

I am at a lunch party in the multi-million-dollar house of my American sponsors, in a suburban Boston. Mrs. Morris's eyes sparkle with tears, and her voice trembles. She loves her sister, loves her niece Julie, and is thrilled to live in the country that can offer the world's best medical care. Overwhelmed by her emotions, Olivia Morris has forgotten that her sister's pregnancy may have had a very different outcome if the latter had not had an excellent health insurance, plus financial ability to leave her job for the duration of the pregnancy.

My mind rushes to a crowded hospital in Leningrad, where three-and-a half years ago my best friend, who was closer to me than any sister could ever be, gave birth to a baby at the twenty-sixth week of pregnancy. There was no health insurance involved, and neither did the hospital send the family any bills. The birth was complicated by an emergency C-section, performed by a tired surgeon in the middle of the night, in an understaffed operating room and with outdated equipment. I don't know if little Alex will be at the top of his class when his time comes to go to school, but he is a fine healthy boy who is running around like any other three-year-old, reciting children's poetry and beginning to learn the alphabet.

I am trying to convey the story to Olivia Morris and her guests, but they shake their heads in disbelief. Olivia's beautiful face expresses contempt mixed with disgust, and the tone of her voice is not any friendlier, when she replies:

"I knew that you were not objective in describing your country, but I did not know that you were capable of lying. My husband and I spent several weeks in Russia, and everyone we met was crying about the lack of medical care, and even basic medicine. People were begging us to bring aspirin…"

If I were given a chance to answer, I would tell Mrs. Morris that I also used to ask my foreign visitors for aspirin—precisely because I was healthy and could not think of any other medicine to request. And the lack of drugs available for sale does not preclude excellent doctors who perform "medical miracles" with less technology and fewer medications at hand than their American colleagues. But the expression on Olivia's face when she turns to me makes it clear that the topic is closed. Her light chatter has flown on, fluttering from guest to guest like a careless butterfly flutters from flower to flower. And suddenly I realize that during the thirty-three years of my life, Olivia Morris is the second person who has ever called me a "liar." The first one was Lev Fedorov.

12

The three big rooms of Aunt Olia's apartment are converted into three bedrooms at night: Arkady snores, and Aunt Olia prefers to sleep separately.

"I see enough of him during the day not to miss him at night," she says cheerfully. "I will certainly enjoy your company much more, especially considering how little time we spend with each other. But let's not stay up late. I have a deadline for an article and would like to work productively tomorrow."

Nevertheless, Aunt Olia and I don't go to sleep until almost midnight. There are two couches in her room, and we talk across the empty dark space of several yards that separates us. Our conversation flows freely, jumping from one subject to another, about nothing in particular and at the same time about everything. With some vanity, I realize that our former relationship of an aunt and a niece has gradually changed to a more equal one of two adult friends.

I know that Olia, being a very practical person, would not have much sympathy for my fruitless love for Volodia, so I try not to mention it. But

she understands completely my problems with Lev, and strongly suggests that I get a divorce. Her own husband is not nearly that bad, but
even she sometimes thinks about leaving him. The most likely scenario
for her is to get a work contract in another country, maybe even in the
U.S.; a year or two in one country, then some time in another...Arkady is
a very conservative person, attached to his daily routine: he would never
follow her. And she would like to see the world—thank god, Perestroika
has finally given people the opportunity to travel abroad...

Aunt Olia's dream is as close to coming true as a dream could be: she
has just returned from an international conference in India where her
presentation was a great success. She has several other invitations from
all over the world, most of them funded by the inviting institutions.

When I finally fall asleep that night, I feel almost happy. Aunt Olia
is very direct when she disagrees with me, and she can criticize me all
she wants, but she knows a magic trick of making me feel good about
myself—something that Lev Fedorov tries very hard to prevent...

"Why are you wearing synthetic underwear?" Olga exclaims in
amazement when I dress up in the morning. "Don't you know how unhealthy it is to wear synthetic right next to your body? I thought you
were smarter than that—don't you own cotton bras and panties?"

"I have tons of cotton stuff, Aunt Olia," I smile at her almost childish
outburst. "But synthetic looks much better, that's all."

"Why does it matter how it looks? You don't undress in front of men
every day, do you?"

"Not every day—alas! But today is the day when I probably will..."

"Ah! That's a different story," says my all-understanding friend with
noticeable relief. Her acceptance of my underwear is as emotional as
the denial was a minute ago. Everything that concerns other people
matters for Aunt Olia, at least everything that concerns people she
loves. And I feel honored and privileged to belong to that exclusive and
lucky group...

* * *

"As your old and trusted friend, I have to warn you; be careful with
these people. You can get into deep shit before you know it..."

Michael shakes cigarette ashes into a small porcelain saucer, and takes another puff. With his thick black beard and curly black hair, he looks like an ancient Hebrew prophet, who has miraculously appeared in a modest photo studio on the seventh floor of a concrete apartment building lost somewhere on the outskirts of a modern city. He talks like a prophet, too: softly, slowly, with an air of absolute certainty. But there is an aura of warmth and coziness around him, and his large Semitic eyes look at me fondly. I feel incredibly relaxed, snuggled by this healthy energy mixed in with a cloud of cigarette smoke, my head light and my body almost weightless.

"What do you mean by shit?" I ask my prophet. He takes several more puffs before he answers.

"The Jewish movement is complicated by a lot of personal politics. People who don't give a damn about anything Jewish use the situation to build up their political capital. They take advantage of naive followers (like you—sorry!) to give their actions more weight, so they can look important in the eyes of the West. You're a smart girl. You'll figure it out while you go along. Just don't get too close; it might be hard for you to wash it off later on...

"I don't like your Chelnov... He is someone new, otherwise I would have heard of him. I will gather some information in no time, though. I won't tell you any more right now. Just trust me: I've been in this business for almost fifteen years now, and I know these guys inside and out..."

I am not sure how closely I will follow Michael's advice—but I will keep it in mind. He and I have just made love on a wide air mattress thrown on the floor of his lab. It felt very natural, something that we meant to be doing, pure enjoyment, absolute mutual trust, and zero stress. We do not love each other, which is probably the greatest thing of all: no need to pretend or to agonize about the future. We are friends, friends, friends—and we are enjoying every moment of physical closeness the way we have always enjoyed mental interaction with each other. I feel no fear of Lev Fedorov, and certainly no remorse: my husband is simply getting what he has long deserved. As for Michael's wife (whom I have never met)—she is his problem, not mine. He has never been secretive about having had mistresses throughout his entire married life. In my heart I disapprove of it, but I have no intention of acting as Michael's conscience. After all, he is an ancient Hebrew, a patriarch, for whom male monogamy is a perversion of the modern world...

13

I had very mixed feelings when I dialed Volodia's number. His mother took the message, and he called back to Aunt Olia's house (which now had a telephone) within a few hours. He was excited to learn that I was in Leningrad: we absolutely had to meet. I thought that the last-minute meeting, just before my departure, would work best for me. I did not want to cherish the hope that Volodia would ask me to see him again tomorrow. I did not want to dream of more than one meeting: I could not be sure that I would be able to behave with proper dignity. One meeting was already hard enough...

In spite of having a very busy social schedule, I could not help counting hours, and then minutes. When walking upstairs to his fourth floor apartment, I had to stop several times: my heart was pounding loudly, and all the blood flushed into my face. A year and a half of separation, living in a different city, having a different life—all this disappeared and was forgotten: I belonged to Volodia again, every nerve, every cell of my body yearning for him and rushing to him.

During a short supper that his mother served in an immaculately clean kitchen, I managed to play the role of a happily married woman dropping by on a friendly visit. We talked a little bit about Perestroika, but mostly about common acquaintances and how new events in the country might affect everyone's life. I cursed my pounding heart, when after supper Volodia and I went to his room: that room caused too many memories... Luckily, it was large enough to allow me to sit as far away from him as possible. The only light came from a small table lamp, and I was hoping that he would not notice my flushed cheeks.

The conversation was progressing somehow, with Volodia doing most of the talking and me occasionally making brief remarks. It was after ten in the evening, and I knew that at some point I would have to get up and leave. I was postponing that horrible moment for as long as possible, when Volodia, probably having realized how late it was, suddenly asked if I could do him a favor.

I said "sure," as matter-of-factly as I could, trembling from excitement and happiness and only being afraid that the favor would be too small to ensure our continuous interaction. He got a folder from his desk that contained a few pages of typewritten text.

"This is an article for a journal (he gave the name) that is published in Moscow. It is due at the editor's next week. I probably still have time to send it via the post office, but it is getting tight, and there is always a risk that the letter might get lost among tons of editorial mail. I wonder if you could give it directly to the editorial staff member I've been working with. No need to go to the publishing house: you will call the journalist at home, and he will meet with you somewhere in the Moscow subway, at your mutual convenience. I thought since you work downtown..."

My heart sank when my fears were confirmed: the favor was too small to have any impact on our future relationship. Volodia wrote the name and the phone number of the person I was supposed to call on top of the folder, but hesitated before giving me the article.

"There is something else...This is the latest version I have, but I've made a few corrections since..." He opened the folder and showed me the manuscript: the pages were filled with handwritten remarks, made in ink in Volodia's fast, unclear handwriting. "I don't know if the editor will accept it this way. In theory, it all needs to be retyped, but I don't know when... You are leaving tomorrow morning, aren't you? I have tennis lessons that I teach starting at eight o'clock in the morning, and I have been going to bed very late the last few nights... I really can't afford to stay up half the night typing. You must have typewriters at work, don't you? The article is not due at the editor's until Wednesday... I wonder if I may ask you... By the way, do you know how to type?"

I looked at him, thinking that I must have heard something wrong. Volodia's last question did not make any sense: he could not have possibly forgotten that, less than two years ago, he and I had spent several months typing a 400-page book together.

"What do you want me to do with the article then, besides giving it to your acquaintance in Moscow?" I finally asked, for the sake of saying something.

"But you did not answer my question: do you know how to type?"

"Do I know... what?"

"Anya, what's wrong with you? I am asking a simple question. I wondered if you might be able to retype this article for me, before giving it to... It's five pages long; it would not be a big job for an average typist... But I don't know if you can type. Have you ever typed before?"

I looked at him again. He was absolutely serious, and probably a little annoyed by my strange reaction. I suddenly felt very, very tired, and completely empty.

"I'll type the article for you," I said wearily. "And I will deliver it to your friend by Wednesday."

"But you do have a typewriter that you can use, don't you? At the office, maybe?"

"I have a typewriter at home," I said. "The same very one we used for typing Eugenia Ginsburg. Imagine, I still have it..."

A faint sparkle of hope that flashed when I pronounced that last phrase died out when Volodia totally ignored it.

"Great! Thanks very much, I really appreciate it. Now, come over, I want to make sure that you can read my handwriting and understand all my remarks..."

It was close to midnight when I left Volodia's house and slowly walked toward the nearest subway station. A fifteen-minute walk took me half an hour, but I did not care. I asked Volodia not to see me off, and he did not insist. The streets were well lit, and a few late pedestrians hurried to get home. I was used to being outside alone late at night, both in Moscow and in Leningrad, and was not particularly worried. Most importantly, I did not want to see any more of Vladimir Sonovsky. Ever.

There was nothing to talk about, nothing to dream about, nothing to regret or miss. He had turned into a shadow. In fact, he had never existed. I had wasted three years of my life loving, worshiping, and dreaming about a man who was alive only in my imagination. "How many times can one repeat the same mistake?" I asked myself bitterly. "The story with Lev Fedorov should have taught me a lesson. Whose fault is it that I learned nothing from it?"

I packed Volodia's article at the very bottom of my suitcase, and did not look at it until later at home when I was about to type it. It was quite a mediocre piece of writing, with some progressive ideas and plenty of emotions, but with nothing particularly new, deep, or out-standing in any way. I thought that Volodia must have had damn good connections in the literary world, to be able to publish something like that in a popular Moscow magazine. Well, his father was said to have been a highly respected journalist, and it was not unusual for the son to inherit some connections (and sometimes even fame), even if he did not inherit the talent.

Volodia called a few days later for a confirmation that his article had been retyped and successfully delivered. I was very glad that Lev was not at home at the time of his call, but other than that had no emotions whatsoever. For the first time ever, Volodia's voice did not make my heart race, and I hung up the phone without the feeling of loss or the sadness of separation. Three years of my life lay dead behind me, stripped not only of pain, but even of memories. I had passed through a black hole that destroyed a big chunk of my soul and my heart, and I was finally out of it, beaten, empty, but still alive. I was thirty years old, and I had to live on.

Chapter Eight

REFUSENIKS. 1988–1990

1

"WHAT IS THAT, IF I MAY ask?" Perlov's tone of voice did not promise anything good.

Damn it, why did he come back? According to Natasha, our department head was supposed to be at various meetings at least until late afternoon. Natasha and Garik knew what I was doing. None of them had any legal right to permit me the use of office equipment for producing personal documents (even the museum director would not have had a right to do that). However, they agreed to look the other way— but only after Garik had shown me how to adjust the printer's settings to my document's format. In short, they were as supportive as they could possibly be; unfortunately, they could not have predicted Perlov's appearance. Now I was caught in the act, and had to get out of the situation on my own.

Like a statue of Justice and Punishment, Perlov stood near the only printer in the office (a bulky machine almost the size of a person—remember that technology of the late 1980s?), watching the pages of the leaflet slowly appearing from the slot.

The activists of ODIKSI (abbreviation for the newly-emerged Society of Friendship with Israel), Jewish Cultural Association, and Jewish Historical Society were in the process of organizing a celebration of Israel's Memorial Day. The plan was to gather people in the woods near the Moscow suburban town of Vyalki, for a big meeting followed by a collective picnic, singing, and dancing. This was not as much a political event as an attempt to bring Jews together and remind them of their national identity. Nevertheless, I could easily be accused of "Zionist propaganda" (which only a couple of years earlier would have instantly cost me my job, and very possibly my freedom).

And, of course, I was not supposed to use the museum's equipment for printing two hundred pages of personal documents, whatever they may have been. Unfortunately, at the meeting of ODIKSI the previous week I volunteered to do that. Now the entire event depended on me, and I would never be able to face any of my new friends, if I failed to accomplish the task.

"I don't know how to stop it," I muttered to Perlov. "It would be very stupid if I break down now," I thought, "and would not help the case a bit..."

My boss came over to the keyboard, and quickly typed several commands. The printing stopped, and I was only half way through.

"I am waiting," he said, standing in front of me like a judge.

I stood up, to be on the same level with Perlov. Looking up at him was intolerable.

"A group of my friends is trying to organize a get-together for Moscow Jews. It is totally secular, and practically non-political," I said, trying to keep my voice from trembling. "And they were looking for someone who could print a reasonable number of announcements. I may have been irresponsible to offer to do it on the office printer (although I have brought my own paper), but I did promise, and now people depend on me. I really cannot come back and say that I couldn't do it. I've never broken my promise to anyone in my entire life. I am sorry, but I must get this done."

Perlov was silent for a while, studying the leaflet and thinking about how to react. Then he suddenly decided to be reasonable.

"How I feel about the subject of this leaflet, does not matter. You should not be using your work time, and especially the office equipment, for your personal business, regardless of who supplied the paper. Neither should your immediate supervisor (he cast a furious glance toward Natasha who was calmly working at her desk) have allowed you to do that. However, since you seem to be almost done, I am going to let you finish, and keep the whole issue within our department. I will trust you to never attempt doing anything like this in the future. Otherwise, next time the consequences will be the most serious..."

I nodded gratefully, and typed the "print" command on the screen. Obviously, I would not be able to do that again. It was a pity: I would have to come up with other ways to make my presence in ODIKSI noticeable.

* * *

I wondered what "shit" Michael had meant. I found the evolving Jewish life in Moscow fascinating as I got more and more involved... Every week I met new people. I liked some of them more, some less, but they all had one quality that I admired and envied: they actively engaged in life, unafraid to be different—and possibly *make a difference*. They organized societies, groups, and seminars. They studied and taught Hebrew, Jewish history, and traditions of Judaism. Most of the meetings were still happening in apartments, but the movement was rapidly going beyond private homes. Research institutes and colleges began to allow lectures on Jewish culture and Jewish tradition, and even meetings with visitors from Israel. It may now seem amazing that the majority of lecturers were not historians or rabbis, but people of totally unrelated professions: engineers, doctors, and teachers—enthusiasts who had learned the material in their own free time. The Jewish theater *Shalom* and the Solomon Mikhoels Cultural Center (both brand-new organizations, rebuilt on the ashes of the Moscow Jewish Theater destroyed by Stalin) had new events almost daily; their programs were advertised publicly—on street posters and sometimes even in newspapers.

Chelnov had become indispensable. As the leader of the Jewish Cultural Association with its ambitions of becoming the umbrella organization for hundreds of smaller groups and societies around the country, he was a necessary participant at every gathering. Every foreign human right activist who visited Moscow wanted to meet with him. As a Hebrew teacher, he was almost inaccessible; it was a disaster, because my main reference source was gone. Nevertheless, I had gained so much confidence teaching my four pupils that I dared to form another group, this time with as many as seven students.

I was happy to find out that there was a support network for Hebrew teachers. Recently formed in Moscow, *Igud haMorim* ("the Teachers' Union") received copies of various language courses directly from Israel. Union members who had access to Xerox machines made as many copies of every textbook as each teacher needed, on a fairly short notice and at a price that students could afford.

Having learned and perfected the *Dusihim*, I decided to try a new course. I ordered and shortly received eight copies of the textbook, neatly bound and printed on a high-quality paper. Another *Igud* member gave me the cassette to accompany the text. Unfortunately, I did not own a double-cassette recorder, so I had to ask one of my new students for the favor of duplicating the tape for the entire group.

I now was busy teaching four evenings a week. Hebrew lessons more than doubled my take-home income, but money was the least of my incentives. Chelnov had been right: teaching turned out to be the most effective way to learn—and learning Hebrew could no longer be dismissed as "useless"—by me or by anyone else. A little light flashed at the end of the tunnel...

* * *

The most amazing thing in my family life was that Lev, who had been so strongly opposed to my Hebrew lesson before, suddenly started joining me in Jewish activities. At first, he accompanied me at my very first "real" Passover Seder organized by Chelnov in his smaller apartment. (My only experience with Seders in Leningrad had been casual get-togethers with Michael Levin's refusenik friends, where matza with canned ham and vodka were followed by jokes and cheerful toasts, but no prayers—and definitely no *Haggadah*.)

"Much more meaningful than our stupid Soviet holidays," was Lev's major remark. He said he liked Chelnov. He was trying very hard to make a good impression on everyone, our host in particular. I had never learned whether my wise Hebrew teacher was fooled by Lev's superficial friendliness, but it was one of the very few times when I felt almost good about my marriage.

In the fall that year, my husband and I went together to the Vyalki Woods, for the celebration of Sukkot. That barely-legal event turned out to be a tremendous success. Even nature was on our side: a light warm wind gently touched the reddish and golden leaves, which looked even brighter against the blue sky. The policemen hanging around the path from the train station to the meeting place did not bother anyone, although they gave only vague directions. Whether police were placed along our route to protect Jews from local hooligans, or to protect the local population from Jewish influence, remained unclear. Per order of the authorities, or by their own initiative, they had removed all the signs carefully placed by Jewish activists the night before. Luckily, the festive crowd steadily streaming through the field toward the birch and pine grove made any signs unnecessary.

The word that Lev was a village dweller about to start his own farm, quickly spread around. Two or three men were in the process of opening their own cooperative cafés and appeared interested in Lev's offer to supply fresh produce, possibly even kosher meat. Not that I believed for a minute that my husband would indeed bother with kosher, but he obviously enjoyed looking important and charming people. He occasionally tried to charm me as well, but (as my reader can guess) without much success; however, I had enough wisdom not to show that.

2

My lessons with the second group of Hebrew students started well. For the first few weeks I had no problems figuring out the new textbook, but a couple of months into the program it started getting more and more complicated. I reached the point when I was only a few lessons ahead of my own students, and while they were making progress, the gap became smaller and smaller. I desperately needed a lesson myself; perhaps not even a lesson, but an extended consultation. When, after a few days of persistent calls I finally reached Chelnov, I got the answer I had expected: my former teacher was extremely busy, but he would try to find an hour for me within the next few weeks.

And, indeed, one fine morning he called. Could I be at his house tonight by nine o'clock? He apologized for the late notice, but he had no idea when he might be able to have another chance. Nine o'clock in the evening worked reasonably well for me: Nadia went to bed at eight; by the time I had to leave the house she would be sound asleep. My next-door neighbor Zoya, who had the key to my apartment, would stop by at ten to check on her. Not the best arrangement, but much better than leaving my daughter alone earlier in the evening when she was still awake. In any case, I had no choice.

Lev arrived in the afternoon. I had not been expecting him, but was not surprised either. He usually showed up about once a week, almost always without any notice. I had mixed feelings about his arrival: no more need to leave Nadia alone; on the other hand, my husband could have a problem with me visiting another man's apartment at such a late hour, even if that man was Chelnov.

To my great relief, this time Lev did not express any objections. The evening seemed to be working out fine, and when at quarter to nine I rang the doorbell of Chelnov's "small" apartment, I was feeling fairly good about life. To my disappointment, I found my teacher in the middle of the group lesson. They started later than he had planned, he explained, and since they had missed the previous lesson, he would need another forty minutes to finish. I was more than welcome to sit with his students and listen; he would spend the promised hour with me after he was done with the group.

I was upset, but had no option other than waiting. Impatient as I was to start my own lesson, I had to admit that Chelnov was an even better group teacher than he was an individual one. His lesson was interactive and entertaining, with the right balance of humor, structure and encouragement for the students to be active. I kept writing down words and expressions that I did not know, and almost regretted my earlier refusal to join one of Chelnov's groups.

The telephone rang in the kitchen every few minutes. Every time it happened, my host asked me to answer. "They know I am here tonight," he sighed. "I should have kept it a secret. Now I can't work. Please, take people's names and phone numbers, and tell them I'll call back later—presumably, when I am finished with you tonight. Whenever that will happen..."

I obediently played the role of Chelnov's secretary, hoping that one of the callers would be my husband; I was sure he would call sooner or later, and preferred to be over and done with his annoying check-up. The lesson kept going on; the phone kept ringing. It seemed that half of Moscow needed Chelnov that night, and I was getting nervous that I might lose in the competition. At quarter to ten the group lesson was finished. I sighed with relief, but too soon. I should not have forgotten that we were in Russia, where no gathering goes without freshly brewed tea. The students displayed cookies and pastries, the host brought a steaming hot teakettle from the kitchen. Cups and saucers appeared on the table that only a few minutes ago served as a giant desk. Another forty minutes went by, with lively discussion and jokes.

The damn phone kept ringing in the kitchen. Chelnov got up and answered two or three times, and then he asked me:

"Could you do all of us a favor? Go to the kitchen, and unplug the damn thing. Let's pretend I have left! They'll call my wife at home instead, she'll take messages."

I thought of Lev Fedorov. He had not called yet, but I could not imagine he would go to bed without making sure that I was indeed at Chelnov's and not with some secret admirer. I did not know how to explain that to Chelnov, especially in his students' presence, but I hesitated to carry out his order.

"Maybe... I'll keep answering the phone? I don't really mind... what if there is something urgent?"

"Nothing can be urgent at ten-thirty at night!" Chelnov seemed a little annoyed at my unexplained stubbornness. "Besides, you and I will start working in a few minutes; you will not be able to keep answering the phone."

With a heavy heart, I slowly walked to the kitchen and unplugged the telephone.

My one-hour consultation with Chelnov turned into two hours. The questions were more complicated than I had expected, and my teacher liked detailed explanations. It was well past midnight when I returned home. To my relief, my husband was sound asleep on the folding bed in our daughter's room (eager to avoid physical closeness with him, I had invented some reason why sleeping together on the couch in the living room was no longer possible). I hoped that he had been asleep for a while and did not know what time I got home. And I hoped even more that he had not called Chelnov's apartment.

* * *

That Saturday in early spring was like any other Saturday, except that Lev arrived home in late morning with flowers and in an unusually friendly mood. I had just finished an English lesson with a group of kids Nadia's age. That winter I had resumed teaching English to children. The main purpose of those lessons was spending time with my own daughter in a way she enjoyed. It also gave her a chance to meet more kids, and for me it was a way to get a sense of the people living in my neighborhood.

The lesson had gone well, but I was feeling depressed and anxious. While my pupils were getting dressed in the hallway, laughing and pushing each other, I was thinking of my husband's flowers. I knew that there must have been a reason for them, and I was correct: as soon as the kids left, he asked me to go to the notary, and sign permission for him to sell the car.

I had long forgotten that the car was "mine". The time when every other week I had to sign notarized POAs to Lev's various friends (most of whom I had never met) to drive "my" car, had passed long ago. Nevertheless, the request made me extremely uncomfortable. I could not understand why we should suddenly sell a perfectly fine car on which we all depended? Lev had promised to start taking Nadia to the village on weekends as soon as it got warmer, and I was still hoping to join them occasionally in summer; but none of that would be possible without a reliable car. Of course, questioning my husband was useless, and arguing with him dangerous.

After lunch, I reluctantly went to the notary and waited in line for about forty minutes before I could sign the paper my husband had required. He almost grabbed it from me, and disappeared right away. He will buy another car shortly, he reassured me before leaving. The next time, it will be in his name, so I will not need to keep going to the notary...

"Another shady transaction," I thought. "Good thing I don't care anymore."

It would have been better if I had cared.

* * *

Two weeks later, Lev and I drove to a bank on the outskirts of Moscow. Our *Moskwich* had been sold, and my husband had borrowed a car from one of his friends. He looked happy, and was very handsome in his new fashionable sheepskin coat. He courteously held the door for me while we were entering the empty office. The clerk at the window respectfully counted seventy one-hundred-ruble notes, for which I obediently signed.

Lev took the pile of cash and safely hid it in his inner pocket.

"Do you need a ride to the subway, or would you rather walk?" he asked, kissing my forehead.

"Aren't you giving me any money for groceries?" I thought of the huge amount of cash that had just disappeared inside his coat.

"Don't you make enough money with your *Jewish lessons*?" He asked mockingly, but opened his wallet and gave me several ten-ruble bills. "Cook something good tonight, we have to celebrate. I'll be home early; should I pick up Nadia from school?"

"Sure," I said.

Then we parted. It was a beautiful sunny day in late March, and I decided to walk to the subway station.

Nothing remarkable happened during the supper. Nadia chattered excitedly with her papa. I served and ate in silence. Later that evening, when Nadia had taken her bath and gone to bed and I was finishing the dishes, Lev asked casually, as if continuing some previous conversation:

"So, where were you *that evening*?"

I had almost forgotten the episode at Chelnov's and didn't understand right away what he was talking about.

"That night, a month ago, when you showed up at home at one in the morning. Allegedly, after "studying" with Chelnov..."

"Lev," I said, feeling sick in my stomach, "I've told you the entire story: Chelnov was in the middle of another lesson, and he asked me to disconnect the phone..."

But I knew that arguing was hopeless. My husband's face had already acquired the familiar scary expression, his skin having turned gray and his eyes red from fury.

"You don't even bother to invent a more plausible lie, f-ng bitch," he hissed. "I called Chelnov; he said he was not in his apartment that night!"

A few days later, having run into Chelnov at one of the ODIKSI meetings, I made a fool of myself by asking if my husband had recently called him. Chelnov was very surprised, but answered negatively. Why would Lev Fedorov call him? Perhaps, he had called his house and left a message with his wife? But even that was unlikely: Chelnov's wife was very good about giving messages...

3

It was a depressing spring, gloomy and cool. Melting snow was turning into mud, and my fancy imported boots, brought from England by my beloved Uncle Victor, were always stained with wet salty spots, no matter how much I polished them. Muscovites were ruder than ever, angry and annoyed at the new government, at their devaluating salaries, at growing corruption and empty stores. Women left their offices during the day and ran around the city, frantically looking for stores that had queues, since queues meant that there was food. The lucky ones who managed to reach the end of the line before the supply was out, did not just buy for their families, but for their friends, coworkers, and neighbors. Returning back to the office, women exchanged goods, thus implementing the basic principal of Communism: "from each according to ability, to each according to need." Cooperation and mutual assistance helped people to survive. When the amount of food on your table depends on your friends' shopping success, working as a team comes naturally. People were angry and stressed, but nobody starved.

Lev came over once a week, with a large cardboard box filled with food. There were mostly canned goods, but high-quality ones: stewed beef, salmon, olive oil, sweetened condensed milk, beans, and imported fruit salads. His packages often included such valuable grains as wholegrain oats, buckwheat, and millet (unjustly unpopular in the U.S.), so we were always set for breakfast. I occasionally allowed myself to buy fresh produce at peasant markets, which added variety to our meals. Fruits were mostly for Nadia; Lev and I made do with beets, carrots, and cauliflower. Even with our relatively high income, paying market prices for fruits for three of us seemed too extravagant.

* * *

Garik received *the permission*. He was working his last days in Tretyakovka, often staying until midnight, eager to wrap up his work before leaving the country. Perlov was quiet and reserved, coiled like a snake ready to strike. Natasha had a job offer in a new cooperative company, and she would start there as soon as Garik leaves. I knew that I had to look for a new job—and that I better find something fast. My time was running out, but I had very few ideas. Library positions were plentiful, and with my education and experience I could easily get one, but they paid close to nothing and were dreadfully boring. I had gotten spoilt by working in exciting places and doing creative research, and the prospect of performing routine operations day after day, sharing a small office with a few depressed women, did not inspire me.

* * *

I remember the gray afternoon, when I was returning from the interview in the Mikhoels Cultural Center. The newly opened Center was supposed to have a library, and the library needed a librarian. After talking to a few people, I envisioned myself as an ideal candidate for the position: I knew a fair amount about Jewish history and culture, was in touch with the current Jewish life in Moscow, could read Hebrew and almost certainly (with my knowledge of German) some Yiddish. For a while I felt excited, thinking of all the connections I would make at that job and all the interesting people I would meet. I made an appointment with my would-be supervisors (without sending any résumé, just through someone's phone call); we had a relaxed two-hour conversation that resembled a friendly discussion much more than a job interview.

Nevertheless, I left the Center feeling disappointed and depressed. It was a full-time job, with a salary barely one-third of what I was making in Tretyakovka. I knew that Jewish organizations the scale of the Mikhoels Cultural Center received huge financial support from the West, and was taken aback by my employer's apparent greediness. And I did not like my future boss. I could not put my finger on what it was that I disliked, except that I knew I would never be able to trust him the way I trusted Garik and Natasha, or even be comfortable with him as I used to be with the simple direct Kharetov.

I was walking slowly through the Taganskaya Square, contemplating the same old question that had been tormenting me since I returned from Leningrad that past winter: to leave Lev Fedorov, or not to leave? I had woken up that morning with the answer "to leave" hanging in the air. I almost certainly could survive without weekly food boxes. Just yesterday my next-door neighbor Zoya brought me a dozen fresh eggs that she had managed to buy in a local store. (Two weeks earlier I had done a similar favor for her.) Other people occasionally shared their shopping trophies with me, like cheese or sometimes even precooked goodies like *pirozhki* or *blinchiki* with delicious fillings, which required only heating. I probably could buy more food at peasants' markets — provided that I kept my current income. And, after all, Nadia, Lev's daughter, would still be living with me, so there was no reason why he should stop supplying us with food.

But now, after that discouraging interview, I was not so sure. Life was uncertain and scary, and was becoming more and more so every day. I felt very lonely in the middle of the crowded square; strangers were rushing past me, nicely dressed, energetic and angry, their faces tense, totally unaware of my presence.

"These are not people, these are wolves," I thought suddenly. "Wolves, roaming around the woods in search of prey. And I have a cub here to bring up, feed and keep safe until it is big and strong enough to survive on its own. If you're a female wolf with a cub, surrounded by stranger wolves, you're better off having your own male wolf to protect you..."

And so that was my decision for the day: stay with your wolf so he can feed and protect your cub... Happiness? I had long forgotten what it was. And who was happy in those days?

I saw a short queue near a fast food place, and driven by a hunting instinct, came closer to see what it was about. My instinct was correct: the cafeteria was selling frozen *pelmeni*, or meat dumplings, a Russian version of ravioli. After only ten minutes in line, I possessed four one-kilogram packages of that delicious precooked dinner. Pelmeni were sold at a ready-food price, that's why the line was so short. I felt a certain pride in being able to afford what for most Muscovites was beyond reach; I also caught myself thinking positively about Lev Fedorov, and how much he would enjoy pelmeni. I dived into the subway station with a firm decision: "no divorce."

4

That evening started like every other evening when Lev was visiting: he played with Nadia; we had small talk at dinner; I read Nadia a book and sang her a lullaby after she'd gone to bed. I was about to take a shower and go to bed myself, when Lev suddenly made some dirty remark about me having sex with other men. I tried to ignore it, but he forced his way into the shower room, where he continued his angry monologue, describing details of my non-existent extramarital sexual life and galvanizing himself with images produced by his own imagination.

I sighed and returned to the living room. My husband followed me, talking dirtily and getting more and more agitated. I tried to shut my mind, not to hear the individual words. My first reaction was disgust, and disgust made me nauseous. But it soon gave way to fear. Fear was pounding in my head, while I tried to control it by self-hypnosis: "It will be over soon. You'll survive, as you survived hundreds of times before. Just don't argue, don't answer, don't show him that you are scared, it will pass... There will be night soon, hopefully, you'll sleep alone, don't listen, don't answer... He will leave for his village tomorrow... it will be all right, just don't let him see your fear or say anything that will make him even angrier..." Then, for the fiftieth time in the last month, I heard the same damn question:

"And who was the fucker you spent that night with? *That night* when you fucking lied to me that you were studying Hebrew with Chelnov?"

At that moment, something strange happened. It felt as if someone invisible turned a secret switch inside me. I had to jump off that swing set, as I did at seven years old. Even if my head cracks open by hitting the ground, I could not stay on that roller-coaster anymore. In one-tenth of a second, I was transformed into a different person; all my fear was gone. The ecstasy that filled me was of the same kind that in the heat of a battle drives a soldier to throw himself on the gun-port of a cannon; the same that makes a slave rip off his chains knowing that he will be killed the next instant—but death no longer matters, since even death is better than slavery. I looked directly at Lev's face, and smiled:

"Do you really need to know his name? The guy is twenty years younger than you, a six-foot tall athlete. He may beat the shit out of you if you try to mess with him... And after all, why is it so important for you to know who I was with *that* night? There have been many other nights, and I was spending them with many different guys. Do you realize how many people I meet in Moscow these days? And you know men: they won't let a beautiful young woman (who in addition has the merit of being married to an old fool who leaves her alone) go to waste!"

I thought he would kill me right away, and was prepared to meet my death looking it in the face. I was sitting cross-legged on our wide couch that for so many years had served as a marital bed, while Lev was standing in front of me, broad-shouldered, strong like a wild beast, a man capable of any deceit, betrayal, murder—and I, a small weak woman, was afraid of him no more.

To my amazement, his face expressed more surprise than fury.

"You... you don't really mean that, do you?"

"But Lev," I said, with a touch of pity in my voice, "my dear husband, you're not a fool! You've known it all along, haven't you? You've been leaving me alone for days and days in a row. I am a young woman, I need sex! Plain f-ng sex, for the enjoyment of my beautiful young body. And I also want to be with young men. Young men, with smooth skin and strong bodies, who don't have erection problems. You may not recognize it, but you are getting old! You haven't been particularly entertaining these days, either. There is only so much one can listen about building a country house or village gossip... My friends take me out to movies... to parities... they dance with me... they talk about interesting things... I was sure you've known it from the beginning... You and I have not been really married since... god, I guess since I left Moscow five years ago and took Nadia to Leningrad. I had someone in Leningrad back then, didn't you know? Since then, we've been just partners, haven't we?.. You had affairs too!"

"Aren't you afraid that I'll kill you, bitch?" he asked. But by that moment I knew that he wouldn't: the momentum had passed. The Lion looked more puzzled than furious, almost helpless, not knowing what to do next.

It could be a lull before the storm, so I had to act fast.

"No," I said. "No, you won't kill me. Or injure me, or do any physical harm. You have too much to lose, to risk spending another few years in prison. You know that court will be much tougher on you, since you've already served one term. If you kill me, you can be sure to get capital punishment: there is no way you'll be able to prove in court that you had a justified jealousy; nobody heard what I said just now, you have no witnesses..."

"Nadia will witness."

"Nonsense. You know as well as I do that courts don't accept testimonies from seven-year-olds. Besides, she does not know a thing. I was careful enough. Do you think I am that stupid? You better leave now: our marriage is over. We just have to go through the boring formalities... They will take a couple of months, then we can divide the apartment..."

Unrealistic as it may sound, I won the battle. Lev, indeed, left. Before walking out of the room, he smashed the lamp that had been standing on the side table. I quickly turned my face away, so the flying fragments of broken glass would not injure it. Next thing I heard was the slamming of the front door. I got up, and turned the inner security lock, which made it impossible to open the door from outside, even with the key. I wondered what I would do if Lev came back and tried to break the door. It was still his apartment, so the police probably would not interfere. And of course, I would have to let him in in the morning, when Nadia wakes up and hears her beloved papa ringing the doorbell. But those were details I could worry about later: my marriage with Lev Fedorov was over, over, over... No matter what horrors the future would bring, I was free from *that* slavery.

I returned to the living room, carefully cleaned the broken glass, then took a long bath, and went to bed. I fell asleep right away—and for the first time in years I felt happy.

* * *

"Lev will not try to break the door," said my neighbor Zoya, when the next morning I came to her place asking for advice. "Why did you think he could? It is not his apartment. He can't even enter it without your permission."

I stared at her in amazement. What did she mean? Of course, it was Lev's apartment! Zoya must have had something wrong. My next-door neighbor was a very sensible person, practical and easy-going at the same time, one of those people who always knows everything about everyone, at the same time being everybody's friend. Most importantly, she was a volunteer passport officer in our cooperative, which meant that all apartment registrations had to go through her before being processed by the local militia (i.e. police department). Out of all people, she must have known who had *propiska* in our building and who did not—but how on earth was it possible that Lev Fedorov did not own his own apartment?

"The ownership in the cooperative is in your name, right?" Zoya could not understand what I was so surprised about. "And Lev removed his registration... mm-m... I have to look up the date. I am pretty sure it's been more than six months ago. When did he start building his village house, do you remember?"

"God knows what my husband has been doing in the village. But I am sure he started the construction before last summer. I remember him taking me to the site, to see the foundation. But what does his village house have to do with our divorce?"

"Because he could not get registered in his new house, without removing his registration from the Moscow apartment!" exclaimed Zoya, amazed at my ignorance. "One cannot be registered in two different homes. And there was no other way for him to legalize his ownership of the village home, without registering there as a permanent resident. I can't imagine you did not know about that. Haven't you guys discussed family things?"

"We haven't discussed much of anything... except my alleged infidelity," I sighed, wondering how much empathy happily married Zoya would feel for such a statement. "That is one of the many reasons why I have no doubts about the divorce. But, since legally Lev and I are still married, can't he do something to register back in our apartment, even if I don't support it?"

"He sure could—for the first six months after he had checked out. That's why it is important for us to know when exactly it happened. But after six months... You, as his wife, will have to apply for his re-registration, and there is no law that can make you do so if you don't want to. And, not being registered, your Fedorov will not dare to force his way into your place. I'll make sure all the neighbors know that you two are getting divorced, and that Lev is not registered. If he shows up and behaves inappropriately, someone will call the police. And since he is an ex-convict, the police will be more responsive than usual. Your husband is not a fool, and he knows the laws. He will not take a chance with the police..."

The news was almost too good to be true, but I felt little relief. I knew Lev Fedorov well enough to realize that he would not just let me get my way and become the sole owner of an apartment that he considered his. Winning in every situation was a matter of principle for him, the principle even more important than the need to have a place in Moscow.

"What if he threatens to do something terrible to me, unless I register him back?" I was thinking aloud, rather than hoping for Zoya's help.

"You think he might?" Zoya sounded doubtful. "An educated man like him, with a PhD? On the other hand, he must have been in jail for a reason... You know what? I suggest you let the local police know. Tell them your husband has been threatening you, and make sure he knows that they know. Do you want me to talk to Vasily? He's a good guy, he'll keep an eye on your apartment."

Vasily was the police officer for our apartment block. He was a friendly guy my age, and we always stopped to chat for a few minutes when running into each other in the yard. I told Zoya that I would talk to him myself, and did so promptly the very same morning. Nevertheless, returning home through the lonely path under thick trees gave me a strong feeling of uneasiness. But Lev Fedorov was not hiding behind the bushes, and neither was he waiting for me in the empty hallway. At home I locked my apartment door with the security lock, which I had previously used only at nights. It was a symbolic measure: I kept wondering what I would do if my husband shows up when Nadia is at home and insisting that I let her papa in.

The phone rang as soon as I returned from work that evening; it was my dear neighbor Zoya. She had just stopped at the passport office, to look at Lev's records. He had checked out of our apartment eight months ago, and therefore had lost all and any right to ever return there. Unless I wanted him to.

5

That spring I became a journalist. It was not an official job, or even a paid job, but here I was—an editorial staff member of the Informational Bulletin on Jewish Repatriation and Culture, with my name printed on the opening page of every issue. The bulletin, published jointly by ODIKSI and the Jewish Cultural Association, was compiled and edited in Moscow, shipped to Israel for printing and then returned to Moscow, multiplied by hundreds, for distribution throughout our huge country. Most of the copies circulated in the capital, but even there the demand for it far exceeded availability.

I had seen and read the Bulletin in Chelnov's house, but had never dreamt of becoming one of its creators...

My new career began at someone's farewell party. There were many of those parties going on in Moscow in 1989, given by friends and relatives of the brave and lucky ones who were about to leave the country forever. Barely in touch with friends I used to be close to, I nevertheless was meeting enough people to be invited to all kinds of social gatherings. Someone introduced me to Fedor Schmukler, the new editor-in-chief of the Bulletin. "Anna is a Hebrew teacher, but she also writes well. I heard you've been looking for new people, so maybe you two can talk," said my acquaintance.

A couple of months earlier I had published an article in "ODIKSI Chronicle", but other than that my writing experience had been limited to high school compositions and later a few short stories written for friends. Nevertheless, Fedor seemed interested. He had seen my article and found it well written. In any case, he had just lost a staff member to emigration, and was about to lose another one, so he was willing to let me try.

Two weeks later I submitted my first chronicle to the Bulletin.

"April 3rd: a demonstration took place in front of the Embassy of Great Britain in Moscow. About forty members of the Jewish refuseniks group "Poor Relatives" from Moscow, Leningrad, Kiev and Kharkov held signs saying: "We support the meeting between Michael Gorbachev and Margaret Thatcher and expect substantial improvement in human rights." The authorities had banned the demonstration under the usual pretext that it would "disturb the traffic". However, their letter was received only twenty-four hours prior to the event (instead of the five days required by law), which made it legally invalid. That is the most likely reason why the police did not interfere, and the demonstration went on as it had been planned, from 6 to 6:30 PM..."

"On April 4 the Jewish Legal Seminar of Moscow held one of its regular meetings. The meeting took place in a private apartment that could barely accommodate forty people. The presentation by Irina Shapiro about the new legislation of the Presidium of the Supreme Council of the USSR, "The new order of conducting public meetings, processions and demonstrations" caused so many emotions that the speaker could barely finish her report..."

"April 5th: the Australian Embassy in Moscow housed a meeting between Mr. Markus Ainfeld, the president of the Australian Commission on Human Rights, and a group of refuseniks activists..."

"April 12: the first meeting of the RAHAMIM Society, the Jewish charity organization, took place in Moscow in a private apartment. 'Rahamim', which means 'charity' in Hebrew, is a several-thousand-year old tradition..."

"The youth theater group from Tel-Aviv led by Nina Mikhoels participated in the International Festival of Theater Schools "Podium-89" sponsored by the Union of Theater Workers of the USSR..."

"On April 15th the Jewish Historical Society held its regular meeting in the apartment of V. Engel. Mr. Engel, the president of the Society, talked about preparation for the International Conference "Human Dignity and Human Rights in Judaism and Christianity" that is to take place in Moscow in June-July of this year..."

There were, obviously, more events in the chronicle section, and I was not the only reporter. The excerpts above should give my readers some idea about Jewish and political life in Moscow in 1989. Keep in mind, however, that the majority of the meetings and seminars took place in private apartments, and therefore could accommodate a very limited number of participants. And, with the exception of theater performances and some concerts, none of them was publicly advertised. One had to be acquainted with a member of the group, or know someone who knew a member of the group, in order to be informed about an upcoming event. Our Bulletin, as well as the ODIKSI Chronicle, another similar periodical, published some announcements, but mostly concentrated on reporting events that had already taken place.

Fedor was satisfied with my first chronicle. The next month I received a more important assignment, to interview a visiting professor from Jerusalem University. I met the latter in his fancy hotel room in downtown Moscow during my lunch break, which the always-understanding Natasha had extended to three hours. The editor-in-chief highly praised the interview, and my permanent position with the Bulleting was established.

Then, without making any efforts (or sometimes without even realizing what was happening), I was elected as a member of the Presidium of ODIKSI, and then a couple of other Jewish organization.

The more I wrote the more work I had. Long lonely evenings spent all by myself now belonged to the past. I was so busy that I often dreamed of staying at home and not going anywhere, not teaching and not spending hours on the phone, writing down reports of some society meeting or seminar. Unfortunately, my new "boss," editor-in chief Schmukler, insisted that I personally visit at least one event per evening, while interviewing leaders of others by phone. He reluctantly agreed that the evenings of my teaching were exempt, but on weekends I always had a choice of several events to go to.

The problem was that none of the above activities (running around town, the deluge of phone calls, new superficial friendships), although had an effect of an anti-depressant drug, could give my life any real meaning. I wondered if having an affair would make it any better; in spite of what I had said to Lev Fedorov, I had no lovers in Moscow, and was not even flirting...

6

At the end of April Nadia fell sick with chickenpox. She and I spent a week in home confinement, together coping with her rash, stinging ointment, boredom, and her temper tantrums; and, finally, the relief of getting better. The doctor advised me to keep her home for another week to avoid possible complications. My daughter was allowed to go outside for a short time, weather permitting, but had to take it easy. At the end of the second week of her sickness, I went out in the evening for the first time. Some important Jewish event that I had to report for the Bulletin required my personal attendance.

Nadia did not mind staying home alone: it was seven o'clock, she had just returned from a short outdoor play, eaten her supper with appetite and was in a cheerful mood. She promised to watch her favorite goodnight show and go straight to bed. Before leaving the house, I made sure Zoya was home; as usual, she would come check on Nadia every hour or so. Lev Fedorov had not shown any signs of his presence for a few weeks. It was a beautiful spring day, sunny and warm. I was happy to be out again and felt almost good about life.

When I returned home at eleven-thirty at night, the windows of my apartment were all dark. It alarmed me: Nadia always left kitchen and hallway lights on when she was home alone in the evenings. My heart pounded anxiously while I was hastily unlocking the front door. The apartment was dark and my daughter's bed empty. The doors of her closet were swung open, its shelves bare, a few remaining pieces of clothing thrown on the floor. The note attached to the hallway mirror explained the horror that had happened here.

"*Mama,*" read big letters of Nadia's childish handwriting. "*I dont laf you and dont wont to lif with you. I wont to lif with papa. We taikin my toys and clous to the viladj. I'll go to skul there and have fan. Nadia.*"

I imagined the events of the past few hours. Nadia was about to go to bed, when her beloved papa rang the doorbell. She had not seen him for a few weeks; she must have been overwhelmed with joy. It was not hard for Lev to brainwash her: her mama had left her alone because she did not love her; she was having fun with other men, betraying her papa. He must have described to her all the fun (mostly imagined) of living with him in the village and making new friends with the village kids. His promise that she would go to the village school was bullshit: none of the villages in the vicinity of Lev's house were large enough to have a school. (The few children who lived in the area had to go to boarding schools, far away from their homes.)

I was pacing the apartment back and forth, having no idea what to do, mad as a lioness who had lost her cub. It was too late at night to talk to the neighbors; too late to try to see a lawyer; too late for everything. Had I lost my child forever? I could not make myself believe that—but the battle ahead of me was the hardest one I had ever fought.

At half past midnight the phone rang. I grabbed the receiver, hoping and fearing to hear Lev's voice. But it was my mother, calling from Leningrad where she was visiting.

"Nadia is with Lev," were her first words (as if I did not know). "I am not asking you right now where you were and why you had left her alone. I just want you to know that she has not been kidnapped. She is at least safe..."

"What do you mean by 'at least safe'?! She is not that safe at all: she is just recovering from chickenpox, the doctor told us to be very careful with outdoors—and what if she develops complications in a village where there is not even a nurse?"

"Anya," said my mother. "The situation is very serious, but there is nothing that we can do right now, except to wait. Lev called me a few minutes ago. He told me that he would return Nadia to us, if we pay him back the 3,500 rubles that you had 'stolen' from him after the sale of his car. I know that you did not see a ruble from that money, but I have no idea how you can prove it legally. You made a mistake leaving your daughter alone for the entire evening—but I am not going to blame you for that right now, because it will not help. What I am asking you for—and, please, I beg you, take it very seriously—is not to attempt to go to Lev's village by yourself. That's almost certainly what he wants you to do. You described it as a remote place: he will simply murder you. He can do it safely: no one will even notice that you're missing."

"What shall I do?" I asked, thinking that my always-anxious mother was probably right this time. "I can't just leave her there..."

"Wait until your father comes to Moscow. It may take him a day or two, but he will be there. The two of you can go to the village together. You may not be able to get Nadia back right away, but at least you will see her without risking your life. Promise that you'll wait for your father."

"I promise," I said. "I am not suicidal. I will not go there by myself."

As horrible as the situation was, I was not alone any more. I took three sleeping pills and went to bed.

* * *

My father's phone call woke me up in the morning.

"Listen," he said in his usual abrupt manner. "I've just talked to *Dadilych* (the loving nickname Academician Alexandrov's pupils gave to their teacher); he will approve my business trip to Moscow starting

Monday. If I fly today, I will have to pay my own money for the ticket. Can it wait for two days, or do you want me to try to catch a plane right now?"

Impatient as I was to start acting, I remembered that the round-trip fare from Novosibirsk to Moscow cost about a hundred rubles, almost a quarter of my father's monthly salary. I appreciated his willingness to pay that money, but it was already Saturday, and two days would not make that much difference. The weather was sunny and warm, and I thought that my daughter was probably OK in the village, even if she spent most of her time outdoors.

"Just make sure you get the first morning flight on Monday."

There was a four-hour time difference between Novosibirsk and Moscow, and only a three-hour flight. Leaving Novosibirsk early in the morning meant an even earlier arrival to Moscow. I could see my father rushing over to Alexandrov's house, to talk about just another family problem that needed his help. I imagined Danilych listening sympathetically; he was eager to help, and was upset by his inability to approve a business trip starting on Saturday.

Early flights on Monday were all sold out, and when my father finally arrived in the afternoon, it was too late to go to the village. We started off the next morning, first nearly an hour by subway, then two-and-a-half hours by suburban train to the provincial town, followed by forty minutes on an old country bus, which dropped us off on demand in the middle of nowhere, near a dirt road heading into the fields and woods.

My father was a fast walker, and I had to make an effort to keep up with him. He had talked too much at home, and now I was glad that we were walking in silence. We reached our destination by mid-afternoon. Lev's house was clearly visible from a distance. Like a medieval castle, it occupied the best location; situated on the high bank of the fast river, it dominated the landscape. About three dozen modest village houses were at least half-a-mile away, looking up at the master house as faithful vassals look up to their merciful and powerful feudal lord.

The lord of the estate had company. It was May Ninth, the anniversary of victory in the Great War, and many people had taken the entire week off. I was glad to see the Gosins, our old and the only common friends in Moscow. Oleg Gosin and his wife Marianna provided moral support to me through the three years of my husband's imprisonment; I even occasionally stayed in their house on my brief visits to Moscow. After Lev's release, they were the people at whose house we could drop off Nadia for a few hours, and with whom we spent holidays such as the New Year. Oleg, a decorated veteran of the Second World War, a man in his sixties, was married to a woman twenty-two years his junior; their daughter, only one year older than Nadia, was her frequent playmate. Gosin's and Marianna's age difference, very unusual in Russia, was exactly the same as Lev's and mine, which made our families even closer.

To my disappointment, the couple greeted me very coldly.

"We don't know what happened between you and Lev, since we only heard one side of the story," said Oleg. "However, if what Lev said about your intent to immigrate to Israel is true... I hope it isn't, because Marianna and I have not perceived you as capable of immoral actions. Nevertheless, if it is true, we certainly have nothing to discuss, and will regret that we have ever considered you our friend."

Marianna, who had always obediently supported her husband, nodded silently. I could barely believe my own ears.

"Israel or not Israel," I turned to Marianna (she was a mother herself, after all—how could she not understand?!), "but a man has no right to take a child away from the mother... especially when he was away for half of the child's life!"

"If the mother does immoral things, he absolutely can—and should," Oleg Gosin, as usual, was the spokesman for both of them. "I am not referring to your alleged affairs—those are strictly between you and Lev—but betraying your country... I would be the first one to take the child away from you, before you have a chance to poison her mind and ruin her life."

"I think you're exaggerating," my father stepped in. He was almost ten years younger than Oleg Gosin, and spoke respectfully. "I have never heard anything about my daughter's intent to emigrate anywhere. It must be one of the stories my son-in-law loves to invent. As for Nadia, my wife and I are concerned that she might develop complications after the chicken pox, and would prefer that she stay in Moscow until she fully recovers. She always can come back to her father's village in summer, when the school vacation starts."

Gosin shook my father's hand:

"Pleased to meet you. I've heard lots of good things about you. You should talk to Lev—I am sure two reasonable people can work things out."

In spite of my father's reassurance about Israel, he and Marianna clearly excluded me from the list of "reasonable people". I turned around and walked away. I was too hurt to think clearly. Hurt and furious, my heart pounded so badly that I could barely breath. I could not believe the hatred that Gosin, a Jew by birth and by passport, felt toward Israel. I wondered what Chelnov and his crew, who were fighting so hard for the freedom of Jewish self-expression, Jewish culture, and Jewish re-patriation, would say about thousands of Soviet Jews like Oleg Gosin...

* * *

I walked around looking for Nadia. From the distance, I could see my father talking to Lev. They looked calm and friendly, which brought a faint hope that I might be able to take my daughter home today.

I found her a couple of hundred yards away from the house, play-ing with the Gosins' girl. Her long hair, unbraided and disheveled, was hanging loose down her shoulders. She was wearing her best blue-and-white laced dress, which my mother had bought for an insane amount of money from somebody who had brought it from abroad, and which was only worn on very special occasions.

I called her name; she stopped abruptly, as if not believing what she had heard, then slowly turned toward me. I repeated her name again, and started walking toward her. My doubts disappeared when Nadia ran toward me and jumped on me, grabbing my shoulders and almost knocking me off my feet.

"There are three weeks of school left, Nadia, darling... You must go home with me, honey, and finish your school year, and then we'll go to Akademgorodok, to Grandma. And why did you ruin your best dress? There won't be another one like that, ever—and now you will have nothing to wear to your friends' birthday parties..."

Someone inside me was whispering that I was saying all the wrong things—but I had been too shocked by the events of previous three days and did not have any time to think, or even to collect myself. Nadia's hold of my body weakened. I tired to meet her gaze, but she was now looking down at her feet. I started kissing her on the head, hoping that she would lift her face, and I could give her more kisses, but she did not move. We stood like that for a few minutes, none of us seemed to know what to do or say next. Then, as in the worst nightmarish dream, my little girl who had just turned seven, too short and slim for her age and even thinner because of the recent illness, looked at me with a childish contempt, and said with her father's intonations:

"You let me go, you, stupid dirty whore. Go back to Moscow to your fucker. I don't want to go to your boring school and I will never live with you again. It's none of your business what I wear: it is my dress, and you just go back to your fucker and leave me and papa alone."

And, running away, with the Gosins' girl by her side, she cried, this time in her normal childish voice:

"And I will never, ever go to Israel with you! I hate Israel!

* * *

"You two should talk alone now," said my father when I, crushed and exhausted, returned to the house. "Your husband and I had a reasonable conversation. He has a point that it is between you and him, so your mother and I should stay out of it. I told him it is nonsense about Israel; you're not planning to emigrate anywhere. And Nadia needs to finish school. I'll go take a half-an-hour walk in these woods; you and I can leave when I return. Hopefully, the two of you will have agreed on something reasonable by then."

I thought that it was a very bad idea and tried to stop my father from leaving, but it was too late: he had already walked away, making seven-mile steps with his long legs, like a magic runner from a fairy tale.

"Let's go inside, we don't need too many witnesses." Lev grabbed my arm with an iron hold, and pushed me into the house. Besides the Gosins, he had two more guests that day, and these guests followed us silently, like two shadows. They were handsome bastards, tall and strong, both not older than mid-forties. A year ago, when Lev had just started building his house, he introduced them to me as his construction crew: they were engineers from the nearby town of Obninsk, who wanted to make some extra money on weekends by helping Lev.

Those two had built Lev's house. They may have participated in stealing logs, pipes, electric wires, iron sheets for the roof, and whatever else was needed for the construction. They had intellectual faces, so they indeed must have been educated people, engineers, not some blue-collar workers. And now, when the house was finished, they were visiting Lev as his guests and his friends. Were they single—or had they left their wives at home? In either case, their presence was strange—and spooky.

The first floor of Lev's home was not livable. It housed the toilet, the village-style *banya* (steam bathing room with a wooden stove), furnace, and some storage space. It had a dirt floor; strong oak pillars, dug deep into it, lifted the second floor above the ground.

Lev locked the front door behind us. The expression of his face clearly indicated what would happen next. I knew that the Gosins were standing right outside the house, and swallowing my pride, cried for help. Someone pulled the door from outside, but, as I said, it had been already locked from inside. Then I heard Marianna's voice ordering:

"Oleg! It is their family business, we must not interfere. Let's go see what the kids are doing."

That quiet bitch, always preaching obedience to one's husband, was not that quiet and obedient after all. And Oleg, a war hero, many-times decorated veteran, followed her order like a child. You learn amazing things about people in critical situations. And I used to consider those two my true friends...

* * *

Lev's first blow hurt me less than the pain caused by the Gosins' betrayal. He was beating me slowly, silently, aiming carefully, almost getting out of breath not from the physical effort, but from the incredible hatred that was suffocating him. His two friends stood silently between us and the door leading to the outside world, watching. There was no point in screaming or calling for help, so I was silent too.

"Do you realize that if your father were not close by, you would remain right here forever, bitch?" Lev pointed to the dirt floor. "Soft ground—it would make a nice deep grave... Nobody would ever find out where you are..."

He stopped beating me—or was he taking a break? His face was tense, but calm. I was sure he meant what he said. (How could my mother have been so perceptive?) I looked at his friends: they were nodding approvingly.

"And you perfectly deserve it," said one of them. "Lev told us everything about what kind of a whore you are…"

"And of course, you believed his every word!" I said, catching my breath. "Don't you think there are laws in our country, which prevent people from getting away with murder? Especially people who have already…"

The two men laughed. Their laughter sent chills through me and was much scarier than the beating. "How long has my father been gone? What if he never comes back?" was the hysterical thought flashing through my mind. That semi-dark basement with the dirt floor would have been spooky even without the three men who wanted to murder me. "I must not show how scared I am. It will only make things worse…"

"Laws? You'll have your laws in Israel… if you ever get there! The law here is *us!*" said one of the engineers.

"Don't you know that the local police inspector and the district judge are here every other weekend, enjoying Lev's *banya*? Lev has lots of friends in the area, who will—same as Pavel and I—testify to everything he asks us. In any court. And you must know that judges tend to trust people with PhDs… Now, have you learned your lesson, or should he beat you more?"

Lev must have decided that I had not learned enough. He hit me again, and again, and again. I fell on the ground. Never in my life had I felt that helpless, that scared, and that full of hatred. Hatred obstructed my breathing even more than the pain. I hated Lev, hated the engineers, hated the Gosins. I hated my father almost as much as all of them, for having left me alone here. And, the most horrible of all, I hated Nadia.

I don't know how long it lasted. It was finally over. Somehow, I was able to get off the floor by myself and walk out of the house on my own feet. The bright sunshine dazzled me. I looked around in despair: my father was nowhere to be seen. I had no idea which way to go to look for him. There were woods and fields around, and he could have gone anywhere. Panic was growing inside me, when I finally saw him appear on the edge of the woods. I waved and started walking toward him, surprised that I could still control my body. He waved back and picked up his pace. We met on a deserted path several hundred yards away from the house and double that distance from the village.

"Finished already? Did you have a productive talk? Where is your daughter—isn't she going home with us?"

I looked at my father in amazement. Was he blind? Couldn't he see that I had been severely beaten? He had never had vision problems...

"What did he say to you?" He asked again, expressing no concern. "Lev must have become more reasonable as soon as he has learned that you aren't planning to go to any Israel..."

I was wearing jeans, so I could not see my legs. But I looked at my arms: no bruises whatsoever. Apparently, there were none on my face either. *Butyrki technique*. Lev must have remembered it. Remembered it, two years after he had left the prison... Simple "muscle memory"? Or had he been practicing it?...

"It was not about Israel, Papa," I said wearily. "And he is not going to let us take Nadia home. We must get out of here at once. And don't you dare to leave me alone any more, even for one minute!"

The only path to the main road led past Lev's house. Feeling safer next to my father, I walked slowly, hoping to see Nadia. I had no idea what it would achieve, but I could not just leave like that, without at least making an attempt to talk to her one more time...

My daughter was nowhere to be seen, but we ran into Lev. He stood in the middle of his large vegetable garden, like a landlord inspecting his property. He sounded almost friendly when he said:

"I'll give you a ride to the train station. There will be no bus to Obninsk for another two hours, and if it is full, it may not even stop. I don't want you to miss the last train and spend the night at the train station. I am doing it for your father, not for you," he turned to me, and the familiar scary light in his dark brown eyes flashed and disappeared before my father could see it. "Don't try to look for Nadia, by the way. She is inside the house with the Gosins, and they will not let her out until you are gone."

I attempted to refuse the ride, even though I had no idea how I could possibly make it on foot all the way to the bus route, but my father insisted on accepting it. Lev and I spent the next forty minutes together in a small vehicle, cursing and scolding each other in a language not suitable for printing. The hatred that we generated overheated the air inside the car and the dirt under our tires. By the end of the ride, even my excessively optimistic father realized that we were unlikely to ever make up.

I hardly noticed the train ride to Moscow. I was crushed, completely defeated, stripped of human dignity. I had lost my child. My situation was too grim to think about. Until I suddenly saw my husband's face, deformed with hatred, and heard his hissing voice: "It's because of you, f-ng whore, that I spent three years in prison… but don't worry, I'll make you serve a longer term—so you'll learn what I've been through…" And, instead of fear or anger, I felt surprise: Lev Fedorov did not sound like a winner. The winner would have expressed cold contempt; instead, he was overwhelmed with hatred.

* * *

When I woke up in the middle of the night, safe in my Moscow apartment, with my father snoring in the next room, a different phrase of my husband's sounded in my head. Those were the words I had heard in the basement of his house, resonating from the dark logs of its walls and the dirt floor:

"*You'll have your laws in Israel. If you ever get there…*"

Until that day I had never thought of emigrating—to Israel or to any other country. Lev Fedorov may have left me no choice…

7

The next morning, I handed Perlov my letter of resignation. There was no point in going back to Tretyakovka. Natasha moved to her new job within a week after Garik had left, taking Aleftina with her. Perlov immediately filled the positions with some shady friends of his, who were obediently serving him like well-trained dogs. The whole crew, including the formerly friendly Communist, simply ignored me. They discussed work, had tea and coffee breaks, walked around the room, and made phone calls as if I were not there. I came in to the office, turned on my computer and played with the museum's new information system, unable to change anything or even ask questions. Nobody wanted my comments, my suggestions, or any input I might have been able to give. To make the situation even worse, the office soon moved into a new building. Suddenly there was no room for me at all: not only did I not have a computer, but not even a desk. I tried to talk to Perlov, but got a blunt answer: "And what are you doing here that you need a computer or a desk?" Complaining to the management is not popular in Russia, and has never been my thing to do. Besides, the management was already aware of the situation, and was entirely on my side—not that it could help...

About a week after Garik and Natacha had left the museum, I ran into the assistant director of the Tretyakov Gallery, who also was Natasha's personal friend.

"Why...why are you still here?" asked that nice woman, her eyes round from surprise. "Hasn't Natasha found you another job?"

"Natasha *promised to* find me another job," I answered undiplomatically. "Unfortunately, she never did..."

"You must find something immediately, or Perlov will *make* you leave," whispered the woman conspiratorially. "I shall call Natasha tonight. Actually, why don't you stop by in my office around five this afternoon? I'll try to think of something for you."

That conversation happened less than two weeks ago—but it belonged to a different historical epoch... At that time, I still had my daughter—and even in my worst nightmares could not imagine ever losing her... It was the following day that Nadia developed rash and fever—so I was conveniently on paid sick leave, and did not have to come to the office. I thought that time was on my side: Natasha and her friend could be looking for a new job for me while my daughter was getting better. But now the holidays were over, and Natasha had called with apologies that she was still looking...

In spite of Perlov's harassment—or maybe exactly because of it—I had decided not to leave Tretyakovka until I found new employment: I wanted to resign on my own free will, rather than giving in to anyone's pressure. But the events of the last few days had broken my strength for resistance. Perlov signed my request immediately, waiving the required two-week waiting period and not even trying to conceal how relieved he was.

I walked out of the museum's administrative building, leaving only ruins behind me where once a beautiful building had stood. I had no idea what work I could possibly do, except picking up more Hebrew students. But first of all, I had to file for divorce from Lev Fedorov.

* * *

Two days later, I was in Leningrad. The woman in the district ZAGS archive had taken my passport and was searching through the volumes of documentation, looking for my marriage records. Through the open door I could see the ceremonial room where seven years and five months ago, in the presence of our best friends, I became the wife of Lev Fedorov. I must have been happy then... Incomprehensible as it seemed now. If I had only known...

If I had known—then what? I would not have married Lev Fedorov... or would I, still? Having an illegitimate baby at the age of twenty-three? I would not have had the courage—or would I? Legally, there was no concept of "illegitimate child:" all children were equal under Soviet law. Single mothers even received some privileges from the government. But socially? No, not with my mother. And not with all the talk that such an event would have generated in my home town. "Anya's boyfriend did not want to marry her... He left her pregnant!" "Why did she get pregnant then?" "She must have thought that he would marry her for sure that way, but it did not work out..." I would have never been able to come to Akademgorodok after that...

"Did you say you wanted a copy of your marriage certificate?" The archive clerk turned away from her book. The strange expression on her face increased my uneasiness.

"Yes, I want to file for a divorce, but I can't find my marriage certificate."

"Then you're in luck," said the woman, looking at me half suspiciously, half pitifully. "Your marriage was terminated a year-and-a-half ago. Here is the record."

She pushed the heavy book on the counter in front of me, and I read: "The marriage between ... terminated on December 8, 1987 by the court of Zhukovsky District of Kaluga Region..."

"That's where you should go to get your divorce decree."

"Oh, no," I cried out. "I can't go there! I have no idea where the damn place is, and I will never go to that area anyway..."

"Oh, wait a second." The woman was now fully sympathetic, convinced of the sincerity of my ignorance. "It was your Moscow district court that made the decision to terminate the marriage. You should go there first—they might be able to issue the divorce certificate for you."

* * *

I was in no rush to leave Leningrad to return to my empty Moscow apartment, so nearly a week passed before the afternoon when I was sitting in the district court, flipping through pages of my thick divorce case. Clipped to the front page was a notarized form in which Anna Fedorova gave permission to the court of S* district of the city of Moscow to conduct hearings on her divorce case in her absence. There was my signature, and the date *December 5, 1987* at the bottom of the form. The court hearing took place on Monday December 7—the next work day, and the divorce was granted. Lev Fedorov must have been in a big rush. I wondered how he had managed to have it all set up in court without having my permission in his hands. Was the judge a friend of his friend? Or was she a woman whom he managed to charm? In any case, my signature was real and the divorce legal. I just could not imagine how I could have forgotten...

* * *

A year-and-a-half ago...

That evening Lev had been friendlier than usual. He told me stories about his childhood, laughed with Nadia, and even helped to clean the kitchen after supper. He was that warm and cozy Lev Fedorov who, had he always been like that, could have probably made me happy again. And then he asked me to go to the notary tomorrow morning and sign that paper. Nadia had just gone to bed, and we were alone in the kitchen.

"I hope you have guessed that our income does not come from my ninety-ruble a month forester's salary" he said matter-of-factly. "Come on, stop looking at me like that! You're a smart girl, you must have known it all along! If I get caught... I hope I'll be able to get out of it, but I am not willing to risk losing our new car, or whatever else *we* have now, for that matter... And I don't want you to be dragged through courts and investigations again. If we're divorced, no one will bother you, or touch your property. Don't you see how much I trust you?"

That was exactly what did the trick: Lev's trust. Other than that, I hated the entire situation. If my husband wanted to mix himself up with the criminal world, it was his business. I tolerated it, as long as he kept quiet about it and I could pretend I knew nothing. I did not want to get involved. Neither did I want a divorce, not even a fictitious one. I had paid a high price for the status of a married woman, and I was not ready to give it up that easily.

"Nobody will ever know about that divorce," Lev reassured me. "Nothing will change in our relationship. You'll keep the same last name. None of us will ever bring it up, unless I am arrested. Which, hopefully, will never happen... But I am asking you—just in case... Please, do it for me!"

And, of course, I "did it for him." I signed that notarized permission, as I later did with the sale of the car, without asking any further questions. Now, whom could I blame for that?

* * *

Lev left for the village the next day. He never mentioned the divorce again, or told me what he had done with my notarized permission. When several weeks later I finally asked, he just shrugged his shoulders.

"I never used it. Sorry you had to waste time sitting in line in that notary. You probably remember that I had to leave early the next morning. When I went back to court the following week, the judge was out sick. The next time the line was too long, and I could not wait. And then I simply had no time to go there. Your permission expired after two months, so I ended up throwing it away. No, you don't need to sign another one: I've made other arrangements, so that our property will not be affected. Besides, it is unlikely that I will ever get arrested. Too unlikely to justify going through the divorce, even a pretend one."

And I believed Lev Fedorov. Or maybe I just did not care enough to think about the divorce: there were too many other problems in my life.

* * *

"My wife left for Leningrad in September of 1983, taking our toddler daughter with her. During my imprisonment between March 1984 and April 1987, she lived with another man, and in fact created a new family. She never visited me in prison, or sent me any letters. Since my release this past April, she and I have had almost no contact. This divorce is a mere formality, legalizing the status of the relationship that has lasted for four years..."

No... That's not it... I don't care about my husband's testimony, and what lies he told about me during the court hearing... Ah! Here it is: "The mother has physical custody of the couple's only child Nadezhda Fedorova. Child support is being paid voluntarily..."

Ok, I did have physical custody—so what was the problem? Why did Lev think that he could keep Nadia in the village and deny me contact with her? I guess I needed to consult a lawyer... A lawyer, again? How many lawyers could a person have during one's short life? And where would I get the one I could trust?

8

"Poor girl! As if you haven't suffered enough..." Svetlana Semenovna's voice over the phone expressed so much sympathy that I almost broke out crying. "Fedorov never deserved you—and you should have left him long time ago... Well, I must not say that..."

Svetlana Semenovna was the only lawyer I knew in Moscow, the woman who had defended Lev and stayed by my family throughout all the years of his imprisonment. But she was also a friend of Oleg Gosin, so calling her was hard. I finally forced myself to dial her home phone number that I used to know by heart. She grasped the issue immediately, but as I had feared, could not help.

"You are correct: I am a criminal lawyer, and have no experience in family law. But this is not the main reason I can't take up your case: I used to defend your husband, and professional ethic forbids me from acting against him. Never mind that he is one hundred percent wrong. However, I have a couple of friends... Wait a second... Yes, this one will be the best for you. Here is the address, and I believe he is in his office tomorrow morning. I'll call him right now; I'll make sure he'll be expecting you and does everything possible..."

Naum Ilyich had one of those faces you trust from the first sight. I would have been comfortable with him even if he had not been a friend of Svetlana Semenovna. Of course, without Svetlana Semenovna I would have never found that humble middle-aged man among thousands of Moscow's legal consultants.

Although the lawyer spent much more time with me than a random person who walks in from the street could count on (for a standard two-ruble fee), he was not able to say anything encouraging.

"It would actually be better if your ex-husband had physical custody," said Naum Ilyich. "Then you could go to court, and demand that it be changed. Now there is nothing for you to go to court for, and therefore, no need for attorney."

I did not understand, and he explained:

"The court cannot order an arrest warrant against your husband for kidnapping your daughter: he is her biological father. In theory, he should not have taken the child out of town without your consent, but Moscow police are not going to chase him in a god-forsaken village in the Kaluga region, just to return the child home. The court cannot grant you physical custody, because it has already done so. If there were reasons to deprive your husband of his parental rights, I would gladly represent you. Unfortunately, I don't see that being a viable option... Try the Department of Education: you might be able to make a case out of the fact that your daughter is missing school; after all, the academic year is not over yet. I am not very optimistic, but..."

* * *

A friendly middle-aged woman in the District Department of Education was sympathetic, but could not offer any reassurance:

"It is the end of the school year. By the time we get the case going... You know how slow our bureaucracy is? Anyway, it will be school vacation long before we can even start anything. If your husband does not return your daughter by September, then the case will look different. He will at least have to submit proof that she is enrolled in a local school: our country has compulsory education for children under six-teen, and that law is strictly enforced."

"But... what if he does submit such proof?" I asked, feeling tense in my stomach and cold all over my body. "There is no school in the vil-lage, but he might send her to a boarding school in the district..."

"Then it will be hard for you to get her back," replied the woman sympathetically. "There is no law that all children have to go to school in Moscow."

But in a minute her face lightened:

"You know what? If she is in a boarding school away from her fa-ther's house, you will just go there in the middle of the week, and take her home! You are her mother, so the school administration will not say a word!"

At the end of May, September appeared to be an eternity away. I could not imagine how I would survive the long summer without Na-dia, or even knowing that she was ok... And even if both of us were still alive in September, taking Nadia from the boarding school would not be easy. Judging by our last encounter, she might simply refuse to go with me. Besides, her father could very well produce a false affidavit stating that his daughter was at a boarding school, while in fact keep-ing her in his village—or in some other village, for that matter...

Has Lev Fedorov won? "No!" cried a voice inside me. "He cannot win like that! He is too evil; God will not let it happen... If people like Lev Fedorov start winning, what will become of this world?"

"Kidnap the child back! Just kidnap her from Lev, the way he kid-napped her from you—and hide in Akademgorodok, with your par-ents—" These were Svetlana Semenovna's last words during our phone conversation. It was the best advice my lawyer could give: the advice of a friend.

* * *

Later I could not believe that the entire nightmare of Nadia's kid-napping lasted no more than three weeks. It seemed more like three years, and it was that summer when, at the age of thirty-one, I noticed my first gray hairs.

The rescue operation was short and simple. My mother, having hastily completed her errands in Leningrad, finally arrived in Moscow. The next morning, taking a beautiful new doll that she had bought for Nadia, she set off for the Kaluga region.

"Aren't you afraid that Lev might try to murder *you*?" I asked, not really thinking that it was possible.

"No, he won't. He does not hate me as much as he hates you. Besides, he knows that you will call the police if I don't return home tonight."

My mother's confidence reassured me about her safety, but I did not understand what her visiting my daughter would change—except that I would learn that Nadia was all right. Would she succeed in persuading Nadia that her mother loved her and had not abandoned her for some other child? I did not know what to expect, and could barely believe my own eyes when, answering the doorbell at ten o'clock at night, I saw my mother and my daughter outside the door, tightly holding hands. In her other hand, my mother was carrying a bag with Nadia's clothes, while Nadia was hugging the grandma's new doll.

"It's all right," said my mother, when I almost cried after Nadia had pulled away from my attempt to hug her. "Right now, she needs a bath and sleep, and school tomorrow. There is one school week left; hopefully, she can still write her tests, and we'll be able to get the paper that she has completed kindergarten. You'll buy us the airplane tickets tomorrow, and the hugs can wait till we're all safe in Akademgorodok…"

A week later, my mother and Nadia left the damn city of Moscow on a non-stop flight to Novosibirsk.

9

The explanation of the miracle was simple: Lev, having proved his point, got tired of Nadia. Even sexual games he played with her in his village *banya*, eventually started requiring more efforts than they were worth. Nadia was one of those kids who needed to be entertained constantly—or else she became impossible. (She loved "*banya* games"— but Lev had limited time to play them, and even when he went through all the pains to prepare the steam room properly, he needed to make efforts to keep the games funny and his daughter happy—and he was not always in the mood for either.) No matter what he needed to do, the girl restricted his freedom. At first, he might have enjoyed taking her along on his day trips, but her presence became more and more constraining and annoying. He tried leaving her with the villagers, but there was only so much of that favor that he could ask from them.

As for Nadia, as soon as the first excitement of living in the village with Papa faded, she became bored. There were no other kids for her to play with, and no structured activities from morning till evening. Riding with Papa in his car provided some entertainment, but the trips were often too long for her, and she would get tired. Besides, he started leaving her in the village with some old people more and more often; they treated her well, but she was bored in their houses even more than in her own.

One fine day, a kind old fairy appeared on the road leading from the woods to the house. Like all fairies, she came unexpectedly, and exactly at the moment when she was most needed. It was Nadia's grandma. "Do you want to go with me to Akademgorodok? All your friends are waiting for you!" she asked Nadia, and the girl jumped for joy and cried: "Yes! Yes!" She ran to the house to fetch Papa, yelling at the top of her lungs: "Papa! Papa! Grandma came to take me to Akademgorodok!"

If Lev had been given a warning, he would probably have come up with some reasons why his daughter could not go. But his mother-in-law's visit was totally unexpected; he lost the momentum for resistance and had to give in to his daughter's pressure. Of course, Lev Fedorov would not have been himself if he had not laid down conditions: my mother had to take Nadia directly to Akademgorodok; his daughter was not supposed to spend any time "with that bitch her mother." My mother, being a good psychologist, sensed that her son-in-law was eager to get rid of the child, and firmly rejected his conditions. "My granddaughter is not leaving Moscow until she has finished the school year; you don't want her to have problems entering the first grade in September, do you?" Lev had to agree.

He drove them to the train station and made sure they got on the next train to Moscow. He must have felt greatly relieved of his burden, but unsure if he had proven his point enough. In any case, he knew that I would never dare to have Nadia live with me in Moscow again.

And the cards of letting or not letting me leave the country were all in his hands.

* * *

That was my saddest summer in Akademgorodok. Nadia was warming up to me, but very slowly. When, a week after I arrived, she asked me to fix a ribbon in her hair, I nearly cried for joy. A few days later, she made a more serious attempt to communicate with me.

"Mama, why are you constantly *pulling money* from Papa?" asked my daughter in an adult tone, copying her father's intonations.

She and I were walking to the doctor's office, and until that moment nothing in our conversation concerned Lev or the time she had spent with him.

"What... what do you mean by 'pulling money'?" I asked, astonished.

"I heard Papa telling his friends that you are constantly *pulling money* from him," she said defensively.

I took a deep breath. One other lie, that's all. I was sure my ex had an unlimited assortment of them; I should never allow myself to get surprised. I spent the remaining five minutes of our walk trying to explain to my seven-year-old the concept of child support, omitting the fact that, in Lev's case, neither he nor I bothered with the money; Nadia's father had too much unreported income, and even my law-abiding parents did not want a pittance that he was required to pay, based on his official salary of a forester.

* * *

My parents turned into my biggest enemies. I did not expect them to accept my decision to emigrate easily, but their reaction exceeded my worst predictions. After they had been so supportive of me just a few weeks ago, the change in our relationship was particularly painful.

My mother's first reaction was that I had not thought well. She scolded me as if I were a little girl, declared that I was even more of a hysterical fool than she had feared, and considered the issue over and done with. When I kept insisting, she first became annoyed, then scared. She tried to use her persuasive power to make me change my mind. After all, I knew nothing about *that world*. My information came from a few foreign movies and novels that probably had nothing to do with reality. There had been, indeed, a few success stories of people we knew, but they were all big families headed by a strong male. My parents had never heard of a woman emigrating alone, and especially of a single woman emigrating with a young child. I had no "real profession," and therefore no chance of finding a decent employment. I had a weak nervous system and would break down at the first hint of a problem. I would go crazy from poverty and loneliness. My parents would not be around to come to my rescue, and I would not only perish myself but also destroy my daughter.

I could find very few logical arguments to present my case to my mother. There was no way to explain to her that I was trapped in a dark long tunnel with no exit, except for one tiny slot that might lead to the light, that slot being a complete escape from my current life and preferably from my current self. If my mother worried about my sanity, she had to understand that, in order to stay sane, I needed to forget Lev Fedorov, Volodia Sonovsky, Tretyakovka—to leave behind my pain, my failures, my memories. I had to make one more attempt to start my life anew. I realized that I could fail, but I wanted to give myself a chance, slim as it seemed. Without that chance there was nothing left for me at all...

Whatever my reasons for emigration, my mother pronounced me "insane", and my dad repeated after her as a child. On the other hand, all of our family friends, including Yurivanych, were surprised by my parents' reaction: everyone knew how strongly they had always supported potential immigrants, and how outraged they were about the Soviet Government not allowing people to leave and return as they please. They could not see any logic in my parents' behavior, except that the idea was too new to them, so I needed to give my mother some time to process it.

That was a perfectly reasonable suggestion—although for a reason completely different from what most people thought: I knew that, as long as Lev Fedorov was alive, I would not be able to leave the country. I needed my parent's emotional support much more than their formal "permission."

My mother had an iron character, and when I was leaving for Moscow in August, she did not say as much as "goodbye". I declined my dad's offer to see me off to the airport: being stuck with him for a few hours only to listen to him repeating my mother's lectures seemed even more intolerable than going alone.

10

Returning to Moscow in early August was stupid: I came just in time for two farewell parties—but other than that, there was nothing to do. In terms of Hebrew teaching, it was still a "dead season:" potential students were all on vacations—at their dachas, visiting relatives in other cities, or bathing in the Black Sea; I was facing a period of a few weeks without any work—and therefore without an income.

My colleagues from *Igud haMorim*, the Hebrew teacher's Union, reassured me that there was a huge need for Hebrew teachers in smaller towns, so they could easily find me a short-term job in one of those places, if I was willing to relocate temporarily. That is how, less than two weeks after leaving my parents and daughter in Akademgorodok, I found myself teaching an intensive Hebrew course in Gomel, a charming provincial city in South-Eastern Belarus. I was as happy to get out of Moscow (which, unlike Leningrad, I always found depressing in summer) as getting busy teaching; the fact that the city was only 80 miles north of Chernobyl, the site of the biggest nuclear disaster in history, was the least of my concerns.

I lived in my own room with a balcony in the neat apartment of a middle-aged Jewish couple. They treated me as their family member, cooked the best meals for me, expressed deep interest in my personal life, and absolutely refused to take any money. In return, I had to teach as many students as they could find in their town, for as many hours a day as the students could afford.

I worked fewer hours than I had been hoping for, but enough to justify living in someone else's house. The weather was sunny and pleasantly warm. In the mornings before breakfast I took a brisk walk to the bank of the wide Dnepr River, famous from novels by Gogol and paintings by Kuindzhi. The huge park that bordered the river was empty at that time of the day. I would spend twenty minutes on rigorous exercise, and another half-an-hour swimming in warm, clear water, enjoying complete solitude. After the turmoil of the previous few months, that sudden switch to peace and serenity seemed like an undeserved gift from life.

Residents of Gomel, however, did not seem either calm or content. Three years after the Chernobyl nuclear explosion, the town still had a highly elevated level of radiation. It was too far from the site of the accident to deserve any kind of federal aid or even official acknowledgment as a high-risk zone, but the increase in health problems was more persuasive than the government's reassurance. People who had never thought of emigration started seeing it as the only escape from their radioactive home. The demand for invitations from Israeli "relatives" coming from that part of Belarus exceeded the capacity of the Israeli government to keep up. Many local Jews looked at a Hebrew teacher from Moscow as a savior with the power to rescue them from an unhealthy environment, collapsing social infrastructure, and uncertainty about the future. I felt awkward and embarrassed, but failed to convince anyone that I was an ordinary person who just happened to know some Hebrew.

A short heavy man in his early forties threw himself into a big armchair in my hosts' living room, unable to catch his breath after running up three flights of stairs.

"I heard you're here... from Moscow... I need the affidavit... right away. Can you make sure my family gets it as soon as possible? My daughter has terrible thyroid problems... Getting worse and worse after the explosion... You know, radiation. We must get out of here... to America, to Israel—anywhere..."

I had been told that the visitor was coming to arrange Hebrew lessons, and suddenly got angry. Those people did not even understand how unreasonable they were. To run away from anti-Semitism, even from a subtle and vague one, was a fair desire. But why should Jews have an advantage in escaping from the radiation? Were Russian, Belarussian, and Ukrainian parents less worried about their children's health, than the Jewish ones? Weren't their children developing the same thyroid and other hormonal problems? Chernobyl was the fault of a bad government and a tragedy for everyone. Instead of uniting to fight the consequences, people were looking out for themselves. And Jews were convinced that they should be entitled to the privilege of being rescued, while others stayed behind. Why?

* * *

"Why?" I have asked my former compatriots in America. "Why were we better than others? Nobody here talks about having escaped from anti-Semitism. I hear "bad economy," "collapsing health care," "inadequate pay checks," "poor housing conditions"—but were we in worse situations than non-Jews? Did we suffer more from the economic turmoil and unstable government? And, an even more serious issue: was Russia ever such a horrible place as Afghanistan, Sudan, Somalia, Sierra Leone, or hundreds of other places on earth? Half of the planet lives in worse poverty and in far greater danger than Russian Jews have ever had—why don't people from those countries automatically get "refugee status" to America just so that they can improve their lives?

I have never gotten a satisfactory answer to any of these questions. Asking them does not make me popular with my fellow immigrants, that's for sure. Neither does it make me feel better about myself. Am I using somebody else's space? Eating the bread that should have been given to someone more malnourished than myself?

* * *

"Why? Why? Why?" were clicking the wheels of the train taking me from Gomel back to Moscow. "Why are Jews convinced that they must have the privilege to escape, when everybody suffers equally? Why is radiation more harmful for Jewish kids than for others?"

"You have no right to judge these people," replied my inner voice. "Your child does not live in a radioactive zone; neither are you stuck in a small town with an inadequate food supply and lousy medical care. You live in Moscow—you are already privileged—and even you want to leave…"

"I do not want to leave my country," I argued. "I would love to stay here and work for its future, but I fear for my life. I am not running away from anti-Semitism, social injustice, or poverty. I must escape Lev Fedorov; he will never leave me alone. He'll destroy my child, and haunt me like a ghost wherever I go…"

"Are you the only woman in the world with an abusive husband?" asked my merciless voice. "You're going to use your Jewish ancestry as an excuse to run away from a man—but there may be others in similar situations who were not lucky enough to be born to a Jewish parent. Are you better than they? More deserving of salvation?"

And finally I had to give up.

"I don't care who is more deserving. Maybe, God is unfair too. He gives a chance to some people, but not to others. No one will ever know what's his rationale, if there is any…

But I do know one thing: if God gives you a chance, it is the greatest sin not to use it. And I will fight for my chance—for as long as I breathe…"

11

By early September, the panic caused by unleashed antisemitism (probably, the direct result of "Glasnost"), crowned by rumors of impending Jewish pogroms, combined with the quickly deteriorating economy and a fear of more nuclear explosions similar to the one in Chernobyl, brought Jewish emigration to its peak. Most of those emigrants wanted to study Hebrew "at home," and come to the Land of Israel as prepared as possible. I now had no shortage of students, and could form as many groups as I wanted.

My total income from Hebrew teaching soon exceeded my father's salary, despite his two government jobs and *doctorate of science* degree; nevertheless, in the eyes of the authorities I was still unemployed. The situation concerned me: sooner or later I would want to find an official job, and my interrupted work records would result in huge reduction of benefits. And what if the authorities decided to question me now about my source of income?

Dima Osotsky, my friend from ODIKSI and its soon-to-be chairman, proposed a solution. He knew a nice Jewish guy in the process of starting a new cooperative company. Among many other activities, the cooperative would organize Hebrew lessons. If they hired me as a teacher, I would still be working at home at my convenience, but registered with an official company. Taxes? I wouldn't have to report all of my lessons, just a few. Dima was sure his friend and I would reach an understanding.

One beautiful sunny morning in early autumn, I met my new boss in a small garden adjacent to a subway station. Dima briefly introduced us and left: unlike me, he had an office job that required his physical presence. His friend, a six-foot tall thirty-one-year-old athlete, did not match my idea of "the boss". We shook hands, and sat down on a bench under a big lime tree. The hiring process took a few minutes. We then engaged in a friendly chat, and parted an hour later with a feeling that we had known each other for years. I watched the strong tall figure of my new employer disappearing inside the subway station. He did not strike me as a serious businessman, but there was something far more important: I knew I could trust him. The feeling was even stronger, because his name was Igor.

* * *

In the Bulletin, I wrote more and more about refuseniks. The Soviet refuseniks' movement was then divided into two mutually-supporting, albeit separate, groups. The first group was formed by people like my friends Michael Levin and Boris who used to have security clearance and therefore were not allowed to leave the country for reasons of "national safety." One of the prominent cases I wrote about was Daniil Kumin, whose security clearance was over two decades old. (Daniil's wife, Irina, also a Hebrew teacher, soon became my good friend.) As a twenty-two-year-old college graduate, Kumin had the misfortune to spend a few days at the *cosmodrome* (i.e. space launch facility) at Baikonur, then a top security location. Many years later, the government of Mikhail Gorbachev not only "opened" Baikonur, but invited a team of foreign specialists to inspect it. Even after the international inspection, OVIR continued to reject Daniil's applications to emigrate on the bizarre premise that, while visiting the cosmodrome twenty years earlier, he might have learned some secrets of high importance...

The second refusenik group, formed in the wake of Perestroika, was more peculiar: it became known as *The Poor Relatives*. This was the group I would eventually join—so, forgive me if I spend a little bit more time on describing it than the history calls for...

Glasnost of the late nineteen-eighties went so far that it dared to reflect the problem in a popular movie, *Intergirl*. The heroine of that movie, a young Russian nurse, marries a wealthy Swedish businessman, and is preparing to move to Sweden to be with her husband. There is only one obstacle: according to Soviet laws, in order to leave the country, the young woman needs permission from her father. The fact that she has had no contact with him since the age of one, makes no difference! It takes the young woman lots of time, energy, and creativity to even locate her father. After the initial shock of meeting a daughter he had not seen for over twenty years, passes, the man demands a payment of three thousand rubles (a sum of money that the girl has never seen in her life) in exchange for his signature. Nothing that she says can persuade him to change his mind: three thousand rubles or you can forget your Swedish husband forever.

In the movie, the young woman eventually finds the money, pays the father, and leaves. In reality, however, those happy endings were rare. It was not unusual for fathers or ex-spouses to demand outrageous sums of money from the prospective emigrants. But no legal mechanism prevented them from denying the permission even after the money had been received. Therefore, those refuseniks suffered not only from their inability to leave the country: they literally became "poor relatives."

* * *

One of my first series of articles on the subject of *refuseniks' movement* was devoted to the family of Polina Peletsky, who became a classic example of the Poor Relatives group, almost their logo. The Peletsky's case, being obviously and outrageously unfair, was the favorite one of human rights activists trying to draw international attention to the problem. It later turned out to be one of their most successful cases—a great example of the power of a well-organized campaign.

Polina was a divorced woman in her late-thirties with twin teenage daughters. An English teacher by profession, she did not need an interpreter to present her case to the world community. Polina's parents and her brother emigrated to Israel when her girls were still babies. Polina could not follow them at that time, because of her husband's knowledge of "state secrets." Mr. Peletsky had promised to go to Israel with his wife and daughters—as soon as he could be reasonably sure that his past involvement in some high security job was no longer an obstacle to leaving the Soviet Union.

However, a few years later Mr. Peletsky changed his mind, and not only regarding emigration: he divorced his wife and married another woman. To make the situation even grimmer, he showed no interest in his own children. Naturally, Polina's desire to join her family in Israel became stronger than ever. Unfortunately, Peletsky must have decided that having *relatives abroad* would not benefit his professional career. He refused to let his ex-wife and daughters out of the country, and without his permission Polina could not even *apply* for emigration. Soviet courts would not take up cases like that, since they were considered "family affairs." Child support was deducted automatically from the father's salary—but that is where government interference ended.

And that's where the refuseniks' organization stepped in.

Polina and her two daughters started with individual demonstrations. Everyone viewed one-family demonstrations as an outcry of desperation, requiring courage and self-control even from adults. Polina's fourteen-year-old daughters may not have been the first children to join their parents in an active protest, but the struggle took a hard toll on them. One of the girls had a nervous breakdown after a police officer had threatened to send her to juvenile prison. Her sister and her mother continued demonstrating without her. When none of the girls could take it any longer, Polina would go to weekly demonstrations alone.

In the comfortable living room of Polina's neat apartment, I studied the posters her children had carried in front of foreign embassies and Soviet government offices: "Mr. Peletsky: you're not our father. Stop tormenting mama and us!" "We don't know you, Peletsky! Let us go to our grandma in Israel!" I thought about the psychological damage the children must have suffered. Being abandoned and betrayed by one's father is bad enough, but having to confront him in front of the whole world seemed to me even more devastating than fighting the government.

But there were the girls' photographs in foreign newspapers and magazines. And there were endless interviews with Polina by foreign journalists. Every visiting Western official in Moscow had the Peletskys' case on his list of questions to discuss with the Soviet authorities.

There was hardly a week when the minister under whose jurisdiction Mr. Peletsky's employer fell did not receive a letter or a telegram from a foreign diplomat, senator, or congressmen about the "unlawful detention of Polina Peletsky's family in the Soviet Union". After the phone call from the Central Committee of the Communist Party, the minister must have decided that enough was enough. He picked up his phone and called the director of the company where Peletsky worked.

"Please, make sure I will never hear that man's name again," warned the minister. "He must either give his ex-wife the papers, or you will find a reason to fire him. But if I ever hear another word about this family..." The company director understood that the minister meant business. He summoned Mr. Peletsky at once.

"Either tomorrow you are signing all the papers needed for your wife's emigration, or don't bother coming to the office ever again. We'll find a way to lay you off..."

Laying off one of the company's top specialists is easier said than done, and the director did everything to avoid that extreme measure. The next morning, upon entering his workplace, Mr. Peletsky was met by the company's KGB representative and two members of the local Party committee. The three men escorted Peletsky to a car, which took them promptly to the district notary office where Polina was already waiting for them. Peletsky must have felt like a prisoner under guard; he was not permitted to leave the notary office until Polina had confirmed that all the papers were in order.

Officials in OVIR, probably following "instructions from above," were quick to make a positive decision about the emigration of the Peletsky women. Within a few weeks, Polina and her daughters had gone to Israel. Mr. Peletsky never expressed any interest in seeing his children, not even to say goodbye.

So, this is my (probably overdue) introduction to the Refuseniks movement. If you are still confused, go back to the Intermission after the Chapter 1, where the term is first mentioned. Or simply read on...

12

Anti-Semitism was on the rise. It happened in spite of Perestroika, or probably because of it. The former totalitarian government tried to keep everything under control, anti-Semitism included. The authorities decided how many Jews to hire for security jobs, or how many kids with Jewish last names to accept to colleges and universities, but those were secret decisions. The government proclaimed equality of all nations and nationalities of our great country, thus denying the very existence of anti-Semitism. Grassroots, or common, anti-Semitism was suppressed, driven underground just like samizdat literature, talks of it exiled to groups of close friends—or communal kitchens (remember my altercations with Klava?).

Glasnost that accompanied Perestroika changed it all. Soviet citizens were now encouraged to speak their minds on wide-ranging issues. People suffering from an inferiority complex could now mask their own imperfection by harassing Jews. That old scapegoat was all too familiar, and attacking it required no imagination. The year of 1988 started with a few cases of vandalism of Jewish cemeteries in Russia's major cities. A few months later, owners of Leningrad dachas, or summer houses, received warnings not to rent their property to Jews. Nevsky Prospect, the city's main street, witnessed one of the first unsanctioned demonstrations in the history of the Soviet Union; the demonstrators carried posters demanding expulsion of all Jews from the country.

The following year was greeted by placards with swastikas linked with Stars of David and with an inscription reminiscent of tsarist days, "Hit the Jews to Save Russia," displayed in Moscow and other Soviet cities. By 1989, Soviet Jews began to be blamed for the failures of Perestroika. During these new times of extreme economic privation, especially food shortages, the Jews, as usual, became easy marks. Complaints like "there is no butter because the kikes took it all to Israel" could be heard increasingly in long lines where frustrated, angry consumers fell back to attacking familiar targets. Jews who succeeded in new private, or cooperative, enterprises were called "profiteers" and "exploiters." For the sake of fairness I must say that wealthy Russians were also viewed with anger and even hatred, but those were healthy feelings, without nationalistic flavor—except for the cases when their less successful compatriots blamed them for being "disguised Jews".

So far, the threats were mostly empty. The very rare cases of physical assault against Jews were acts of hooliganism dressed for convenience in ideological garments. The government, however, did almost nothing to stop anti-Semitism from getting out of control, and that was the scariest thing of all. Rumors about pogroms periodically sprung up in Moscow and Leningrad, then died out, only to revive a few months later. I heard of a family whose Leningrad apartment was burned down in the middle of the night, after they had applied for emigration to Israel. Luckily, the owners were out of town, so no one was killed or injured. The police refused to investigate: there had been three other similar fires in the city that very night, all involving Jewish apartments, and the authorities clearly preferred to stay out of the sensitive issue.

* * *

It was late September of 1989, when I finally dug out the affidavit from an Israeli "aunt," requesting the Soviet government's permission to reunite with my "family" in the land of my Jewish ancestors. I had received several of those "invitations" from various imaginary relatives; all of them were neatly stored at the bottom of a drawer in my bookcase. I did not think I would ever use one, but kept them anyway—just in case. I attached the latest invitation to other papers required for the emigration application. Two critical documents were missing in my file: my ex-husband's and my parents' permissions. Then I took a subway to the district OVIR, and after having waited in line for only three hours, received a formal rejection from a young clerk in a military uniform. My papers were incomplete; he could not accept my application.

I walked out of the building feeling that I had taken an important, probably irreversible, step in my life: I became a refusenik.

* * *

"It looks like a totally hopeless case," said Yuri Semilevsky, the head of the Poor Relatives group. "We can fight your ex-husband, or your parents, but not all of them at the same time. I wish we could help you, but we can't take on hopeless cases. There are only so many failures we can afford, while still maintaining the prestige of our organization."

I was neither surprised nor upset by Semilevsky's response. My case was even more complicated than he thought: I was not even sure that I wanted to emigrate. I wanted to become a refusenik, and so I did.

I needed a support group that would at least know if something happened to me. I was ready to play by the group's rules, for the sake of membership. But I could not imagine Academician Alexandrov receiving phone calls from abroad about my father not letting me go to Israel. As for Lev, he seemed out of reach. There was nothing that international human rights organizations could do with a humble forester living in a god-forsaken village on ninety rubles a month salary—especially when that forester was the head of the local mafia.

"Nevertheless, that's what we do," replied Semilevsky. "If you don't want us to bother your father, don't even mention him. But give us the name and address of your husband's employer. The information about the local Party and Union officials would be helpful, too. Whether our campaign against him would help or not, I don't know. But if you want to be in our show, you have to play by the rules of the game."

And so there I was, back in the Kaluga region. That time, instead of going to Lev's village, I headed to the district center. I did not dare to go alone: Igor Koganov, my new "boss" and my friend, accompanied me. Nevertheless, nightmares of accidentally running into Lev Fedorov while on our mission had kept me half-awake for three nights.

In spite of my fears and numerous warnings I had given to Igor, everything went as smoothly as in a movie. Our taxi driver found the townhall without much difficulty. It was a modest two-story wooden building, with only a few rooms. Several bored women sitting behind their desks welcomed my appearance as a distraction from their routine, and were very friendly.

Did they know where the forester management office was? Of course, in that very building, the second floor, first door on the right. The forestry clerk was out sick today. Was there anything they could help me with?

I replied positively and told them my simple story. My ex-husband, the forester in their district, was not paying me child support. Getting tired of struggling with poverty, I decided to take him to court. The court understandably wanted the information about my ex-husband's employer: their address, phone number, the name of the supervisor...

The information was not a problem, responded the friendly women. Was I Mrs. Fedorova? How bizarre—everybody was sure that Lev's daughter lived with him in the village after her mother had abandoned her...

"No", I said, "That was just one more lie of your highly respected forester. I have never abandoned my daughter, and she has not set foot in her father's village since the end of May. Actually, she is with my parents in Siberia right now, but I still need to provide for her; daddy's child support would be of a great help."

"Oh! He makes much more money than his official salary," advised the women. "Several times more. Make sure the court takes that into account: you don't want to raise your child in poverty when her father has all that money... Just think of it: he told everyone that his daughter lived with him! Such a nice man, who could have thought that he was such a liar!"

After a few minutes of a pleasant walk, Koganov and I reached the district Communist Party headquarters, where I repeated the same story, with the same result. Friendly women clerks gladly provided me with all the information I needed. I even learned that the chairman of the local party committee was Lev Fedorov's best friend...

* * *

A few weeks later, I was standing in front of the Soviet Peace Defense Committee on an individual political demonstration. Yuri Semilevsky and his group had done their job; now it was my turn to do mine. Letters to appropriate district officials had been written and mailed; foreign human rights activists had my name of their lists.

I was alone, my child still too young to join me (never mind that she was in Siberia, guarded by her grandparents). Two support group members hung out nearby (but not too closely) with their cameras ready. The November wind went through my imported jacket exposing me to the winter chill, trying to rip off the posters hanging from my back and chest. "Further stay in the Soviet Union places my family in danger," read the front poster. "Forceful detention in the Soviet Union is illegal and contradicts international laws," said the back one.

Passers-by glanced at me contemptuously and walked on, paying no further attention. A correspondent from some foreign newspaper took my picture and left, looking for more important events to report. I felt as if I were chained to a pillory. "Half an hour. I must remain here for half an hour, no matter what..."

A policeman showed up ten minutes later. "May I see your permission for the demonstration?" "I mailed my request to the City Hall ten days ago, but I never received any response..." "Then you must leave right away." "But my demonstration was never prohibited. Here is my receipt for the certified letter to the City Hall..." "You are interfering with the public order..." "Not at all, I am just standing on the sidewalk. There is no law prohibiting citizens from standing on a sidewalk..." Standard responses used many times by others.

"You have to drag on for another twenty minutes," I kept silently talking to myself. "Don't get yourself in trouble. The support group may like seeing you arrested, but it must be an illegal arrest. You shouldn't give the authorities any reasons to say that you've been violating the law..."

So far, the policeman hadn't used any force; he had not even been verbally abusive. It was just a conversation. He had instructions, too. Ten more minutes... somehow it was less embarrassing to stand there arguing with the policeman than all by myself. "You'll leave right now, or I'll arrest you!" He sounded as if he meant it. Has it been half an hour yet? I didn't want to be arrested, regardless of what Semilevsky said. Lev Fedorov was not any more likely to let me go even if I became a world-famous prisoner of conscience...

I slowly took off my posters. The demonstration was officially over. The support group members looked at me disapprovingly. "Twenty-four minutes," they say. "You should have carried on longer, or let him arrest you. In any case, we've taken enough pictures. We'll send them to everyone who needs to have them. You'll get your copies, too..."

We walked to the subway station together. They made sure that nobody followed me, and then we parted, going our separate ways.

13

A very sad thing happened that winter: Michael left.

He called me one fine evening, and casually asked if he could stay at my place for a few days, starting tomorrow. Of course, I said "Yes." I would have been overwhelmed with joy, if not for the unusual situation that Michael was suddenly coming to Moscow. A presentiment of grief pinched my heart.

"Have you... received *the permission?*"

He hesitated before answering. He had probably planned to tell me in person, and was unprepared for such a direct question.

"Yes," he said simply, after what had seemed to me an eternity of silence.

"And when are you..." I had to make an effort to pronounce the terrible last word "...leaving?"

"Not for a while. We'll see each other again before then."

Oh, Michael, Michael! He always had to be unpredictable, and I hated uncertainty more than anything else in life.

"Ok, I'll ask differently. Do you have plane tickets?"

He hesitated again.

"Yes."

I should have stopped there. But something was wrong in the way my friend's voice sounded, as if the biggest and most important truth was still concealed. I should not even have thought of that, but almost against my will, my tongue asked the most inappropriate question:

"*Where* are you going?"

"I am not *going to* anywhere, I am *leaving from* here."

No, that wasn't what I wanted to hear. He should have laughed at my question, or even scolded me for assuming that he might be going anywhere except Israel. Hadn't the Holy Land been his dream for most of his life? Hadn't he gone through years of poverty, humiliation, denying his family a normal life, for the sake of reconnecting with his people and his historical motherland? I remembered his endless statements that Jews who were given a choice to live in Israel but chose another country did not deserve to be called Jews, and that God himself turned His face away from them...

I was not sure why it mattered to me so much where Michael was emigrating to, but something very important depended on his answer. I should have waited until the next day, and tried again when he and I were together, but I could not stand having to wait that long.

"What's your destination?"

"Free world," he answered, confirming my suspicion even further.

"Misha!" I called him by his nickname. "I will know sooner or later — what is the point of avoiding the answer? Your tickets are from Leningrad to...?"

"...Vienna." I knew that he had to make an effort to say that.

My heart pounded, and then nearly stopped. Vienna was a transition point for Soviet emigrants going to the United States. The route to Israel went through Budapest.

"Why... why are you doing that?"

"Anya," he said softly, "You and I will have lots of time to talk tomorrow. Can you wait?"

* * *

Two days and two nights came and went too fast, and he was gone. Not yet to America, but only to Leningrad—eight hours of train ride away, but still to another world. We were very close during those two days, like husband and wife who are each other's best friends and most desirable lovers—only our union lasted for an incredibly short time. He returned to Moscow a few weeks later, to receive visas for his family, but our time together was even shorter. Before leaving, he asked me to come to Leningrad to say a final good-by to him.

I had never cried so much in my life as during that night in Michael's apartment, bare of furniture, but full of people, most of whom I had never seen before. Family members and guests alike, were busy packing miscellaneous things piled on the floor, while Michael's older sister worked her endless shift in the kitchen, serving fried potatoes with hot dogs and salad to those who got hungry, tired of packing, or just needed some distraction from the anxiety of departure and separation.

During the course of the night, I managed to neatly pack two huge bags, but my tears never stopped. They kept streaming down my face, until the collar of my blouse, and then the blouse itself got all soaked as if I had just come in from a heavy rain. After a while I stopped wiping them, stopped attempting to talk, and was just working like a machine, neatly folding shirts, sweaters, and trousers and trying to squeeze them into a suitcase as tightly as possible.

Soft white snow was falling outside, but the beauty of the night was wasted. In contrast to outdoors, the apartment was warm and brightly lit. It was full of people who loved Michael, people who would forever remain part of his life regardless of where he ended up living. I did not belong to that privileged group; I was a stranger there, an intruder into their close circle. People in the apartment may not have known it, mistakenly considering me one of them, but their kind words of support and encouragement almost made me feel worse. Michael was packing in the next room, but his physical presence did not change anything: he was already gone to a different world, having taken a piece of Leningrad and a huge chunk of my life with him.

At the end of the night, minutes before getting into a taxi, he found a moment to find me alone and hug me. It was four-thirty in the morning, and the winter Leningrad night had many more hours to go before turning into a gray empty day.

"I will call you from Vienna," he said.

"You will not have the money," I answered, not ready to believe in such promise.

"Hopefully, it will not be my last money. And if it is the last money... well, then it won't matter anymore, and I'll call you anyway."

The last frantic hours before departure were over, and Michael was again his normal self—calm, confident and slightly ironic. I finally stopped crying, not because the pain had subsided, but because I must have run out of tears.

14

Leonid Sotov, the head of the Moscow Jewish Legal Seminar and the current leader of the Soviet refuseniks, was holding a brief press conference in his apartment. There were about ten independent journalists, representing various unofficial periodicals, nervously taking notes. Sotov confirmed the worst rumors, which most of us had refused to believe: America had betrayed Soviet Jews.

The sky started darkening a year earlier, when in September of 1988 Washington revoked its several-decades-long practice of automatically giving refugee status to Soviet Jewish emigrants. Still, a majority of those who applied to the American Consulate in Rome, were granted admission to the United States. The unfortunate ones faced the choice of going to Israel, or returning back to the Soviet Union—the country that they had just left having burned all bridges. I personally heard of no one who was brave enough to come back, although I am sure some cases did exist. As I mentioned in the beginning of this book, the majority of emigrants who left Russia with Israeli visas, Jews and non-Jews alike, had no connection with Israel and no desire to live there. Their plans and hopes for the future were in the United States; Canada, Australia, and New Zealand accepted a small number of immigrants from the Soviet Union—but I was never able to figure out their criteria.

The panic changed from moderate to high when on October 1 of 1989 the Bush administration put into practice a new policy of admitting Soviet émigrés. For a long time, Washington had chastised Moscow for restricting free emigration. Ironically, now it looked as if it would be the American government doing most of the restricting—of immigration. Before that date, emigres from the USSR had been channeled through Vienna and then Rome. Yet after October 1, Soviet Jews wanting to move to the United States had to apply at the U.S. Embassy in Moscow, which would screen them and decide whether they qualify to enter as refugees. Moreover, the American government imposed a ceiling of 50,000 immigrants per year. Washington claimed that under *glasnost* most Soviet Jews were no longer in danger of discrimination. Of course, the real reason for the restriction had nothing to do with "justice" and "fairness": it was a cold financial calculation. The cost of each refuge being approximately $7000, the U.S. could no longer afford to pay for an unlimited influx of Soviet Jews.

After describing that grim picture for almost an hour, Sotov unexpectedly ended on a bright note:

"But the State Department assured us that refuseniks would be exempt from the new rule... especially the long-term refuseniks. They will still need to go through the regular application process, but then it should be a mere formality..."

"And how do you apply to the American Embassy?" asked someone everybody's question. "There are tens of thousands of people eager to be interviewed. You can't just walk into the embassy and fill out a form..."

"That's what we are working on right now," replied Sotov. "Don't worry, I'll keep you informed of all updates..."

I was amidst those events, yet I felt as an outsider. My comrades' anxiety and despair touched me very little. I had no idea how strongly

I would prefer emigration to the United States over emigration to Israel: both options seemed out of reach for me...

* * *

The one-day hunger strike ended at five. It was nearly dark, but fresh snow made the world look lighter and brighter. I was slightly hungry, but felt reasonably good after a full day of socializing. About fifteen of us had spent the day in the apartment of the leader of the Moscow Women's Refuseniks Group. Women only: even the hostess' husband was at work. I suspected that the strike had ended in time so that, coming home after an exhausting day at the office, the master of the house could enjoy family dinner in peace and quiet. I had no doubt that his wife would join him for the evening meal. Most of the other strike participants would eat as soon as they got home. No one talked about it openly, but there was absolutely no point in going to bed hungry. It could not bring us any additional publicity, or make our case stronger. No one would know what we did after we left our meeting place. After all, we had done our duty: nine to five, the full day spent in a small apartment—with nothing except water. Not even tea. Of course, nothing had prevented the women from having a full breakfast. A few of them had arrived as late as nine-thirty, and even nine forty-five. You can eat an awful lot before nine-thirty in the morning.

My breakfast had carried me until almost three in the afternoon. It was probably the case with most of the other women, because exactly at that time our lively conversation started slowing down. But generally, we had a good time, the company compensating for the lack of food. Two of the participants had arrived from Leningrad, and one lady was our guest of honor from the United States. Ten years ago, she had also been a refusenik, but her family managed to escape Russia on the previous wave of emigration. She now came back as a visitor—a typical foreigner, except that she spoke Russian. The center of today's little group, she was bursting with stories about that wonderful world on the other side of our planet, where the land was flowing with milk and honey. The life that was hard to believe in, but yet real for some lucky people who managed to make it to the U. S. Life without lines in OVIR, refusenik demonstrations, food and goods shortages.

Like everyone else, I envied that woman. Unlike others, I did not envy the fact that she was an American, with pockets full of convertible dollars, free to board a plane and fly to almost any place in the world without as much as getting a visa stamp in her passport. I envied her stable family life, the fact that she had three children and a husband whom she apparently loved and could trust. I thought that a family like that was more than enough for happiness; I certainly would not have thought of any emigration, had I been in her shoes...

We were slightly disappointed that none of the foreign journalists had paid us a visit. There had been plenty of phone calls, though. Calls from the news reporters and human rights organizations stationed in Moscow, calls from our fellow refuseniks in other Soviet cities, even calls from abroad. We wrote an Appeal to the Women of the World, requesting solidarity and help. The American guest was the main editor of the English version. I thought that she had made a few grammatical mistakes, but my corrections were scornfully dismissed: how could I dare to think that, after living in the U.S. for ten years, a person could not know English as well as her mother tongue? I did not dare to think that, and shut up.

I had missed Irina Kumina, my only real friend in the Moscow refuseniks' world. She had to be at the airport early in the afternoon, to meet some foreign visitor who brought insulin for her husband, a long-term "secret" refusenik Daniil Kumin, who suffered from diabetes. She regretted greatly that she could not join us for the strike. She announced that she would fast anyway, and asked us to include her name in the list of the participants, and sign the petition for her. I thought that Irina was probably the only one who honestly fasted all day.

* * *

I reached the subway station, and suddenly felt depressed. A brisk walk in the crystal cold winter evening had kept my spirit up, and the chat with women walking with me distracted from unpleasant thoughts. But as soon as I was alone and motionless in a closed subway car, I could not avoid feeling that our "one-day hunger strike" was hypocritical and false. Worst of all, people who would publish our Appeal and write articles about our selfless struggle, perfectly understood the hypocrisy—but pretended not to notice it. Irina Kumina was almost certainly feeling the same. I wondered if that might have been the real reason for her absence.

"There is a lot of dirty politics in the refuseniks' movement," I remembered Michael's words. "Be careful!" It was easy for Michael to say, "be careful." He did not have to deal with Lev Fedorov's revenge...

15

Did I want to emigrate, or just be a refusenik? I asked myself that question periodically, coming to different answers depending on my mood. Generally, I tried not to think about it. Regardless of what I wanted, I could not imagine Lev Fedorov ever giving in to any pressure from the outside and signing the permission for me. The events of that winter confirmed my worst fears.

It all started with a phone call one quiet afternoon in the late fall. A pleasant male voice in the receiver asked to speak with Anna Andreyevna. He sounded informal, almost intimate, and when he introduced himself as a lieutenant of the KGB, I first thought it was a joke. However, it was, indeed, the KGB, wanting to "meet to discuss issues of mutual interest."

Being totally unprepared for that kind of offer, I gave the first answer that came to my mind:

"So, what's the problem? If you know my phone number, you must know where I live—come over, we'll talk here. I can even offer you a cup of tea..."

"Many thanks," the voice on the other end of the line answered politely. "I would not talk to you myself: there are other people in our department, better trained to do that kind of work. I am just trying to set up an appointment... And it has to be here—we prefer to talk to people on our grounds..."

"Well, I prefer to talk to people in my own house. I also have lots of work to do—so I have no time to waste on commuting in Moscow. Your guys get paid for your travel time, and I don't. You want to talk to me—you come here."

"You may regret your decision," said the lieutenant softly, before hanging up.

* * *

The KGB called several more times before I finally gave in. The last phone call came in early December, and it was from a major; they clearly had gone up in the ranks.

"Don't you want to see the letter that your ex-husband wrote about you?" asked the officer. "You understand, we can't bring it to your house: it's part of our dossier... But it might be helpful for you to know what is in it..."

Was he hoping to scare me, or counting on female curiosity? In any case, it was the curiosity that worked. I could not imagine Lev Fedorov having anything to do with the KGB, not even for the sake of avenging a woman who left him. Yes, I wanted to see the letter. I scolded myself for letting the KGB win so easily, but agreed to set up an appointment.

"Oh! Come right now! You don't have lessons at this time of the day, do you? It's three o'clock, it should not take you more than forty-five minutes by subway..."

"Ok, give me your address."

"That's not possible," replied the major. "Our address is a state secret. But I can give you verbal directions. Do you know where *Detsky Mir* is?"

And so, there it was—a gray-and-yellow four-story building at the end of Dzerzhinsky Street, across from *Detsky Mir,* Moscow's central children's department store. I must have walked past that building many times, without noticing it. I was told to use one of the side entrances, and since there were no outside signs, I hesitated about which one to go into. I finally pushed the heavy door and walked in, to find myself in a semi-dark hall that looked like a reception room of any other office building. The security guard asked my name, and without requesting an ID, disappeared into the back rooms. Two minutes later he emerged to report that major N* was expecting me.

He showed me into an office that, like any normal office, had a window, a large desk and even some plants. Two officers behind the desk greeted me rather informally. One was my telephone acquaintance

Major N*, the other one introduced himself as a colonel. I understood nothing about shoulder insignia, so he could have been a general or a sergeant—I would not have known the difference.

On my way there I promised myself that I would be relaxed and casual, no matter what, and at first it seemed to be an easy task. Sitting in a comfortable chair on the other side of the desk across from the officers, I got engaged in a conversation resembling a friendly talk much more than an interrogation.

The officers wanted to know more about my activities. What exactly were my duties as a member of the Presidium of ODIKSI? I was an active member of *Igud haMorim*—the Union of Hebrew Teachers—I must have been doing other things there, rather than just teaching Hebrew... And what were my connections with *Irgun Zioni?*

The last question annoyed me. They were so well informed that they should have known that no one in Chelnov's circle wanted to have anything to do with the *Zionist Union*, a new organization created by our fellow Hebrew teacher Tolik Goretsky. I never understood the politics behind the relationships of our Jewish leaders. Goretsky was a chairman of *Igud haMorim*, which should have automatically made him "one of ours." And I did not see any harm in creating an organization whose goal was preparing Soviet Jews for life in Israel. Nevertheless, since Chelnov and Osotsky, whom I proudly considered my personal friends, denounced Goretsky and his new Union, I had no choice but to look at it only as a journalist, coldly observing and reporting meetings and activities while avoiding any personal involvement.

"I am not familiar enough with the program and strategies of Irgun Zioni to make a responsible decision about joining the organization," I answered. "Besides, they are only a few months old, so their work is still to be seen..."

The officers seemed to have accepted my answer, but were not ready to dismiss me.

"So, you must have learned a great deal about *B'nai B'rith*—you joined their organization at the first meeting..."

That question was tougher. I had, indeed, joined B'nai B'rith a few weeks earlier, without doing any research or even thinking about it. It happened during one of the dinner receptions in café *Vltava* that I loved so much to attend. *Vltava* was one of the first private, or cooperative, restaurants in Moscow, and a very good one. Its convenient location in downtown, its cozy atmosphere, excellent service and, most importantly, the fact that the owner was a Jew preparing to emigrate (at some point, he was also my Hebrew student), made it a favorite reception place for Jewish events. Several nights a month the restaurant was closed to the public because of some private function. Very few people were privileged enough to receive invitations to those parties. I was probably invited to less than half of them, and I treated every such occasion as a great honor.

The food was always excellent and free; presumably, someone paid for it, but certainly not any of the participants. Soviet Jewish movements must have received good financial support from the international community. Some people whom I met there were my friends, or the ones I was hoping to become friends with. But many times, I saw guests who were so high up that I would not dare to approach them.

The reception for American B'nai B'rith leaders was one of those occasions. There was food, and wine, and speeches, and more food, more wine, and more speeches. The atmosphere was festive and relaxing, everyone talked to everyone as if we were all close friends. Someone (Chelnov? Osotsky? Or one of the Americans?) announced the evening to be the birthday of the Moscow Branch of B'nai B'rith, and everyone who was in the room lined up to sign their names in the new members' book. I had absolutely no choice but to follow everyone's example, and no reason to doubt that I was doing the right thing. A few minutes later, we all posed for a group picture. The photograph appeared on the cover of the next issue of the B'nai B'rith monthly magazine, where the creation of its Moscow office made headline news.

I had heard about the picture, but had not seen that issue of the journal. Until that fine afternoon when it was placed in front of me on the desk in a modest office of the KGB headquarters.

"You are a beautiful woman, Anna Andreyevna. And very photogenic, too..."

I had never been photogenic, but had to admit that the picture on the cover was one of the best I had ever had.

"Very flattering... good photographer..." I muttered, to win some time. "So, what's your question?"

"You seem like a reasonable person. What prompted you to join this foreign organization on the spot? Have you just given in to their cheap recruiting technique?"

"You are perceptive," I wanted to answer. "Actually, my friends were there—or people who are my allies and supporters, if 'friends' is too strong... I did what I felt right at the moment, and so far, have had no reasons to regret my action. It is rather flattering to see your picture on the cover of a foreign journal..."

"B'nai B'rith is a well-known international organization," I said. "I respect their goals, their program... and the people who support it. By the way, I did not come here to give you a report of my life that you seem to know better than I do. I came here to see the letter from my ex-husband. I hope you do have it—or I am leaving right now. We've talked enough, and I still need to prepare for my evening lesson..."

The officers turned to each other, as if hesitating whether to show me the letter. Were they playing a well-rehearsed game? I was just beginning to doubt that the letter existed, when the major produced three pages covered with painfully familiar neat square handwriting. It was a report by the man I used to love, adore, almost worship, for whom during some period of my life I was ready to die, addressed to the KGB. I read it as slowly as I could, trying to memorize every sentence. I had decided long ago that Lev Fedorov would never surprise me anymore, but that letter exceeded anything that I could have ever imagined. I knew better than anyone in the world, how much the author hated everything that came from the government. Yet he was writing as a law-abiding citizen, faithful and trusting, convinced that he was helping the authorities to fight high treason and possibly contributing to saving his country... Saving from?...

He listed every anti-Soviet book that I had ever had in the house. He quoted my phrases against the government and socialism, while totally omitting the fact that he himself had initiated most of the conversations that provoked them. Worst of all, he named people who used to come to our house, who read and discussed samizdat books and listened to the tapes of Vysotsky and Galich, and with whom he shared the bitter stories of his unjust imprisonment. He reported the Passover Seder in Chelnov's house as a "Zionist meeting", and described my teaching Hebrew as a part of a "Zionist conspiracy". I recognized my husband's style and heard his voice in every phrase, yet I still could not believe that he had fallen that low.

I read the letter twice, before reluctantly giving it back.

"Do you admit the facts mentioned in this letter?"

"I am not going to admit, or deny anything," I said. "We have not agreed on an interrogation. You invited me here for a discussion, right? Now, if you are interested in discussing this letter, I'd like to ask you how could the author know about those conversations and "Zionist meetings", unless he himself was a participant?"

"Mrs. Fedorov," said the colonel sharply. "Today's meeting is not to discuss your ex-husband. It is to discuss *you*. When your husband's time comes, we'll deal with him. Now, please, answer for yourself. What are the reasons that you want to emigrate from the Soviet Union?"

As if he wanted to prevent me from denying that horrible crime, he put several photographs on the table. Those pictures were in black and white, but large and on high quality paper. It was my November demonstration in front of the Soviet Peace Defense Committee. One could clearly read the poster hanging on my chest: "Further stay in the Soviet Union places my family in danger."

"Here's my answer to your question," I said, pointing to the sign. "Consider that the reason for my desire to emigrate. By the way, I wish I knew your guys were there—I would have felt less lonely..."

"Could you explain what you mean by "danger to your family"?" asked one of the officers, turning friendly again.

"You've just confirmed it by the letter you've shown me. Don't you agree that it might make a woman feel insecure?"

"Are you afraid that we are going to persecute you?"

"Oh! Not at all. *You* are not going to persecute me: it is 1989, after all, not 1939. I am far more concerned about persecution by my ex-husband. He will not let it go, and neither your organization, not the police are powerful enough to protect me from his revenge. I will not feel safe until I am out of physical reach of Mr. Fedorov..."

"Emigration is not an answer to this kind of problem. You can solve your family problems without reverting to treason!"

"Treason?" I acted surprised. "I thought this attitude toward emigration belonged to the past. Eduard Shevardnadze keeps referring to emigration as a basic human right that everyone in the civilized world must enjoy. And our current government is struggling to have the Soviet Union join the civilized world..."

"Shevarnadze is a politician," smiled the colonel. "And politicians say what is expected of them at a particular moment. Tomorrow your

Shevarnadze will be saying something totally different... Or maybe we will have another foreign minister, and then *we* will talk to you very differently..."

I thought the colonel was much closer to high treason than I. To say such things in front of his subordinate... I wished I knew how to respond to that. I wished I could have a telepathic connection with Michael: he would instantly think of some sharp, witty answer that would show the officers that they had gone too far.

"I do not know what happens tomorrow," I suddenly felt very tired. "And neither do you. However, as of today, Eduard Shevarnadze is the Minister of the Foreign Affairs of the Soviet Union, respected by the entire world. His statements are consistent with the general line of our Communist Party, which I respect and support. And the last place I expected to hear criticism of my government is the KGB headquarters."

"We are glad to hear that you respect the government," smiled the major. "Unfortunately, your actions do not quite support your words. By the way, do your parents know about your activities? Your father is a Jew, isn't he? A highly respected scientist, with a great job in Akademgorodok. He must be very supportive of his only daughter becoming a Zionist activist, isn't he?"

What were they getting at? Were they about to threaten me that my father could lose his job? I doubted that they had enough power; it was probably just a scare tactic. And what could I do, in any case? Tell them that my parents called me insane for wanting to emigrate, and stopped talking to me?

"My father does not know much about my life in Moscow, and does not support me, or even approve. Moreover, I am thirty years old, and I do not need my parents' permission, or approval, to do anything. I do not understand why you're bringing this up..."

"We do not want your father to have problems at work," was the response. "He has been with the Institute of Mathematics for so many years. It will be a disaster if he loses that job now, when he is nearing retirement..."

That threat was cheap, too cheap and too outdated to take it seriously. I looked the officers straight in the eyes, and said slowly:

"My father has many more years before retirement, and he is valued enough in his institute not to have fears about job security. And my so-called "activities" have nothing to do with his job: our country has a democratic government, and democratic governments do not punish parents for the misdeeds of their adult children, or vice versa. By the way, I'd like to use the bathroom. Would you show me where to go?"

The officers looked at each other as if my question was the most amazing thing they had ever heard.

"We don't have bathrooms in this part of the building," said the colonel. "All our facilities are *inside*, where only employees are allowed... I don't know if we can make an exception for you... Andrei Mikhailovich," he turned to the major, "would you kindly go and inquire if we can allow Mrs. Fedorov to use our bathroom?"

The major was absent for a good five minutes. The colonel apologized, and started reading some papers. The major finally emerged with the negative answer.

"Absolutely not possible," he said apologetically. "No one can be allowed inside the security zone, unless you have a special permission and a security clearance. But Anna Andreyevna certainly raised a good question. Indeed, we interrogate people here for eight hours in a row, and more... No one has ever asked to use the bathroom... But I imagine it can come up again, especially with older people... Should we bring up the question at our next staff meeting?"

"Definitely, definitely," agreed the colonel. "But now, Anna Andreyevna, would you mind answering one last question?"

"Yes," I said. "I do mind. Even if we had not been talking for over two hours, I still would leave now, to find a bathroom. I hope you don't consider me rude: I have been trying to do my best answering all your questions... but it is hard to satisfy the KGB!"

"Rude? Oh, not at all! You are a charming woman, Anna Andreyevna, and it's been a great pleasure to meet you. Unfortunately, you are a bit too stubborn. In any case, your dossier will stay with us forever. We are afraid that you will provide us with new material to add to it... Just remember: politics change—and next time you may not be able to walk out of this building as easily as today..."

When the heavy double doors closed behind me, I turned and looked back at the building that had horrified my country for decades. There was nothing special about it, nothing that would distinguish it in the architectural ensemble of downtown Moscow.

It was early evening: the sky had turned dark, but streets and squares were brightly illuminated. Fresh white snow glittered in electric light, making the city look festive. Nicely dressed people were going on with their errands, doing shopping, meeting friends, rushing to the subway stations. The world seemed peaceful, a stable and well-run place.

I had an hour before my evening lessons—more than enough to get home in time. I walked slowly to the subway station, trying to sort out my feelings. I did not particularly need to use the bathroom: I would have found one in the *Detsky Mir* if I had to, but I remember going straight home. I wanted to get out of the crowd, to spend at least a few minutes alone before my students arrived. I did not understand whether I was scared, confused, angry, or just very tired. One thing was clear: Lev Fedorov would not let go. However, the fact that he had turned to the KGB was reassuring: if he had been planning to kill me, he would not have written a letter that drew attention of the authorities to both me and him.

* * *

It was nineteen-eighty-nine, I reminded myself. Don't panic. Fifty years earlier, I would have disappeared from the face of the earth, followed by everyone mentioned in Lev Fedorov's letter. Lev Fedorov would also have disappeared, although probably not until the KGB had used him to arrest as many people as possible. Ten years ago, I could have been sentenced to a couple of years in prison, and my friends reported by my ex-husband would all have been interrogated, some losing their jobs, some possibly arrested. The case of Sasha Radzinsky served as a perfect illustration of the latter scenario. Today, I freely walked out of the KGB office, demonstrating the world's tendency to improve. Was the improvement irreversible? I doubted that God himself knew the answer to that question...

16

Early next morning, I called Leonid Sotov at home. There was an urgent matter that I needed to discuss with him, but I could not talk about it over the phone. The head of Soviet refuseniks, being used to these kinds of requests, immediately named the time and place where we could meet. Having made the appointment, I sat at my desk and wrote down my entire dialog with the KGB officers, as closely as I could remember. The only detail that I omitted was the name of the author of the report. I called him "someone whom I used to know well," and concentrated on other aspects of the meeting. I particularly emphasized the critique of Shevardnadze's foreign policies, and skepticism about Perestroika expressed by my interrogators, as well as on their threat that my father might lose his job.

I titled my little essay "The KGB during Perestroika." My typewriter allowed only five copies on thin paper. I gave the first two copies to Sotov that very afternoon. He complimented me for having informed him, and promised to make the case known to as many people as possible. A few days later, I gave another copy to Chelnov and the fourth one to Osotsky. They both found my story rather amusing, but promised "to give it to someone who would put it to use." We all agreed that there was no immediate threat from the KGB: it looked as if the officers felt increasingly insecure about their place in the society and their very jobs, and could only pray that the Perestroika failed. However, no one could ignore the KGB warning: *Times might change...*

Still, I was far more scared of Lev Fedorov than of the KGB.

* * *

Within a few weeks, the report of my unpleasant encounter appeared in a number of foreign periodicals. The KGB must have taken note of that, or maybe they found more interesting cases to work on, but they never bothered me again, and neither did they ever fulfill their threat to contact my father's employer. The letter that Academician Sergey Sobolev, the world-famous scientist and the director of the Institute of Mathematics of the Siberian Department of the Academy of Science, received regarding my father, did not come from the KGB; it came from Lev Fedorov.

The old academician was appalled. He handed the letter to my father with profound apologies. His first instinct had been to tear up that dirty piece of writing and throw it in the garbage basket. But then he decided that his duty as a human being was to warn my father of his former son-in-law's evil intentions. "If he hates your family so much, god knows what else he could write, and to whom. You should tell your daughter to be very careful…"

* * *

To be very careful… That was a good advice, easier said than done. Every time I walked from the subway station to my house in the evenings, I imagined Lev Fedorov stepping from behind the dark bushes, and chills went through my body. I dreaded unexpected rings of the doorbell, and always stopped and looked around me cautiously after entering the hallway leading to my apartment. But week after week went by, and Lev Fedorov did not bother me with his personal appearance. Neither was he inclined to let me forget about his existence.

A few days after the meeting at the KGB, I found an envelope in my mailbox, with the official stamp of the district probate court. The letter inside confirmed my long-term fears: it was a court summons, alleging that I had pocketed the money from the car that I had bought in the marriage with Lev Fedorov, but sold unilaterally after the divorce. My ex-husband was seeking his portion of 3500 rubles, the amount of money equal to about seven months of my father's salary.

The hearing was scheduled for the middle of January. The New Year being only a couple of weeks away, the timing for finding a good lawyer was not great. Luckily, one of my students had a friend, an experienced attorney who could take on a sensitive issue and would treat me informally. Two days later, I was sitting in the office of a young woman, very inconveniently located in one of the Moscow suburbs, two hours away from my house. The lawyer was understanding and sympathetic. She seemed to have fully believed me, but admitted that legally my case was very weak.

"It looks like your husband wants to make sure that you will never leave the country," she said. "From his point of view, it is a smart move to turn you from a politically oppressed person, a refusenik, to a criminal offender trying to escape paying her debt.

You will never be able to prove in court that your husband got all the money. Even if the judge believes you, legally your case can not be won. However, we can make sure your husband does not win either. How? I can drag this case out forever, until he gets tired and gives up."

"What if he never gives up?" I asked, not reassured.

"He will never get the money," said the lawyer. "And you will never have to pay. Of course, as long as there is a court case against you, you will not be able to leave the country, or even blame the government for a human rights violation. But you have other reasons why you can't emigrate right now, don't you? Why don't you keep working on them — and when everything else is resolved... well, if worse comes to worse, you'll have to pay him 3500 rubles... I know it is a lot of money — but people pay much more for the emigration papers."

17

Dec. 19, 1989 [7]

I should have kept a diary... So many events happened that winter, causing anxieties, stress, fears and hopes, that right now I cannot lay them out in any logical order. In my memory they are all mixed together, jammed, tangled in a conglomerate of emotions. As they move farther and farther into the past, trying to sort them out to create a coherent story is becoming an increasingly hard job.

I remember sitting in the Moscow Central Cinema. There is no movie or show on the stage, but speakers who replace one another. They talk about growing anti-Semitism in the USSR, new opportunities for Jewish cultural and religious practice, repatriation, and strengthening ties with Israel. I know approximately half of the speakers, but must catch the names and positions of the others. As a journalist, I am obliged to report the minutes of the First Congress of the Soviet Jewish Communities and Organizations. But I am also a delegate, Representing ODIKSI and *Igud haMorim*, with the right to make suggestions and vote.

Only two years ago the possibility of such a meeting seemed hardly possible, but Perestroika had been making seven-mile-long steps. There are about seven hundred delegates, representing nearly two hundred Soviet Jewish organizations and communities, and about a hundred foreign guests, from human rights activists to former prominent refuseniks.

The Congress's main organizational goal is to establish an open group that would coordinate the activities of Soviet Jews. By the end of the day, the delegates created a *Va'ad*, Hebrew committee, with my teacher Mikhail Chelnov as one of its co-chairs.

I am watching history happening, but feel almost no excitement. My mind is drifting away from the speeches and discussions to my lawsuit with Lev Fedorov, my encounter with the KGB, my emigration that will probably never happen, my daughter whom I have not seen since last summer, my parents who have not been talking to me because of my involvement in the very movement I am here for ...

The Congress concluded with a dinner reception. This time we met not in the modest *Vltava*, but in a fancy restaurant far beyond the reach of regular mortals. There seemed to be even more guests at the reception than there were participants of the Congress. The floor had several levels, and on each level, there were tables for six or eight, set with the finest china, and a buffet dinner with more entrees than a human being could possibly try in one evening. In the spirit of approaching New Year, an enormous pine tree was glittering with lights and ornaments in the middle of the hall, piercing the space through all levels of the restaurant. The orchestra was playing soft music, which contributed to the festive atmosphere but did not interfere with the conversations.

For a few minutes, I was wondering who was paying for all that—but quickly pushed that thought away: I did not need that information for my report in the Bulletin...

The central and lowest level of the giant hall was separated from the upper ones by a balcony, forming a small stage. The evening was not even half way through when a strange performance, like I had never seen before, began there: young men and women engaged in elaborate dance, were slowly taking off their clothes... Within about fifteen minutes they were all but naked, save for the tiny piece of silk covering the crotch—their bodies breathtakingly beautiful, almost unreal in their perfection. They continued gracefully moving to music, as if in a trance, unaware of their nudity or of several hundred people watching them.

I had heard of striptease, but always considered it belonging to the capitalist culture, unacceptable in our stern society. Had I moved into a different stratum not subjected to rules obligatory for common folks, or were we witnessing another sign of Perestroika?

That party was so unreal in its luxury, so beyond everything that I had ever experienced or even imagined, that I would now consider it a dream, if not for a conversation that happened there that eventually changed my entire life.

I was more or less enjoying myself, until a woman at my table named Zhanna, a Hebrew teacher and a long-term refusenik, mentioned an interview at the American Embassy that took place just a few days ago. As a result, about two dozen people received Political Refugee status, which gave them and their families the right of permanent residency and eventually the citizenship in the United States. She named several people in that group whom I knew well, but who had never told me anything about being invited to the American Embassy. Zhanna herself belonged to the second group whose interview was scheduled for mid-January.

Viewing my own emigration as some unrealistic dream, I had never thought about moving to the U.S. versus moving to Israel, but my colleague's story unexpectedly hurt me. My latest information about the possibility of immigrating to America came from the meeting at Sotov's home over two months ago. I remembered Sotov's statement that refuseniks would be exempt from the new restrictions, but I never worried about practical implications of that promise. Things, however, were happening right next to me, with me knowing nothing about them and with no one thinking of including me. Wasn't I a refusenik? Haven't I worked in the Information Bulletin, taught Hebrew, participated in Jewish meetings and committees, even gotten in trouble with the KGB? I felt left out and almost betrayed by people who called me their friend.

"How do you let Americans know that you want an interview?" I asked Zhanna, trying to sound as casual as possible.

"You do not let *Americans* know!" answered someone else at the table, amused by my ignorance. "You have to get on Sotov's list; he is the man who submits the names to Washington which, in turn, notifies the Moscow embassy whom to invite for an interview. Why, are you upset? Go talk to Sotov right now: he is working on the new list; he should be able to include you if you ask. You are a refusenik, after all, so you must be eligible!"

It was all too sudden. I needed to think whether I really wanted that refugee status. And I felt very uncomfortable talking to Sotov with all these people around. What if he turns me down? I had been a refusenik for less than three months; there were hundreds of others known in the West for years for their political activities and trouble with the government. Did I dare to hope for the same privileges as they had?

My feelings must have been quite visible on my face, because Zhanna gently pushed me towards the end of the restaurant where she had last seen Sotov. "Go find him right now! You don't want to miss getting on another list! Go, go—you must not be shy! Nobody will invite you for the interview unless you ask!"

It was not hard to find Sotov. Like Chelnov and other leaders, he was surrounded by a large group of people eager to talk to him. I reluctantly walked toward that circle and waited for my turn, feeling awkward, embarrassed, and fearful that Sotov would simply reject my request. Naked men and women down below continued their surrealistic dance, bending their bodies in almost acrobatic movements. I suddenly felt a sting of envy: they must have been so confident, so sure of themselves, never shy or afraid of failure, taking success for granted.

When I finally approached Sotov in the few seconds he was not talking with anyone else, he was friendly. Had the KGB bothered me again? He hoped not: his friends in the West were aware of my interrogation, and the KGB was notoriously afraid of publicity.

I swallowed the lump in my throat, and asked about an interview at the American Embassy. I tried to think how to accept Sotov's refusal with dignity, and hoped that no one overheard our conversation. To my surprise, Sotov's response was quite favorable:

"But of course! I was convinced that you wanted to emigrate to Israel—otherwise I would have included you in my previous list! But do not worry: it is not too late. I am working on the new list right now; it will go out to Washington at the end of January—just be around at that time, you'll have to fill out a long questionnaire. Somebody from my group will contact you.

No, you do not need to call me with a reminder. I do not forget things like that. Actually, I am writing down your name in my special notebook right now... Worry not—I am sure you will provide the

Americans with more than enough reasons to give you the refugee status..."

That's how easy it was.

18

For the New Year of 1990, I went to Akademgorodok. The prospect of spending the holiday with my parents did not appeal to me at all, and for a while I was cowardly thinking of going to Leningrad instead. But I had to see my daughter. Having packed a full suitcase with expensive gifts, I bought a plane ticket home—for the first time ever with my own, rather than with my parents' money.

To my surprise, my mother greeted me with her former warmth. Lev Fedorov's harassment had done the job—although almost certainly not the one he had been hoping for. My parents were scared out of their minds for me. The last straw was Aunt Olia's phone call, reporting the letter she had just received from my ex-husband. The letter started innocently as a New Year greeting, but concluded with the description of my terrible crime of infidelity and betrayal and the promise of a horrible revenge. I couldn't imagine what Lev had been thinking while writing it, but if he wanted to help me get my parents on my side, he could not possibly have done better.

"What if I won't get the refugee status to the U.S.?" I asked my mother. "The only other alternative is Israel—would you let me and Nadia go *there*?"

"I would strongly prefer that you two move to America," was my mother's honest answer. "But since that may not be possible... I'd rather have a live daughter in Israel than a dead one in Russia. If you manage to get out, I'll bring Nadia to the airport—in Moscow or any other city—just before you are ready to board the plane. Lev must not know about your departure. He will do everything in the world to prevent it, and kidnapping the child would be the best way to achieve his goal."

It was a far better New year than I had feared. Unfortunately, this time I could not allow myself to enjoy my family, my childhood friends, or my home town. I had to return to Moscow before Nadia's school break was over. In addition to impatient Hebrew students, my work in the Bulletin mounted like wet snow.

* * *

"Pamyat" in Russian means "memory," or "remembering." The group carrying that name appeared at the dawn of Perestroika, with the innocent program of the restoration of traditional Russian culture nearly destroyed by decades of the Communist rule. They were very critical of the Socialist Revolution and especially of Stalin. They were concerned about rebuilding Russian historic monuments. Those were all noble goals that any reasonable person would support. But they were also talking about returning Orthodox Christianity to its former place in the society, and that's when intellectuals started feeling uneasy. No other religions were mentioned in the program of *Pamyat,* and the emphasis on the word "Russian" in the multi-national country caused concern.

By late 1989 and early 1990, Pamyat had become increasingly open and bold in its anti-Semitic slogans and activities. In the fall of 1989, Muscovites witnessed an unprecedented event: an unsanctioned rally in Red Square. People of all nationalities watched with horror as several hundred robust guys in identical black uniforms with swastikas marched in front of the Kremlin. They broadcasted through the microphone inflammatory charges against the "Jewish-Freemason conspiracy" and other "dark forces" that they deemed hostile to Russia. They carried openly anti-Semitic slogans, calling for the extermination of Jews and other non-Russians who infested our holy land.

Two decades earlier, an unsanctioned demonstration on the Red Square had lasted for a mere four minutes. That's how long it took the government to arrest its seven participants, all of whom were sentenced to lengthy jail terms shortly thereafter.* The neo-Nazi rally during Perestroika went on uninterrupted for almost forty minutes. After a good half-an-hour, a police officer emerged from the Kremlin, approached the leader of the group Smirnov-Ostashvili, and politely asked to see the permission for the demonstration. When the latter replied that he had no such permission, the officer requested that the guys disperse. They obeyed, but not before making another full circle around the country's main square...

---

* The rally against Soviet invasion in Czechoslovakia in 1968

"When things turn this way, even I want *to fly* out of here, and as soon as possible," said my former Tretyakovka boss Natasha (being a "pure" Russian without relatives abroad, she had no chance of ever getting a refugee status to any country). "If I were Jewish, I would probably be hysterical now," she added a minute later. "But you... your last name is so typically Russian, and what does it say in your passport? You aren't registered as a Jew, are you?"

Of course, having a Russian mother, I was "Russian" in my passport. And the last name "Fedorova" was a "typical" Russian name, as Natasha correctly pointed out. But in her reassurance, Natasha forgot about my ex-husband. And Lev Fedorov, having written to the KGB, would not hesitate to contact Pamyat and ask them to add me to their list, or even go as far as joining the organization. There was talk that Pamyat leaders required prospective members to furnish the names and addressed of at least four Jews. If they decided to move from threats to actions, they would not be checking passports...

* * *

I wrote about Pamyat activities in the Bulletin, accurately reporting whatever information was available from rumors and—partially—from official sources. It didn't scare me, though: it was too surreal.

More often than not, it felt like my very life was surreal, a bad movie I was watching in a company of drunk acquaintances (violence, sex, love, betrayal, expensive parties, political turmoil... what else was missing?..). I knew I needed to stop, to interrupt that nightmare, walk outside into the fresh air, look around me, listen to the birds... go home, plan for the future... But for some reason, I could not do that. Loneliness and depression changed to dissociation, when I comfortably moved to an imagined world. Dissociations provided huge relief, but they had their faults, too: coming back to reality was always painful. All in all, it must have been adrenalin rush that allowed me to survive. I lived on adrenalin, as an alcoholic lives on wine. Contrary to all known psychology, adrenalin and depression often managed to coexist.

The most real image I had, was my ex-husband waiting for me late at night behind the dark bushes outside my house. It was much more terrifying than the marching guys with swastikas and anti-Semitic slogans...

19

It was the evening of January 13, known in Russia as the Old New Year. Young people often used the occasion as an excuse for having another party. For my former classmates who ended up in Moscow, it was a traditional reunion night.

That night, for the third year in a row, the reunion took place in the apartment of my divorced classmate who, through his grandfather's high position in the scientific world, happened to live alone in a very large place. Every year I had been looking forward to that party, carefully preparing my dress and spending hours on the phone with Tanika and other women figuring out the potluck supper.

This was the first year when I had decided not to go. It was the day before my first court hearing: the next morning I had to face Lev Fedorov accusing me of stealing the money for the family car.

It had not occurred to me that it was him who owed me fifty percent of the cash received for the sold car, until my lawyer pointed it out. Still, the money itself was the last thing on my mind. It was seeing Lev Fedorov that terrified me.

Besides, the entire situation was too dirty to share with anyone. And I could not imagine coming to the party and acting cheerful and happy as if everything were fine. My former position as the wife of a prisoner had been grim and depressing, but not embarrassing; it elicited empathy and respect—at least from people I cared about. Being involved in a petty financial litigation with the ex-husband was shameful and humiliating, and would cause nothing but pity and contempt. There had already been too many things in my life that separated me from my childhood friends by a hundred-foot-high wall, and tomorrow's court hearing made that wall even higher. We belonged to two different universes, and crossing from one universe to another in one evening seemed an unfeasible task.

At six o'clock in the evening, I called Tanika and a couple of other people with whom I was relatively close, and told them that I was sick. At eight-thirty, I was on the couch in my robe, studying Hebrew and feeling at least calm if not content: the usual dull pain had been replaced by emptiness, and I was grateful for that emotional break. Suddenly the phone rang.

The voice on the other end of the line threw off my calmness, my feeling of inadequacy, and my desire to be alone that evening. It broke the fragile vessel of indifference in which I had been hoping to hide from my own emotions. It was the voice of Igor Scheichman.

For a few minutes, I tried to fight myself by inventing reasons why I absolutely could not come that night. I was not feeling well ("Oh! Come on! Take some aspirin!"); it was too late anyway: by the time I would make it to the party it would be almost ten o'clock ("Nonsense: call a taxi, you'll be here in half an hour—we'll all pay for it if the money is a problem"). I almost told him that indeed, money was *the* problem, although not the money for a stupid taxi that I could ride every day without noticing a difference in my budget—but I bit my tongue in time.

The last thing I wanted to discuss with Igor at that moment, were Lev Fedorov, or lawsuits, or emigration. Suddenly I was seventeen again, a girl going crazy with unreturned first love, dreaming of her hero calling her at home asking to come to a party, because the party was not a real party without her. In an instant, from a depressed tired woman, I turned young, beautiful, sexy, wanting to be among other young people, to dance, to be admired while coquettishly pretending that I was not noticing the way men looked at me...

That ecstasy disappeared almost as suddenly as it had started. Forty-five minutes later when the taxi stopped near my classmate's apartment building, I was wondering if I had done the right thing coming here. It was too late to go back, however, and I slowly walked up three flights of wide stairs in a brightly lit hallway.

The semi-dark living room was full of cigarette smoke. There were only two women at the party, and guys, having nothing better to do, had gotten more or less drunk, with the exception of my friend Yuri and of course, Scheichman. (In all the years I knew Igor I could never imagine him drunk.) They both came out to the corridor to help me take my coat off; Igor then took my hand and led me into the room as his girlfriend for that evening. He was a good dancer, and I enjoyed feeling his hand on my waist—but by then I had remembered that we were not seventeen, but thirty-one, and that I was a divorced woman with many failures in personal life, with a court hearing awaiting me the next day.

My earlier depression returned with full force after two glasses of wine. I continued to dance, not just with Igor but with other guys as well (women being in deficit, none of us lacked dancing partners), but the image of Lev Fedorov and the thoughts of tomorrow's trial did not allow me to relax. I dragged myself through the party, and if not for Igor, who acted as a caring and attentive friend, I would have left after the first hour.

At two o'clock in the morning I finally decided that I had done enough to be social, and dialed the number for the taxi, but with no luck. The phone either rang busy, or no one answered: it looked as if the folks at the taxi office had simply gone to sleep.

"There is a taxi stand ten minutes from here," said a voice near me. "I'd like to leave, too; let's walk there together." Igor stood behind my back, and I suddenly felt warm and secure, almost the way I used to feel with Michael.

We walked slowly, turning ten minutes into fifteen. Neither of us was in a rush to get into a taxi and part for God-knows-how-long. The night was quiet and peaceful. The full moon lit fresh white snow and sleepy buildings, and the cool air felt refreshing after the stuffy smoky room.

"Is it true that you are planning to emigrate to America?" asked Igor suddenly.

"Where did you get that?"

"People are talking... I do not want to give names. I hate gossiping, and I'd rather not... I hope it is just a gossip—isn't it?"

"I do not know if I want to emigrate, or not," I wanted to say. "I wish my life were different. I wish my ex-husband, whom you all liked so much, had not reported me to the KGB. I wish he had not been threatening to kill me, or to kidnap my child. Tomorrow—actually, today, in a few hours, I will face him in court on the accusation that I stole money from him—even though I had not seen that money. I wish I had a reliable job and a normal family. I wish I could say, "This is my country, and I want to live and grow old here." But I do not know whether it is my country anymore, because I do not feel safe here. I don't understand what to do with my life. If I am thinking of leaving, it is out of desperation, not in search of a nicer life. And even if I were sure I wanted to emigrate, I still would need my ex-husband's permission—and he will never give it to me..."

We had almost reached the taxi stand. I could see two cars with plaid-colored doors, their drivers snoozing behind the wheels. There was not enough time for serious talk. Not enough time for anything.

"Are you taking the taxi all the way to your town?" I asked, instead of answering his question. Igor lived in a post-graduate students' dormitory in a suburb, where he worked after successfully defending his dissertation.

"Oh, no. That would be too expensive. I'll go to the train station, and wait there. The first train leaves in three hours. I have a book with me. I'll just sit there and read. Or take a nap on the bench..."

Igor spending three hours at the train station... When I need to talk to him so badly! Who knows when we might see each other again? It could be a year from now, or even longer. And what happens between now and then? A year from now he might be in love, or even happily married—and we will never feel that close again; or I might be disabled or even dead, destroyed by Lev Fedorov's overwhelming need for revenge. If he leaves now, I will have to face all those hours until the court hearing alone, almost certainly sleepless, trying to figure out why I had failed to choose a normal man for a husband... Having a friend to talk to would make all the difference. If Igor doesn't understand me, doesn't connect with me, then who will? Maybe, he will help me understand myself better?... What if, after talking to him, I realize that I don't ever want to leave my country— no matter what Lev Fedorov does?... We had wasted so much time at a stupid party...

I had to make an effort to say the following phrase, but there was no time for hesitation:

"Are you sure you want to spend the rest of the night at the train station? I will be glad if you see me all the way to my house... It is only half an hour from here, and you can take a subway in the morning."

"Are you ...inviting me?" He made particular stress on the word "inviting".

I sighed. He misunderstood, but there will be time to clear that misunderstanding later.

"Yes, of course," I said.

* * *

We did not talk in my house, but went straight to bed. I was prepared to have sex with him, although sex was not my primary objective. I thought we would sit down in the kitchen, make ourselves some tea, and talk first. But Igor acted rather aggressively, and I decided not to argue. After all, many of my best talks with male friends happened in bed right after sex. And there will be morning, when we wake up after a few hours of refreshing sleep. We could continue talking then...

I used to love that man. It was strange: I felt nothing but friendship right now, mixed with moderate physical attraction. Nothing wrong with having sex first, before talking. We were both single, and we had known each other since we were little kids.

It could have been enjoyable. We were both experienced lovers, with young strong bodies, and we liked each other. I was about to drift into the relaxing nowhere, forgetting for a few minutes about Hebrew lessons, refuseniks, and Lev Fedorov, transformed into a new person, pure and innocent, with no knowledge, no thoughts, and no worries, when a blow from my partner knocked me down to the ground:

"Oh, honey," he whispered, "I am so happy it is finally happening! You and I have been waiting for this moment for thirteen years..."

"Oh, shut up!" I cried internally. "What are you doing, for heaven's sake? Do your thing, and shut up!"

But he did not shut up. He carried on and on, about the childhood love that never dies, the dreams coming true for those who have patience to wait, all that nonsense that we both knew he did not believe in. That damn boy, he always tried to do everything right, I should have known that he would follow some stupid "sex psychology" book...

He had ruined everything. I did not relax during sex, and was almost glad when we were finished. He tried to stay awake for a few more minutes, following the same stupid books that teach that a woman needs affection after intercourse. There was no way I could talk to him about tomorrow's court, or the KGB, or emigration. Our closeness was gone, gone, gone... There was some faint hope for the morning, but when we woke up a few hours later, Igor was as distant as if last night had never happened.

We drank coffee in my kitchen in silence, feeling awkward and tense. I might still have attempted to tell him about the court, if only he had given me some encouragement. He could have asked me about the real reason for inviting him last night, or why I had not come to the party until he called me, when I obviously wasn't sick. He could have said that he had noticed that I was sad at the party, or that I looked as if something was bothering me, and if he could help by at least listening. He could have attempted to save the situation; I still might have been able to talk to him, although we had lost many precious hours. But instead, he said:

"You never answered my question about emigration. Are you really planning to go to America?"

And I had no choice but to lie:

"America does not give Jews refugee status anymore; it is an abandoned practice. Jews who want to emigrate from the Soviet Union go to Israel. I've never thought about moving there—and I have no idea who spreads such stupid rumors, or why..."

Was he satisfied with my answer? I would never know—and it did not matter in any case. A few minutes later he quickly kissed me goodby and left, without asking any more questions. I did not have time to get depressed, or regret what I had done: I had to get ready for the court.

It was the last time I saw Igor Scheichman.

* * *

Lev Fedorov had grown a thick beard that made him look at least ten years younger. He was such a handsome bastard, in a new sheepskin coat (he must have replaced the old one that was confiscated during his imprisonment). He carried an air of a frontier life, and made me think of the wild woods where he had just come from. I thought that if I did not know him, I could possibly fall in love with this man, wanting to share the roof and the bed, have children with him and grow old together.

We sat as far apart from each other as the small court room allowed. He avoided looking at me, probably for the same reason I avoided looking at him. He told the judge a long lie about me having sold the family car and then having pocketed all the money, with an honest and persuasive voice, without ever acknowledging that I was in the same room. I asked my lawyer to answer for me: I had lost my energy for fighting. My mind drifted away again: I saw another court room, when Lev Fedorov did not look like a forest knight, but was a humble prisoner who was seeking my eyes, and where I thought that I would still be able to trust him and love him...

As my lawyer had promised, the judge ordered another hearing. It was scheduled for the end of March, exactly when I was hoping to take advantage of Perestroika, and spend a few weeks abroad for the first time in my life, to take a glimpse of the rotten capitalist world... My Uncle Victor had finally sent me an invitation to visit him in London. My lawyer said the timing was great—she would take care of every-thing... She wanted to drag the case on forever, and so far, her plan seemed to be working out...

Six weeks later, I had an interview in the American Embassy, which granted me Political Refugee status.

20

"He signed it," said my mother. "But, please, understand that he *will not* give it to you. The reason he signed was to harass you, to have you beg and cry... do not humiliate yourself—it will only make things worse..." I thanked my mother, and hung up.

It was end of May 1990, and Nadia had just finished her first school year, attending my own special English-language school, with the same elementary school teacher, Panna Andreyevna (which may ex-plain why she had been accepted to the still prestigious school without any questioning). Lev arrived to Akademgorodok two days earlier, to pick up our daughter for a couple of months in his village. Even though he had not given my parents any warning, they decided that it was now safe to let him take her. I was very uncomfortable with their decision, but my mother was convinced that things had changed. Nadia had grown up, was attached to her grandma, her school, and her friends in Akademgorodok. "He won't keep her against her will," my mother re-assured me. "It would be too hard a job—after all, she is his daughter."

Angry as my parents were about the car money, they did not find it to be a sufficient reason to deprive their granddaughter of having a father. Had they known about the games their former son-in-law played with Nadia in his village banya, they may have felt differently.

But not only did they not know: they had no idea that such things existed, and probably would not have believed it even if Lev himself had told them...

Nadia was disappointed that Papa had to live in the hotel, instead of sleeping with her in her bedroom. And she was astonished when her hospitable grandma did not ask Papa to stay for dinner. Grandma and Papa sat in the kitchen for a while and talked, and then both left the house.

I don't know how my mother managed to talk Lev into going to the notary office. What she said to him remains a mystery. There must have been hypnosis, or maybe my ex-husband saw some profit for himself from my emigration, but he walked with my mother to the notary, and signed the waiver to all financial claims that he might have had on his former wife, which included the permission for his daughter to move to Israel. Unfortunately, he did not give the paper to my mother as she had been hoping, but folded it neatly and put into the inner pocket of his sport jacket.

"I'll give it to Anna tomorrow," he said. "She and I will need to talk first."

That's when my mother called me. She repeated five times that I could not possibly be in the house alone when Lev arrives. Nadia was too young to protect me—and he could easily ask her to go play outside, or simply leave her with his friends. But even without my mother's warnings, I was scared enough of my ex-husband. I wouldn't dare to face him one on one in a closed apartment.

* * *

I was in the middle of my Saturday morning Hebrew lesson when Lev and Nadia arrived. With eight adult students in my house, I felt reasonably safe. Lev had to run errands: he dropped Nadia off at my house, promising to pick her up in early afternoon for the trip to the village. He looked and sounded like a normal human being, reasonable and almost friendly, and I had to remind myself not to trust his friendliness, and stay alert.

460

He must have hoped to find me alone with Nadia when he returned a few hours later, because when he saw my friend Irina Kumina, he could barely contain his anger.

"I don't want to talk to you in front of strangers!"

"She is not a stranger, she is my close friend, and I have no secrets from her."

"Well, she is not *my* friend! And probably we have nothing to talk about anyway. Give me Nadia's things, and we'll go. See you in two months."

"The permission is only good for a month," I thought with despair. "Of course, he may not have it any more: he has probably thrown it away, of left it with somebody whom he visited this morning..." But if he leaves now... This is a slim chance, but there may never be another one..."

"I'll walk with you to the subway station," I said. "I'd like to spend an extra few minutes with my daughter, in any case..."

I returned to the living room, and asked Irina not to leave my house until I have safely returned, no matter how long I am absent. She understood the seriousness of the situation very well, and I knew I could count on her.

Lev, Nadia, and I slowly walked between apartment buildings to the subway station. Trees and thick bushes around us created a nice shade, protection from the bright sun. The path we were walking on was quiet enough to permit a personal conversation, but not too deserted to make me feel threatened. Nadia, only recently excited about going to the village with Papa, sensed that something was terribly wrong, and was quiet.

Lev and I kept silence, each one waiting for the other to start the conversation.

"Why don't you give me the paper you signed yesterday?" I finally asked, trying to sound casual.

"The paper? Which one? Ah! That permission! I don't have it anymore!" answered Lev carelessly, but I instantly knew that he was lying, and remembered my mother's warnings.

"Oh, that's all right! Sorry my mother went through the trouble of dragging you to the notary. She really thinks Nadia and I should go to America, once we have such a unique chance. She is scared to death about this AIDS epidemic... You know, they expect something like forty percent of the population to become infected within the next thirty-forty years—mostly because of the lack of disposable syringes ... It is probably an exaggeration, and Nadia may well fall into the lucky sixty percent. But you know my mother; she always expects the worst... And then, of course, the health care system is collapsing, the economy is getting worse and worse... She thinks Nadia would be better off in a stable society".

"So, now you're blaming everything on your mother? It was all her idea, huh? And you never wanted to emigrate?" There was some uncertainty in his voice. I became as tense inside as an Olympic athlete seconds before the start. I must have been doing something right, but to proceed successfully, I had to rely on intuition rather than on logic.

"I *did*. When I started a year ago, I thought I wanted to emigrate. I had problems at work; besides, several of my friends were leaving... you know, women are weak... Things have changed since. I am one of the most popular Hebrew teachers in Moscow, and I am making three times more money than my professor father who works two jobs. Working from my own home, mind you: no boss, no commuting in rush hour...

I have never had so many interesting friends. Last week there was a reception in the American Embassy, for refuseniks only. The Ambassador himself was hosting the party. I am not talking about smaller receptions in restaurants and such, which are going on all the time. And all these people who call me every day, invite me to their homes etc. I've never had so much fun in my life. Only a fool would want to leave all that, in exchange for the uncertainty of immigrant life in America."

While I was talking, I kept carefully watching Lev, not to miss the tiniest change of his facial expression. But now I glanced down, to see my daughter's face. She was looking up at us with huge scared eyes, her sun-tanned face suddenly having turned pale. What had she understood? She had certainly heard much more than was appropriate for her age—but I had no choice except to continue. I put my arms on her shoulders and, turning to Lev, said:

"I have just been abroad for the first time in my life. I met dozens of young people—some only ten years older than Nadia—traveling around the world. They graduate from high school, pack their backpacks, and wander from country to country, wiring home to their parents when they run out of money. They do not have to wait in endless lines in OVIR, or to worry about being denied an exit visa. There is a big world out there, and I am sorry that our daughter will not be able to be a part of it. And who knows? Maybe those predictions about HIV epidemics will turn out to be true... I've lived my life, but she... she is just beginning. Why deny her opportunities that kids her age in other parts of the world take for granted?"

Was I imagining it, or did Lev's eyes soften? Have I touched something human in him? I looked at my daughter for support. She was totally lost, turning her head from her mom to her dad, and finally whispered:

"Pa... Maybe, mom is right... Maybe, we should go to America—and you can come visit us there, OK?"

My heart beat so fast that I had trouble breathing and was afraid of losing consciousness. "God, help me..." I wished I had the power of hypnosis. Just for the next few minutes. "God, just make him reach into his inner pocket, and give me the damn paper. I don't care what happens next. Just make him give me that paper..."

"What will happen with your apartment if you leave?" Lev suddenly asked coldly, all traces of human expression having disappeared from his face.

"I will sell it. You know, there is a new law in effect: now citizens can sell their apartments to whomever they want. And I will need money in America, so I will sell for hard American dollars."

"I will give you the *permission*, if you sell that apartment to me. I'll find dollars for you."

So much about caring for his daughter's wellbeing. He is ready to sell her—just as he was a year ago, when he requested thirty-five hundred rubles from my mother, in exchange for returning her to Moscow. Good thing she does not understand that. But now he is talking business—cold, pragmatic business. He will try to cheat me here, as he cheats everybody else. But I must not let him...

I suddenly became calm.

"I cannot sell the apartment until I am ready to leave—not to you, not to anyone else. And in order to leave, I need that piece of paper with your signature... Vicious circle!"

"I promise to give you that permission—or sign another one if this one expires—as soon as my name is on the title. What—you don't trust me? Don't worry, I am not going to leave you and my daughter home-less."

"It is not about *trust or no trust*," I said. "I can't afford complicating my case by messing around with my residence. You know our Soviet bureaucracy... I must receive the government permission to leave the country *before* I can do anything with the apartment. But, if you are cooperative, I can promise to give you the first choice. Provided that you'll have the money to pay."

"I don't trust you!" he said bluntly.

"Well... sorry! You have no choice. Your only chance of getting this apartment is if I leave the country. If I remain here—than you never get it."

"Unless you die," he said quietly, so that Nadia could not hear. "Then I could move in as Nadia's legal guardian."

"Good luck with this one," I looked straight at his eyes and forced a smile. "You know, I am noticeable enough... the American ambassador knows me... Even the KGB knows me. And the local police inspector is my friend, as you must have figured out. Besides, everybody knows that you've been after me. Better get a good alibi, or your next prison term may be much longer than three years..."

"Pa! Shall we go?" Nadia pulled her father's hand. "I am bored with you two arguing here. What is it all about? Just give mom the stupid paper—and let's go to the village!"

"You'll be stuck with her forever if I die," I nodded at my daughter. "It may not be as much fun to keep her all the time. And when she grows up, she may hate you for having denied her the opportunity to live in America. Just give me the stupid paper, as Nadia said—and get going. The weather is beautiful; you're wasting the day."

"Do you *promise* to sell the apartment to me and no one else if I let you two go?" I could see that he was still hesitating. Another second—and he could turn around and leave, taking my permission with him.

I looked away, pretending that I was watching a colorful butterfly dancing in the sunlight over the tall grass.

"I already told you: yes, I do promise. It will take at least a few months to get the permission, tickets etc.—but then the apartment will be yours. And I am tired of going back and forth on that. My friend is waiting for me, and I have plans for the day. We can leave things the way they are, for all I care. In ten years, I'll explain to Nadia what happened today. Or my parents will, in case I am not around..."

I watched him with my side vision. He reached into the inner pocket of his jacket... My heart stopped. "Just don't show him how nervous you are, don't show him, or he'll leave... My god, what if he is just reaching for his handkerchief?"

But there was a piece of paper in his hands. It was folded, so I had no idea what was in it. It must have been something important, because Lev's face displayed a mixture of strong emotions that I was too agitated to analyze.

"Don't you dare to deceive me," he said in a voice that sent chills through my body. Then, turning to Nadia, he added in a totally different tone:

"Let's go, Lady Bug!"

I have no memories of the rest of the day, but Irina told me that when I came home that afternoon, I scared her. I walked into the house like a zombie, handed her the paper without saying anything, and burst into hysterical tears. She ran to the kitchen to find valerian drops, and then stayed with me for a few more hours, making sure I would not do anything that might damage the precious document. Together we went through my papers and collected everything required for the application to emigrate. It was Saturday, and I had to wait for two more days until OVIR reopened. I feared that Lev Fedorov might try to break into the apartment to take his permission back, and did not want to stay alone. Irina agreed to sleep over for the two remaining nights. The wife of Daniil Kumin, a long-term refusenik, she understood about emigration...

On Monday morning, the familiar officer in OVIR went through my papers several times, as if they were the most amazing thing he had ever seen.

"What did you do to your poor ex-husband that he suddenly signed *this*?" He asked in amazement, after making sure for the fifth time that the notary was real.

I shrugged my shoulders.

"If I could understand Mr. Fedorov, we probably would be still together. Maybe he met another woman, and got over the fact that we had broken up..."

"It will take three or four months for your application to be reviewed," said the officer. I thanked him and left. Three months was the standard review period, and many people waited much longer for an answer.

* * *

In the middle of September, I pulled a thin envelope with the government stamp from my mailbox. Without opening it, I knew what was inside. My Hebrew students were constantly talking about receiving such a letter, describing every line that it should contain. They lived in expectation of it, dreamed about it, saw it in their sleep, and woke up in fear that it would never come. It meant the end of the ordeal with the Soviet authorities, symbolized the beginning of a new life, the transformation of the recipient into a new being. All of them would have considered me crazy if they had known that for four months I kept the envelope at the bottom of my desk drawer, without even opening it...

21

Sasha Radzinsky proposed to me. It happened in late spring, a few days after Lev had given me his permission. Why should important things in my life happen all at once? I had been dreaming of finding a man who loved me, rather than just wanting sex. I had been longing for a stable family, for a new father for Nadia, for the opportunity to have another child. Sasha's proposal should have seemed like a dream come true—but I rejected it.

I wouldn't have been able to give a logical explanation as to why I had done that. Sasha was one of the closest friends I had ever had. There had hardly been an issue that I was not comfortable discussing with him. We loved the same books and the same music. We shared friends and political views. I had more confidence in his moral standards and honesty than I had in my own. Love? I had long forgotten what it was; all I wanted was unconditional trust—and Sasha gave it to me in abundance. But was I ready to give up on emigration now, when I had come such a long way to be closer to it than ever? I had thought that I would grab on any excuse not to leave; instead, I was watching that last straw float away—and made no attempt to hold on to it...

Sasha came to Moscow on business, and as usual, asked to stay at my place. As usual, I was happy to see him. We had just finished dinner and were sitting in my kitchen, when Sasha confessed that the meeting at the Lenin's State Public Library was just an excuse for his coming to Moscow. He came here to see me. I had suspected for a while that Sasha's feelings for me were stronger than those of a friend, but was still surprised when he asked in a trembling voice:

"Maybe... you could marry me?"

I was silent for a few minutes, thinking of how to refuse without hurting him, then said:

"I applied for emigration yesterday. In a few months I should receive my permission... I might be gone before the end of this year. It looks like all good things in my life just happen too late..."

"But you don't need to leave, even if you get the permission, do you?"

"I've invested so much into *applying*"—I tried to smile—"that it would be a sin not to use the permission if I get it. Of course, if I get refused...

"Will you consider marrying me if your application gets rejected?" asked Sasha.

"Yes," I said. "I can promise that."

I thought that he was selfish when he said passionately:

"I will hope and pray that they will refuse you!"

* * *

My exit visa was only ten weeks from its expiration date, when I realized that I was as far from being ready to emigrate as I was a year ago.

My political refugee status theoretically guaranteed me entry into the United States, but before letting me in, the Americans required a sponsor who would make sure that Nadia and I would not end up sleeping in the street. I was told that HIAS, the Hebrew Immigration Aid Society based in New York, would find us a sponsor sooner or later, but it would take many months, and we would have no choice about where in the United States we'd go. The advice I received from knowledgeable people, was to find a sponsor myself.

I called everyone I knew in the United States, but with no luck. My American friends were all recent immigrants struggling for survival, who had no money to sponsor anyone. But before I had time to get seriously worried, I received a phone call from the person I had been counting on least of all: it was Michael Levin, now living in San Francisco.

"Do not leave Moscow within the next few days," he told me. "Someone coming over from the USA will want to meet with you. It's important—otherwise I would not bother you..."

A few days later, I met Mr. David Morris, a wealthy American lawyer and human rights activist from Boston. A Jew of Russian origin, Mr. Morris dedicated many years of his life helping Soviet Jews to get out of the country. As a person of law, he was particularly interested in refuseniks (that is how, many years earlier, he had met Michael's family). I had been on Mr. Morris's list of people to meet in Moscow; it was just coincidental that Mr. Levin, who he deeply respected, had just asked him to help his friend Anna Fedorova. So, what could he do for me?

Oh, sponsorship was not a problem for him; he could start the paperwork as soon as he returned to the USA. Unfortunately, it may take weeks and even months—and I was running out of time... "I can try to pull some strings," concluded Mr. Morris—"but I can't promise..."

Unlike so many foreigners I had met before, who usually promised much more than they actually ended up doing, David Morris proved to be the opposite: he did more than he had promised. He, indeed, pulled all possible strings, including calling a senator, his former classmate from Harvard Law School. The sponsorship documents arrived at the US Embassy in Moscow in a record-short time. From the point of view of the Americans, Nadia and I were all set to go. Unfortunately, in the eyes of the Soviet government, we were emigrating to Israel. The reason Soviet authorities were letting us out of the country was the agreement with the state of Israel about the reunification of families. My readers may remember that an invitation from an Israeli "relative" was an essential part of my application package.

I was naïve to think of the Israeli visa as a mere formality—and I could have paid dearly for that naiveite, as well as for my procrastination. The Israeli consulate was swamped: Jews, scared by rumors of pogroms and doubtful that the new democracy would last, were leaving in unprecedented numbers. Zionists called it "exodus," but I was mostly thinking of "panic." Whatever it was, it seemed to be contagious. When most of your friends and relatives are running away, it is very hard not to start packing your own suitcase.

At first the Israeli government welcomed the flow of highly educated Soviet Jews to their country. It was Israel that had been pressing America to restrict Jewish immigration to the United States, and its efforts finally were rewarded. Israel even reached an agreement with Moscow to provide direct charter planes to Tel-Aviv, so Soviet Jewish expatriates did not have to be routed through Budapest any more. But when it became harder and harder to absorb the increasing numbers of immigrants, the Israelis imposed some restrictions, too. Copying the shameful practice of the Soviet government, they started checking the national background of their prospective citizens. Starting some time in 1990, it was not enough to have at least one Jewish parent in your birth certificate to receive an Israeli visa. That parent had to be "a Jew" not just on paper, but following the rabbinic laws, be born of a Jewish mother.

My first visa application was rejected by the Israeli consulate right away: with the amount of paperwork they had to process daily, they did not want to bother with someone whose last name was so obviously Russian. I tried to explain that the name was my ex-husband's, but got a crude response: "So why don't you take your maiden name back?"

So I did, although somewhat reluctantly. Due to my good relationship with the local police inspector, I had my new passport, with the name of Anna Andreyevna Chernetsky, within just a couple of weeks.

When my application for the Israeli visa was rejected for the second time, I got annoyed more than nervous. The consulate had no way of knowing that I was going to America; I would not have been the first person with American refugee status who would not use it—so the status was not an issue, I was told. However, my birth certificate stated that I had a Russian mother; yes, my father was written to be Jewish—but who were my father's parents? Was he a Jew from his mother's side, or only from his father's?

I could not believe the pettiness of the Israeli government, but had no choice but asking my father for his birth certificate. As I had feared, he had lost it years ago. Luckily, my father was born in Leningrad, only eight hours away from Moscow. Without much ado, he sent me a no-tarized telegram allowing me to request any documents on his behalf, and I was off to Leningrad, on an unprecedently short one-day trip.

When the Israeli Consulate rejected my application for the third time, I started panicking. The birth certificate was a duplicate, and consular workers knew very well that documents could be easily forged for a small fee. My duplicate was real, but I had no idea how to prove it. There was no way to present the original of the document that had been lost decades ago. Had I gotten through all the turmoil of fighting Lev Fedorov, to be stopped on what was supposed to be the last and the easiest step? My friend Dima Osotsky, the chairman of ODIKSI, reas-sured me that there must have been a mistake.

"I am to have tea with the Israeli consul tomorrow evening," he said, when I called him, half-crying. "Just bring me your papers, and I'll take them with me. Hopefully, you'll have your visa tomorrow night."

And that's exactly what happened. Two days later, Dima brought the visa to my home. He told me that the consul had apologized: he had heard of Anna Fedorov, and had no doubts that she deserved to live in Israel, regardless of who her grandparents were. He did not real-ize that the woman who applied was the same person. It seemed like a happy ending, except that I could not help feeling guilty: had Dima known that I was planning to use the Israeli visa to emigrate to the United States, he would not have done anything to help me.

To my defense, by that point, I barely cared where I would go: all I wanted, was to leave the Soviet Union, leave Moscow, be as far from Lev Fedorov as humanly possible. If I could go to the moon, I would have done that. Israel, even during the war, was not half as scary as the prospect of remaining within the reach of my ex-husband.

22

American air forces were bombing Baghdad. Soviet television showed the ruins of the Iraqi capital, but the commentary said that it was Jerusalem. Whose cruel idea was that? Most Soviet citizens, overwhelmed by problems in their own country, could not care less about the war in the Middle East, except for the small percentage of those having personal ties with Israel. People who had never been in Jerusalem were easy to fool. They watched with horror the images of bombs dropping on the city where they thought they would live soon, or where their loved ones lived already.

Charter planes from Moscow to Tel-Aviv flew half-empty. If the Soviet government wanted to stop their Jewish citizens from emigrating, it should have invented the Gulf War.

And yet many people I knew were leaving. Dima Osotsky resolutely packed his suitcase and declared that his family had no fear. The Kumins' teenage son received permission *to visit* relatives in Israel. His father still being a refusenik, Stas could not use the standard formula of "reunification of families;" there was no way for the authorities to give him permission to emigrate, as willing as they were to do so. However, giving in to the international pressure generated by his father's case, they made a compromise move, allowing the boy out "on a guest visa." No one doubted that he would not return—but that was no longer the government's concern.

Stas Kumin had just turned eighteen, and was to be enlisted in the army during the spring draft. An intellectual boy with a typical Jewish face, too short and slim for his age, he had almost no chance of survival in the brutal Soviet Army where authority was based on seniority and physical strength, and officers used to look the other way when older soldiers harassed the younger ones. Leaving the country was the only way out for him. Irina put her only child on the charter plane to Israel, not knowing if she would ever see him again.

The next day, Western radio stations reported that several Iraqi missiles had hit Israel. Stas Kumin did not call from Tel-Aviv upon arrival, as he had promised his parents. For three days Irina did not know if her son was still alive. She finally managed to reach some distant relatives in Haifa, who brought her back to life by confirming that Stas was staying with them; the phone lines being in complete mess, the boy had been unable to get through to Moscow, although he kept trying several times a day...

A few weeks before the expiration of my exit via, I still did not have plane tickets to the United States. I had made a firm decision that if two weeks before the date, Nadia and I still had no tickets to America, I'd go straight to the Israeli Consulate, request two seats on a charter flight to Tel-Aviv, and leave with my daughther on the next plane.

Bombs or no bombs, Saddam Hussein had nothing personal against me, and therefore scared me much less than Lev Fedorov.

* * *

My first attempt to reserve plane tickets to the United States was a disaster. The only office in the capital allowed to sell tickets abroad maintained a waiting list, and that waiting list was nearly a year long. Apparently, there was an alternative way—by knowing someone or simply giving a bribe—but I had no idea how I would find the right person to pay to. Moreover, even with my fairly high income I hardly had enough money for the two plane tickets, let alone the bribe. It looked as if we might have to go to Israel, after all...

Then someone told me about SPAID. I have long forgotten what the abbreviation stood for, except that it was the name of the office set up by HIAS in Moscow, for the purpose of arranging transportation for political refugees to America. SPAID was established in the late fall of 1990, and did not advertise itself. Nevertheless, thousands of people from all over the country rushed to its only room located on the second floor of a modest building on the outskirts of Moscow. How they had learned about the organization, remains one of numerous Russian mysteries. But the most amazing thing was the very existence of the organization that was, indeed, in the position to book airplane tickets.

When I first arrived at the SPAID agency, I had very little confidence that I would get help there. Having to stand in line for over four hours on a crowded staircase reinforced my pessimism. A stern policeman at the top of the stairs made sure that no one rushed in and disturbed the order of the sanctuary, but other than that paid no attention to the snake-shaped crowd below.

It was the end of December, but the approaching New Year did not lighten the atmosphere of the overcrowded waiting area. People in the queue, suspicious that someone might get in ahead of them, were full of anger and hatred. Outbreaks of verbal violence sprang up here and there, thickening the air and making everyone around feel even more tense. Hatred reverberated off the walls, multiplied tenfold, and filled every inch of space in the narrow stuffy corridor, making it even harder to breath.

Inside the small office, the atmosphere changed entirely. In a clean and empty room, polite and knowledgeable agents spent as much time with each customer as was needed. Unfortunately, in the SPAID database I was listed as Anna Fedorova, while both my visa to Israel and the Government permission to leave the Soviet Union had my maiden name, Chernetsky. (In order to get the exit visa, I had had to surrender my Soviet passport—so, technically, I was now a citizen of no country—which sometimes made me wonder if I existed at all...) A friendly woman behind the counter spent a good half-an-hour trying to figure out what to do with me—and finally suggested that I return in a couple of weeks: she would see what she could do to clear the confusion. But it took me several more visits before finally receiving two airplane tickets for a non-stop flight to New York.

Every time I came to the SPAID office, the atmosphere on the staircase seemed to become tenser and tenser. I could not understand what was going on: HIAS guaranteed tickets to every refugee, so there was no need for competition; what made people get so angry then? Where did that mutual hatred come from?

But what shocked me the most, was an obvious, showy wealth of my future travel mates. I had never in my life seen such expensive furs in such quantities. Many women wore coats worth two years of average salary—much more expensive than a flight to America. Long diamond earrings hung from their ears, reminding me of New Year tree decorations. Contrary to Russian custom, men did not bother taking off their big mink hats. When they opened their mouths (usually to curse a neighbor), I could see golden teeth glittering in the dim light of the waiting room. I knew that SPAID was only serving *political refugees*, and could not believe that even the world's most cynical government could recognize those people as oppressed in any way...

How had I ended up being one of them? I did not have any jewelry on, and my four-hundred-ruble Afghan-made sheepskin coat that I had been once so proud of, must have looked like Cinderella's rags, compared to all those furs and diamonds. But their behavior appalled me even more than their appearance. Those people were the luckiest of the lucky; they should have felt guilty about their undeserved luck, sad because they were about to leave their own country, anxious about the unknown future—but none of that was present on their made-up faces...

There was a moment when, after having spent two hours on a crowded stuffy staircase, I was about to turn around and go home. Never mind that many of my friends had left or were about to leave—the ones who were the most important to me were not thinking of emigration, but were determined to stay in their country and work for its future, hard as that work could be. And I belonged to them, not to those fat shiny creatures in furs and diamonds, who were cynically taking places that should have been reserved for the starving, oppressed, and misfortunate around the world.

But a second before I was about to give up my space in line, I remembered Lev Fedorov, the dirt floor of his new country house and the faces of his friends silently watching him beating me—and I stayed.

23

I will never forget that New Year, my last New Year in Russia.

On January first of 1991, the country entered not only the last year of Perestroika, but the Soviet Union itself. In less than eight months, the planet's last empire would collapse, after over seven decades of dominating the world's politics. No one could imagine such an outcome on the night of the year's birthday; still, people were feeling anxious and depressed. Following the holiday tradition, they tried to act cheerful, got dressed up, and had parties as usual, but the anticipation of the hard times ahead was hanging in the air.

It was another "hungry year" in Russia—something people had not experienced since the end of the Great War. Food shortages did not last long enough for anyone to starve to death. Most families had sufficient supply of food in their homes, and those who did not got help from friends and relatives—but poverty and misery were quietly creeping in. Stores stood empty, and more and more cafés and restaurants closed; prices at peasant markets, where food was still abundant, were far beyond the reach of most citizens.

* * *

Sasha Ranzinsky and I spent New Year's night at Nina's home in Leningrad. Nina's parents were out, and her children slept soundly in their room. The four of us had the entire apartment to ourselves. Shortage of food notwithstanding, the table was set as usual, covered with a white tablecloth and a dozen entrees, to be followed by the main course and five kinds of dessert. Russia's most famous actors and actresses were singing and dancing on the TV screen; they contributed to a special atmosphere but did not interfere with our conversation. Even Leonid, having drunk a couple of glasses of champagne, was unusually social.

We talked very little about my emigration, but everyone remembered that it was the last time the four of us were likely to be together like that. Our hidden pain unspoken, we all understood that the most important words were the ones not pronounced. Everyone masked grief with small talk—but we all knew that it was just a mask...While the night progressed, we felt closer and closer to each other.

At five-thirty in the morning, Sasha and I left Nina's hospitable house, the tree sparkling with ornaments, the table full of unfinished food, and walked slowly toward the subway station along empty and quiet streets. The sky was dark—moonless and starless—and the main light in the world seemed to be coming from the fresh white snow crunching under our feet. I remember Sasha accompanying me all the way across the city to Aunt Olia's place where I was staying, and how he tried to warm up my suddenly cold hands in a subway car. I remember our long "good-by" in the semi-dark hallway outside Olga's apartment, where he would not let me go...

"Will you come to Moscow to see me off to America?" I asked.

"I don't know," he said. "It may hurt too much..."

After my departure, Nina would have no more friends in her country. A few weeks ago, she and I saw off the two people who were the closest to Nina after me. Rita and Mark had come to my life as Nina's childhood friends, and stayed there; we shared many a night listening to forbidden singer-songwriters, exchanging typewritten books, or just having fun. The only gateway from the Soviet Union was through Moscow, so that is where the couple and their two children stayed during their last two days, before leaving forever for Israel.

I made up the beds for the children in Nadia's empty room, and had matrasses and sleeping bags arranged on the floor for the adults. However, none of us attempted to lie down. Rita and Mark kept packing and repacking like two madmen, as if trying to catch something that was slipping away... Nina and I spent both nights sitting on my sofa-bed in the living room, talking.

"Will you come here again to see *me* off when my time comes?" I asked my friend.

"Do you realize that after you leave I will have *absolutely nobody* left here?" she replied instead of answering.

* * *

I am slowly walking up the familiar staircase. How many times did I come here, my heart pounding from excitement and anticipation of happiness, or aching from pain? How long since I've last been here?

Tonight, I am here for the very last time. I now have confirmed tickets to the USA, two weeks before my exit visa expires. There will be no time to come to Leningrad between now and then. I am almost calm, barely having any emotions, except the sadness of saying good-by. The person whom I am going to see in a few seconds could be in America right now. He received his refugee status over a year ago, even though he does not have golden teeth or wear a mink hat. He is not poor or oppressed, either. He has never been hungry, or imprisoned, or persecuted in any way. He just happened to be born in the right place at the right time. And to the right parents. He could now be living somewhere in New York City, close to his mother and his twin sister. He is young and healthy, and speaks decent English; he would have made it there. But he has chosen to stay in his own country. If there had been nothing else to respect Volodia Sonovsky for, I would respect him for that.

Am I saying farewell to Volodia, or to my entire life that had included him as an essential part? I don't know the answer to that question—and probably don't want to know.

The apartment feels empty: the warm and loud family that used to live here is gone. Tonight, Volodia's mom has not cooked supper for us in the kitchen. His sister does not stick her head into our room to ask me about Nadia. I think that it must be spooky here at night, with all these big empty rooms and the twelve-foot-high ceiling. My other quick thought is that, with Russia's perpetual shortage of housing, Volodia must be one of the most desirable bachelors in Leningrad; but that thought comes and goes, before I have the time to register it.

Volodia's unrequited love, Svetlana, is also in New York, living not far from his sister's family. Has he given up on his dream about her, as I had given up on mine about him? Our conversation is fairly personal, but we are carefully avoiding anything concerning love. We are sitting on the same couch where we had slept together so many times in the past, in a semi-dark room, listening to the soft music and talking. It feels very good and very close.

"Next time I'll see you in America," says Volodia in a melancholy voice. "... but when? I have just visited my mother and my sister, and it will be a while before I get around to going there again. Too much work here..." He suddenly moves closer to me, grabs my shoulders and presses me against his chest.

"You're not going to leave just like that, are you? I *want you* so much! You must stay here tonight. Like it used to be, remember?"

Do I remember? I wish I could forget those endless hours that I spent waiting for his phone call, unable to do anything or even think about anything else except to look at the clock and count minutes... Those lonely weekend evenings that I hoped to spend with him, while he chose to be elsewhere... I wish I could forget Volodia rudely pushing me away, and his disdainful words: "I am tired of hearing about your feelings, Anya! It is *boring*—don't you understand?"

I gently pull away from him, but Volodia Sonovsky is not a man accustomed to hearing a woman say "no" (unless the woman is the wife of his best friend). He draws me back, passionately kissing my lips. "Don't leave... I want you. Please stay..."

Something inside me is about to give in. After all, what harm could it do if we make love one last time? It could not hurt me any more—or could it? I hesitate, passively allowing Volodia's hand to wander under my blouse... then under my skirt... It is not too late to get up and leave— but why should I? I will not stay overnight. It is infinitely more comfortable sleeping at Aunt Olia's, but I could spend one more hour here...

"How long has it been since we were together like that? Oh, how much I want you!.."

Suddenly, I pull my hand from under his pants, and jump from the couch. He has not said anything that I wanted him to say. "I am so sorry,

Anechka... I was such a selfish son-of-a-bitch... I must have hurt you so badly. Will you ever forgive me?" What is going on now is closer to a rape than to making love. It will be over in a few minutes—and then he will lose all interest in me. Haven't I had enough humiliation from this man? Have I lived through all these years, endured Lev Fedorov's harassment and my lonely life in Moscow, become a refusenik, attended all those political demonstrations, and now am about to emigrate to America—to come back to this man's feet? He *wants* me?—Tough luck! He'll has to find another *female* to satisfy his sexual desires...

"I have to meet someone at nine-thirty," I am saying, fixing my hair and my blouse. "I did not realize how late it is. Sorry—but we'll have to postpone this until we meet in the United States."

"Call and cancel your appointment." He is not ready to give up. "You can meet that person tomorrow."

"My tomorrow is fully booked," I reply. "And I was not planning to stay here for that long, anyway. We had a good talk; we won't have better memories of each other if we make love now. It is too late, anyway..."

He offers to walk me to the subway station, but when I refuse, he does not insist.

* * *

It was past nine o'clock in the evening when I left Volodia' house and slowly walked along the familiar street. I did not have any more dates that evening, but was looking forward to spending a relaxed hour with Aunt Olia, before she went to bed.

How many memories can one street bring? My late grandfather lived here for many years, and I still visit Sofia, his widow, every time I come to Leningrad. My beloved uncle, my father's cousin, used to live around the corner from Volodia. He passed away two years ago, and his family emigrated to America. I will almost certainly see them when I get there, but we are unlikely to have the same close relationship we had when Uncle David was with us.

At the end of this street, in a three-story building above the subway station, is the backpackers' club that my college friend Irina and I attempted to join many years ago, when we were still single and looking for guys. Next to the club is one of the best movie theaters in the city, where I have been with virtually all of my friends. And across the street from the theater is the supermarket where my mother's cousin, Natasha's mom, still works as the head bookkeeper, and where I come sometimes to buy delicatessen unavailable to common folks.

The street is light from the bright windows above my head, and from the powerful streetlights. People rush past me, unaware of the fact that I may be walking here for the last time in my life. They probably would be envious if they knew... Or hateful and contemptuous? Or all of the above at the same time?

In a few weeks I will be walking along a totally different street, on the other side of our planet. That street will have no memories. Whom will I visit there? Who will miss me, or worry if I don't call for a long time?

Why am I leaving? I knew the answer in the basement of Lev's house where he beat me until I fell on the dirt floor, while his two friends with PhDs silently watched us. I knew it on the cold winter morning when I was standing alone in front of the Soviet Peace Defense Committee, posters demanding freedom of emigration hanging on my chest and back. I knew it at the dock in France, where I was not allowed to board the ferry to London, because my passport was the wrong color—bright-red, instead of darkish blue or green (the colors they use for passport covers in the "free world"). I knew it when the impudent young officer in OVIR turned down my emigration papers... But here, in the city of my youth, I forgot the answer.

I stopped and looked back. Volodia's house had disappeared around the corner, but I suddenly imagined him showing up at the end of the street and running after me, his fur hat in his hand and his jacket unzipped.

"You can't leave like this, Anya," he would tell me, catching his breath and putting his hat on. "I am so sorry: I said all the wrong things. You must stay here, and forget America. Think of our poor country: if all the decent people leave, what will become of Russia?

Me... I acted like a swine tonight, and I am very ashamed of myself. I just did not have the courage to say... Maybe, I did not fully understand it until just now—but I love you, Anya. You are the woman I want to be with. I want to live with you, raise children with you, and I want to work for our country's future together with you. Please, Anya, it is not too late... Just stay in Russia. Stay here with me..."

This image was so vivid, so real, that a warm wave of happiness came over me, my chest expanded, my breath became deeper. I smiled, and with tears of happiness on my eyes stretched my arm to touch his hand.

Alas! It was just a mirage.

I turned around and walked to the subway station as fast as I could. It was too cold to cry outside...

It was January 2, 1991.

24

Five weeks later, I woke up wondering if my entire life had been a prelude to this day, or was I about to make a grave mistake. I kept asking myself that question for many more years in the United States, but the answer to it depended on my mood even more than on the events of my life. Eventually I gave up, having surrendered to the reality. After all, the world has changed, and now I can go back and forth. At least for now—until another change reverses the flow of history... (I have never forgotten the KGB's dire prediction...) I just wish we could travel like that in time, not just in space...

Which moment would I want to return to, had I been given a chance? When would I have said "time, stop!"? Many days come to mind—and no one feels the best. Maybe, I would come back to my last New Year night in Russia? Or to that day in Moscow in February of 1991, when so many people I loved were around me at the same time, and everyone tried to believe in the happy future?

"Everything is for the best in this best of all worlds," says Olga Petrovna—who will forever remain my Aunt Olia—shaking off the light snow from her new winter coat. "Never mind, I will miss you incredibly... You've been one of my closest friends... much more than just a niece."

My father steps out of the kitchen, and gives Olga a bear hug.

"Sorry... something got into my eye," says Olga, and reaches for her purse to look for a handkerchief. "Andrey... We've lived long lives, you and me—haven't we? Remember, when we first met—could we have thought...? You must be proud of your brave daughter... I am proud of her...—ok, Anna?

"I thought you did not approve of emigration," my mom steps into the conversation.

"There are circumstances... and there are circumstances," says Olga. "She is doing the best for her and her daughter. Besides—time will change, and she will be able to come back to visit!"

Both of my parents shake their heads. I know what they are thinking: their friend Olga has always been an optimist. Her predictions are simply too good to be true. Yes, they know there would be changes. Everybody understands it right now: the time of stability (or stagnation—whichever way you want to look at it) is over. Things must change because right now they are too unstable to last. The question is, how will they change? Where will Russia go? To join the Free World, where everybody can travel back and forth? To the abyss of civil unrest, hunger, Jewish pogroms? That seems more likely right now. In any case, Nadia and I have one-way tickets to the other side of the world, leaving tomorrow morning, on a transatlantic jet. As emigrants, we need to be at the airport twelve hours in advance, which means tonight. That is all we know. We have today—and it is more or less predictable. Tomorrow is murky and dark—and is it real, in any case?

I glance out of the kitchen window—and suddenly feel that something has gotten into my eye, too. Nina, Leonid, and Sasha Radzinsky—all came on the same overnight train from Leningrad—are slowly approaching my house. Nina, afraid of slipping on the fresh snow in her three-inch-heel boots, is walking between the two men, holding on to them for dear life. I close my eyes, trying to imprint this picture in my memory, and suddenly whisper a prayer that time would stop, and this morning would never, ever be over...

We have just finished the third serving of pancakes and are boiling the tea water for the second time, when the door bell rings again. Somehow, today I am not afraid of the sound; today, I am not thinking of Lev Fedorov, terrified that he would suddenly show up at my doorstep. Nadia has not asked about her father, which is great—because if she did, what would we all say?

Lev does not know we are leaving today. He called my parents in Akadmegorodok only a few days ago, and my mother lied—probably for the first time in her life: "They don't have plane tickets yet... May not for a while... We'll keep you posted..." Mama must be very afraid of her ex son-in-law, if she chose to lie, which was not her thing at all. "Lev must not know when you two are leaving," she repeats for the hundredth time. My father agrees with her: "The bastard is getting away with not paying child support for at least ten years," he says. "And after all, it is all his fault that Anechka (the tender nickname he gives me) has to leave... No remorse necessary."

The two people who have just rang the doorbell are my mom's best childhood friend from Tver (then still called Kalinin) and her son Kyrill. They have just arrived in their own car—still a rarity in Russia. (This car, however, is bought with the honestly earned money, Aunt Ella has nothing to hide—or to be ashamed of.) They will spend the next twenty-four hours in Moscow, and drive home tomorrow, after my plane has taken off... I've been visiting my second family in Tver every couple of months, but today they need to be here. "God knows if we will ever see each other again," says Aunt Ella, her eyes strangely wet ... "You know... I have two great sons. But you have been... more than my niece... more like my daughter... Sorry, Masha—I hope you are not jealous..."

No, mom is not jealous. She is very calm and composed, probably trying to push the reality away. Live today, don't think about tomorrow. Pretend that nothing has changed... And why should it? We are so happy together: my mom and dad, Nadia and I... Tomorrow we'll all board a plane and fly together to Akademgorodok... And then, I will return to Leningrad... and probably go back to work in Saltykovka... On weekends, Nina and I will go to movies together. And maybe I will marry Sasha... Life has so many possibilities, it takes my breath away just to think of all the wonderful things that could be in store for me here...

* * *

It is getting dark, and more and more people are coming. Tanika arrives with a big homemade pie. Her beautiful face is all smothered with mascara; she says it still snows outside, water has gotten into her eyes. Our former classmate Yuri is already here with his wife; those two have been great support for me during all these lonely years in Moscow—even though they did not know ninety percent of what I was really going through... Yuri and Tanika hug, remembering some mischiefs they had done together as little kids. Then the phone rings—

and there are Anyuta and Tanyusha, calling from Anyuta's home in Akademgorodok. The former best friends do not see each other very often: each one has work and family, and a separate life—but today they are together. They need to complete our old Tanya-Anya quartet. They talk with me, then with Tanika, then with me again. "You promise you'll write?" each one of them asks for the tenth time. It's so hard to hang up... It is so hard not to say: "Hey, stop wasting money on stupid phone call—I will see you in summer! Can we plan a short girls' get-away again?"

We sit around the table, which has been fully unfolded and moved to the middle of the room. There is hardly enough space for all the wonderful food—where has it all come from, when the stores have been empty for months? Another mystery of our ever-mysterious country...

We have just started filling our plates, when the phone rings again. At first, I do not recognize the woman's voice at the other end of the receiver. "Monsieur d'Artagnan?" I do not understand... what kind of silly joke is it? "Monsieur d'Artagnan! Athos speaking..." and then I catch my breath, and yell into the receiver: "Al-ka!!"

"Alka, Allochka—where the hell are you?"

"At the train station," replies my childhood friend. "Just arrived... I am not too late to see you off, am I?"

Alla is married, but she still keeps her maiden last name, Kotova. She is very proud of her family heritage, proud to be the daughter of her father, Yuri Ivanovich (or Yurivanych) Kotov, who by now has authored several well-known books in physics, and—unexpectedly—in art history. Alla's brother Ivan, the little Vanyusha of our childhood, has become a professional musician with the Moscow philharmonic orchestra. Alla is an artist, employed full-time by the drama theater as the chief scenery designer in a provincial town not far from Moscow. She also paints at home, and periodically arranges her personal exhibits. Life has driven us apart—but today all the years that passed don't matter: we are girls again, close as we have ever been. As soon as she arrives, she, Tanika, and I begin sharing memories about having played musketeers together. "Is our club Victoria still around?" asks Alla, who has not been to Akademgorodok for years.

"Yes, it is. But it looks like a very different place right now... Just a regular fencing club..."

"The world is a different place, isn't it?" Alla appears to be another impossible optimist—maybe even more so than Aunt Olga... Where do they get that belief that, after all, everything will turn out for the best?

* * *

"Get out of the room," said Leonid in his usual slow and quiet manner, "you are in no condition to do anything reasonable right now." It was almost ten o'clock, and I was trying in vain to close my suitcases. In less than an hour, Leonid re-packed all four of them (and, of course, they closed just fine). Four suitcases, two per person, was all that the Soviet government permitted us to take out of the country. Each emigrant was allowed two suitcases and three hundred dollars in cash—no matter how much of your life was left behind... (Good thing that my Uncle Victor in London could be a keeper of the twenty-five hundred dollars that I had received for my Moscow apartment; he would find a way to get them to me once I'm safely in the United States...) Many former restrictions to emigration had been lifted—but we still had to remember who we were: traitors, abandoning our motherland in times of trouble; we needed to know our place.

At midnight we left for the airport.

The Muscovites had gone home. Allochka had departed to spend the night with her brother. The rest of us set off in two cars: Kyrill drove my parents, Nadia and me, in his own car. Sasha, Aunt Ella and Leonid went in a hired taxi. Among all of us, eight-year-old Nadia was the only one who did not look sad or scared. Her excitement earlier that evening had turned into a complete indifference. She had spent nearly four hours in her bed, but did not fall asleep, and was probably very tired. Instead of a doll or a teddy bear, she carried in her hands a souvenir from Siberia, a huge cedar pine cone.

There were two people who stayed behind, to spend the night in my, no-longer-mine, home: they were Nina and Aunt Olia. Nina suffered from elevated blood pressure—a condition that she experienced more and more often, in spite of her almost unhealthy low weight and a Barbie-doll figure. Aunt Olia was supposed to make a presentation at a mathematical conference the next morning, so she wanted to be well rested.

"You are not going to notice me at the airport anyway," she said. "I've seen people off before. Departing emigrants are so stressed that they are hardly aware of those around them. But I will see you in America. I haven't been there for a while. They keep inviting me, and now I will finally have a strong incentive to accept."

Aunt Olia, indeed, visited me in Boston the following summer. She always kept her promises...

Many years later I keep wondering if some mystic forces were responsible for the fact that my two best friends spent that night together in my abandoned apartment. They both died almost a year later, one day apart from each other, under completely different circumstances.

No, I know: there was no mystic force. Just a plain coincidence. A cruel joke of Her Majesty the Life...

* * *

Nadia and I spent our last night in Russia in the Moscow international airport Sheremetyevo. Aunt Olia had been right, but only partially: I barely noticed the people who were there to see me off—but I would have been unable to manage without them either.

All of a sudden, we were alone. We had gone through at least five different control points, which had taken most of the night. I remember sitting in the departure hall, which was absolutely empty, except for me and Nadia. (I am now sure it could not have possibly been true: it was already morning, and planes were leaving one after another; there must have been other people there—but I was completely unaware of them.) The cafeteria had just opened; I spent my last Russian rubles there, forcing myself to swallow a piece of cupcake and trying to persuade Nadia to eat at least something. She finally agreed on ice cream, but left most of it untouched.

I looked back to where we had just come from. Behind us was a wall with a security door that opened one-way, and one-way only. The people I loved remained somewhere on the other side. I knew that they would not leave the airport building until our plane has departed, but that knowledge did not help. I thought of all the things that I wanted to say to them—and did not. I never told my parents how much I appreciated their help and support. I didn't tell Kyrill never to divorce his wife, because she was wonderful, and I loved her. I never kissed Sasha. I suddenly remembered Sasha's eyes when he was looking at me seconds before I bravely went through the first passport control—eyes full of pain that his forced smile could not hide. Will another man ever love me like that? Aunt Olia said I was doing the right thing. She must have been thinking of Lev Fedorov; she did not know about Sasha.

I must not cry... What will I say to Nadia if she asks me why we are doing this? I no longer know the answer myself...

My daughter was sitting quietly, drawing with a pencil in her sketchbook. She took off her hat and carefully placed the pinecone inside it, as if making sure that it was comfortable.

"Why didn't you bring a doll?" I asked, just to say something.

"Dolls are stupid," she said, and continued drawing.

"And I don't like people," she added after a prolonged silence.

I then thought that she meant "toy people..." But later I decided that she might have meant more than that...

I looked at the piece of paper on my daughter's lap. There were several pine trees, with disproportionately large cones, a four-story apartment house, and two kids on skis in front of it.

"Is it Akademgorodok?" I asked.

She nodded silently, and turned the page.

* * *

All comes to an end, even the day of your emigration. Even the longest night at the airport. We are now inside the plane, having taken our seats. An experienced air traveler, my daughter buckles her seatbelt without reminder. The pinecone is carefully placed on the folding table in front of her, next to the sketchbook. In her eight-and-a-half years, she has been through a lot. She has too much of a life, to just leave it behind like that, without saying a word.

Is this the moment I have been trying to imagine for years? Am I really *leaving*? Flying to that forbidden, free, fairy-tale world that every Soviet citizen has dreamed about since early childhood, but never expects to see? That world, on the other side of our round planet, where things and people are upside down, and that I will not just visit, but will have the privilege of actually *living* there? I have always wanted to know what I would feel at the moment of final departure... Now I should find out the answer.

Is it happening *for real*? Maybe I am daydreaming again, and Nadia and I are about to fly home? Three hours from now we will land in Novosibirsk, to see my father waiting patiently at the airport—never mind the plane is late again; after another hour-and-a-half, we'll walk into our dear old apartment, and my mother in a new apron will rush out of the kitchen, and the house will smell of freshly baked pies, and Nadia will laugh and run outside to play, and I will pick up the phone and start calling my childhood friends...

But why are the signs on the plane all in English? Why is the captain making his announcement in two languages? As in a dream, I watch a stewardess locking the door. Now the red "fasten seat belts" signs come on, now the plane starts moving, at first very slowly. I can still clearly see the airport building that I had seen so many times and that I know I will never see again; now the building disappears. The plane pauses for a moment, only to roar with all its engines and start accelerating, accelerating to an enormous speed. The airport is flying back past the round window, and for a split second, I can still see the ground that has been *mine* all my life and that I have been taking for granted. I can still see houses, trees, tiny cars back there on the ground, and I know that I am leaving it all forever, forever...

I close my eyes, to concentrate on my feelings.

But I feel—nothing...

EPILOGUE

1

ARE MY READERS LOOKING FOR the happy end?

That might be tough to do... But you have already gotten the Happy Beginning—isn't that enough?

Remember, in the Preface to the book, the heroine comes to Russia (which is no longer the head of the Soviet Empire) for a visit—as an American citizen, with her American husband. She presumably takes him to her birth city, Leningrad (which is no longer Leningrad, but St. Petersburg), and then to the place she has grown up, Akademgorodok (which is still Akademgorodok, the scientific center of the country). They arrive in the capital of Siberia, Novosibirsk, on one of the hottest days of the summer, and the world traveler Walter (who's never been to Russia before—never mind Siberia) is blown away by the bright colors of the hot summer day.

The heroine's parents are welcoming her, their new son-in-law, and their granddaughter, to their home (which is still the same home she has visited throughout the years). Isn't it a great Happy Beginning?

Anna returns to her country in the second half of the 1990s, when Russia's first democratically elected president, Boris Yeltsin, is struggling to overcome the grim inheritance of the seven decades of Soviet regime, and bring Russia on par with the first-world economies. Life is still difficult (in some respects more difficult than before), but people are hopeful and excited: belief in Russia's bright future is prevailing. (Take just one fact: Anna is an emigrant, who, only a few years ago, did not think she would ever be able to leave the Soviet Union. Now she is back on vacation, and has no fear about being unable to return to the U.S.).

Most of us know (from the news, if nothing else) that the Pamyat Society, although it continued its crude anti-Semitic propaganda well into the 21st century, failed to organize Jewish pogroms, or move the grassroots anti-Semitism to any level of violence; their leader, Smirnov-Ostashvili, was the first person under Soviet law tried and imprisoned (although briefly) for the crime of inciting "inter-ethnic hatred and enmity."

Poverty and injustice have never disappeared in Russia, but food shortages and lines in grocery stores now belong to history. People are no longer afraid to openly criticize their government, and books by Solzhenitsyn can now be bought in bookstores or borrowed from a library, and CDs by Vysotsky and Galich are sold everywhere.

Presumably, Anna and Walter will live happily ever after (no one knows the future, of course—but there is no indication of impending marital problems). Presumably Anna's teenage daughter Nadia will develop into a psychologically healthy young woman and will not suffer from various mental disorders caused by her birth trauma and even more traumatic childhood...

Hopefully, memories of past horrors have not crippled Anna into a life-long sufferer of post-traumatic stress disorder; she stopped mourning her friends and family in Russia, and has fully adjusted to life in the United States—both economically and culturally. (At least we know that now she can smile again—remember the opening scene at the Novosibirsk airport?)

There is a hint that she has never lost touch with her old life, which is admirable, and fits the happy ending... Sorry, the Happy Beginning—because the Preface could not be the ending, but only the beginning—maybe of another book, which I am not yet ready to write...

So, should I end my story with the moment when the trans-Atlantic jet takes off, with Anna and her eight-year-old daughter on board, bound from the oppressive Soviet Union to the free America?

I could certainly do that—but what about people who were left behind?

Maybe, I could just leave Anna's friends at the airport, waving good-bye to the departing plane; each one of them will return to his or her everyday life, which will continue without Anna—just as it continued without their other friends who had left earlier, carrying one-way tickets...

Or would it be fair to them—and to Anna, for that matter?

Does connection between people who love each other break like a string, when the distance between them becomes measurable by the width of an ocean?

If that is what you believe in, please close this book now: you have finished reading it.

2

Was there another New Year? Already?

How could the time had gone by that fast? Or maybe it was still just a dream? Although, I rarely had dreams lately: I got too exhausted during the days—nights came and went in a flash. I put my head on a pillow—and there was a ring of the alarm clock, and I had to drag myself out of bed... then get Nadia up, to have her ready for school before I leave for the day...

My daughter and I lived in a small rental apartment with donated furniture, which we still could not call "home." I was back at school, repeating my library degree (my Russian higher education diploma appeared to be useless here)—but I had no friends in college. Overall, the relationships between the students puzzled me as much as relationships between students and professors: there was neither closeness, nor intensity which in Russia everyone had taken for granted; people were brushing against each other with superficial smiles on their faces, but no one seemed to touch anyone else's life, or wanted his or her life to be touched...

In the Reformed Jewish congregation that had sponsored us (which Mr. Morris belonged to), we met new people almost daily; they wined and dined us, showed us around the Boston area—but even the best ones could barely qualify for "acquaintances" (never mind that most of them referred to me as their "friend"). I was getting desperate that, with that attitude, I would never make any real friends in America. I was beginning to think that it was for the best—after all, I was over thirty, long past the age when one could acquire real friends; maybe, I should just live in the past, and don't bother with trying to reinvent life that had been lost forever?

It had not taken me long to understand that all my American acquaintances wanted in exchange for their hospitality, were horror stories about life in the Soviet Union. When I was unable to produce those, people appeared disappointed and outright angry. They had read enough newspapers, they heard narratives of other refugees...

I could not tell anyone about Lev Fedorov, or Volodia Sonovsky, or Perlov's harassment in Tretyakovka—or even the fact that the last name *Fedorova* was not Jewish. Surprisingly, no one wanted to hear about Akademgorodok, or teenagers skiing through the woods to an abandoned hut, or the white nights in Leningrad, or playing musketeers with my childhood friends...

"How come your grandfather was a lawyer, when he was a Jew? Weren't Jews oppressed under the Soviet regime?"

"Why did you grow up in Siberia? Were you exiled there? Even in spite of the fact that your father was a scientist? Well, of course, he was a Jew—so being a scientist clearly did not save him..."

It seemed to me that people already knew the answers to all questions, but wanted some kind of validation. Unfortunately, I could neither validate their knowledge, nor share mine. It is possible that I just knew too much to share it with anyone?.. I had been used to being a misfit, and it shouldn't have bothered me—but in Russia I could always escape that by finding a group where I *did fit*... There seemed to be no such group in the United States.

How come I always looked so serious, not to say unhappy?—enquired people around me. Hadn't I been one of the privileged few who managed to escape communism and anti-Semitism? Wasn't I excited to live in America, where I could be openly Jewish, and where my daughter would have so many more opportunities? People smiled at me—how come I was not smiling back?

But, no matter what, I could not smile. What no one among my new acquaintances understood—or even less appreciated—was that I was no longer crying, either... Nor was I ever thinking of killing myself: those times belonged to the past.

Nadia behaved horribly when in other people's houses—so badly, that soon both the Americans and other Russian immigrant families stopped inviting us over. What they did not know, was that Nadia and I had become much closer to each other than ever; at home we spent our short time together cuddling, or watching English cartoons on the old TV bought in a Salvation Army store... Nadia would ask me to help her with homework, or read her books in Russian. I could talk to her about my feelings without worrying that she would accuse me of being "ungrateful." I could trust her to get on her school bus on time after I had left—for work, then for college, and then for more work—early in the mornings. I knew she would be at home when I returned late at nights, sleeping on the couch in front of the TV, her food left in the microwave untouched, her hair disheveled, the tap in the bathroom not turned off... I would kiss her, and undress her, scold for not having eaten, and put her to bed—and I did not, not, not need to worry about Lev Fedorov appearing on my doorsteps and snatching her away...

* * *

Nadia was quick to learn English, and succeeded in finding a few kids in the neighborhood to play with during the day. She was convinced that she and I would go to Akademgorodok next summer, so she just needed to survive the winter. In the beginning, she was asking me to buy her a pair of skis, but then accepted that there was not enough snow for skiing, anyway. She often talked about her grandmother, or her Russian friends, but never about her father. She never failed to play a little monster when there were other adults around— but it only happened when I was present as well: at school and vacation camps she was one of the best-behaved children—smart and creative, according to teachers...

On December 28, I picked up a still-perfectly-fresh tree, thrown away by neighbors after Christmas. I stuck it in a bucket with sand in the middle of our small living room, and Nadia was busy for a few days, making tree decorations from colored construction paper. I wish I could afford tree lights—but realized that that might have to wait till the next New Year... Meanwhile, I was trying not to think of how I would be able to pay the rent when the twenty-five hundred dollars received for the Moscow apartment ran out... My income from the two jobs was barely enough to cover gas and car maintenance, plus parking downtown (the car, very old and in poor condition, had been given to us as a tax-deductible donation by a family from the congregation); food and second-hand clothes were of relatively low cost—but together my expenses by far exceeded my earnings...

Still, there were bright moments in my life, and memories of them helped me to keep my head up. There were Michael Levins's calls from

San Francisco every weekend; during those calls I could not only smile, but sometimes even laugh. Michael's life was far from easy, but his unique sense of humor never left him. Twice, Nadia and I drove all the way to New York City, first visiting our remote relatives from Leningrad, then Volodia's friends Svetlana and Ivan who had a daughter Nadia's age.

The most important and joyful event, however, happened last summer, when Aunt Olia came to visit. She had been offered a two-year contract in one of the universities in New York City; before accepting it, she came for reconnaissance, and attended a few-days-long mathematical conference; of course, half of her time was spent in suburban Boston, in my less than modest apartment. For whatever reasons, sightseeing with Aunt Olia was so much more interesting and exciting than similar activities with my American acquaintances—even though I hated driving in unknown areas. The one week Aunt Ola was visiting, was my only truly happy time in this country; but what really lifted my spirit, was the knowledge that very soon she would live nearby, and we would be able to speak and see each other constantly.

In summer, I was still receiving many letters. I tried to respond right away—but, with nights becoming longer and lonelier, money tighter, and time disappearing under the burden of full-time studying and two part-time jobs, I wrote less and less frequently—and also with shorter replies. I had been determined not to complain, no matter what; at the same time, I was not good in lying, especially lying to my friends. In any case, I did not have time for either...

* * *

It was January First, and I decided to invite a few people over. New Year was not much of a holiday for anyone, besides Nadia and me—but I wanted to celebrate it, anyway. Smiles or no smiles, but we both put on our best dresses brought from Russia—and of course, I cooked Russian food—or the closest I could manage, with the ingredients bought in American supermarkets.

I had expected Michael to call to wish me happy New Year. But when the phone finally rang, his tone of voice was so strange that I started feeling uneasy—something that had never happened between Michael and me before.

"Is everything all right with you guys?"

"My family and I are fine," said Michael in the same strange voice. "But an awful tragedy has happened in Leningrad."

There was a long silence. I tried to guess what he was referring to, without anticipating anything too serious, when he said:

"Nina will never come here.

She is gone..."

At first, I did not understand. Nina...gone? Where? The news that she was not coming to the Unites States did not seem too upsetting to me: I had never believed that her talk of emigration was serious. But why did Michael sound so grave?

"Boris called her last night, as usual," explained Michael. "You know, he always calls her on the thirty-first. Her mother answered. "She can't come to the phone," she said. "No, don't call later... She will not return... ever. It happened two weeks ago..."

He hung up. At first, I felt almost no pain. The world was very empty—as if I were alone in the whole universe. Me and my nine-year old Nadia. I could not imagine some strange people coming over in an hour.

Michael must have been wrong, I thought. That bastard Boris misunderstood something. Probably he was drunk. Or it was one of his strange jokes. I had just sent Nina a twenty-five-page letter. I had told her everything—about my desperate search for human relationships, my loneliness, and my doubts that I had done the right thing by emigrating. I explained why I had not written for so long... I knew she would understand. I did not want to write a *desperate letter*; both she and I had read too many of those letters sent by recent emigrants who were too weak for America—I did not want to sound like one of them. But until last week, I could not write anything different and be sincere. I had to survive that first semester in college, at least. And Nadia's tantrums every time she and I went out, and working seven days a week for virtually no money, and having no one to talk to... Twenty-five pages long—I mailed that letter only a week ago... I was wondering if there was any chance that Nina would get it in time for the New Year...

Nadia came out of the bedroom to ask me something, but I could not understand her words. The world stopped making sense. It was worse than waiting for Volodia's phone calls, worse than Lev's imprisonment, worse than anything I had ever been through in my long, long life. Except that very deep in my heart I was still hoping that there had been a mistake.

Suddenly I came to a very simple decision: I picked up the phone, and dialed Nina's Leningrad number. I did not care how much the phone bill would be: money did not matter anymore. Rachel Naumovna answered the phone. I could hear her as clearly as if I were calling from my old Leningrad house across the street.

*Nina was working late on Friday. Then she did not go to bed for a while, because she was writing a letter. On Saturday morning we thought she was asleep. Leonid was also asleep; he often sleeps till mid-day, because he writes his programs at nights... Nina's father and I took care of the children, making sure they would not wake her up... But she was not even home. She had left very early, to meet a person who was about to leave for the U.S. She wanted to give him two letters, so he could mail them from America—letters for Boris and for you, Anya. She went over there to give him a letter **for you**... It was such a terrible day: windy, cold... Nina had not been feeling well for a few days, but continued going to work. She should have taken a sick leave... Or at least gone to bed on time... She fell on the street. Probably, at first nobody paid any attention. You know, people are so angry and frustrated these days, everyone hates everyone... We don't know how long she was lying there alone before the ambulance came. It came too late. Nina was dead.*

We waited for her all afternoon. We had thought she was asleep in her bed, until Leonid got up and told us otherwise. Toward the evening, we started to get worried, but not very much. She had often left like that, without telling anyone, you know... Then the police came. They brought Nina's work ID that she always carried in her purse.

It happened on December 14.

* * *

Neither Aunt Olia, not her family, were that "lucky." Olga was going to a concert, and had left her university ID at home. Her husband Arkady had to make dozens of phone calls before he was finally told that a woman had been hit by a car in front of their house the night before and was rushed to a nearby hospital...

The accident occurred in the middle of October. Russia had already had its first democratic presidential elections; the Communist Party of the Soviet Union had been banned; dissolution of the Soviet empire was going full-speed, losing one republic after another. I remember how excited Olga had been last summer, when she was leaving my Massachusetts home.

"How do you see Russia without socialism?" I asked her.

"I don't see it,"—she answered. "Russia will never be like America—and thank God for that. Russian socialism has been in need of many improvements—and I am happy that the current leadership can see it, and is prepared to look outside the box... The system's faults will be fixed—you'll see; then everyone in the world will finally understand that socialism is the most economically fair system. When I finish my assignment in New York, you and I will go back to Russia together..."

"Everything is for the best in this best of all worlds?" I asked with a smile.

"You are learning!"—replied Olga, her face remaining serious. "Study, study... Learn English to perfection, learn about this country... You will be able to do lots of good things in Russia when you come back in a few years..."

A few days after Olga left, I picked up a third job. Then a fourth. Then I had to drop two of them, when my full-time studies in Simmons College started. I switched into survival mode, and had no time and energy to follow politics in Russia...

* * *

That night Olga was going to the concert in the philharmonic, the first one in her season ticket. (She had always bought season tickets to the philharmonic grand hall.) She had invited my mother, who was in Leningrad briefly to arrange care for her old aunt, to come along, and my mother accepted with enthusiasm. She waited for Olga outside the concert hall, but her friend never showed up. My mother began to worry, but then decided that she had gotten the day wrong, and returned home, somewhat anxious but not panicked.

After the car driven by a drunk man hit Olga on the crosswalk in front of her house, she did not feel pain or fear: she lost conscious before hitting the ground. She was still unconscious when the ambulance delivered her to the nearest hospital. It was a weekend, and the emergency room was severely understaffed. Hours went by before Olga was seen by a doctor, and almost two more days before the necessary surgery was performed. A lot of precious time had been lost, but Olga's strong spirit was still fighting. She regained consciousness, requested pen and paper, and attempted to write some letters. She wrote to her friends scattered all over the world, and she wrote to me. Arkady was in no rush to mail those letters, so it was already December when I received a short—but, as always, optimistic—note from my aunt. She mentioned the car accident and the hospital stay as if they were minor inconveniences; she wrote that she was about to be discharged, and was hoping to catch up with her work before the year ends. She was still excited about the events unfolding in the country: too bad the newspapers arrived at the hospital with at least two days delay, and she did not trust her husband to relay the news to her without bias...

It was hard not to believe her; however, when my parents called to wish me happy New Year and, at the end of the conversation, I asked whether Olga had been discharged, my mother's "yes" sounded somewhat stern, even grim—and she rushed to complete the call and hang up. I dismissed her tone; it was New Year eve, after all—and I needed to feel if not happy, then at least content. It's an old Russian belief that the year will go the way it has started: have a happy New Year—and the next 365 days will be happy and successful... I had too much invested in the year ahead, to risk ruining it all...

* * *

I thought the guests would stay forever—but at least now I could cry openly, without fear of being blamed. I had just learned about the death of my best friend, and even in America you are allowed to grieve in cases like that. Nadia, luckily, was playing with the two girls who came over, and that made visiting somewhat worthwhile. The first day of the year was almost twenty-four hours old, when I finally went to bed. My tears had stopped coming—or they were giving me a break, I was not sure: Nina's death still belonged to the world of the Impossible. For a few moments, I thought that all I needed to do, was just fall asleep; in the morning it would turn out to be just another nightmare, that's all.

And then I remembered Aunt Olia. It was early morning in Leningrad—and I was sure Olga and her family were still sleeping; but I knew she would forgive me for waking her up. Yes, of course—how could I not think about it before? Olga knew Nina's family well enough, she would reassure me that nothing bad had happened there... Or maybe... maybe it is true—and Aunt Olia would say... "Oh, how horrible! Two little children—and so young..."—but she would *share* my grief, and she would find the right words, the words that would soothe my pain and give my life some new meaning... Yes, that's what I have to do... Just call Aunt Olia right now. I don't care about the money...

And suddenly I turned so cold as if the walls of the house disappeared, and I was lying naked in the snow. I remembered my mother's awkward "yes" on the phone, and something became very clear to me. The truth that I had been pushing away since last year, flashed in my mind like lightning: *I will not call Aunt Olia. Because Aunt Olia is dead too... How did I **not** understand it right away?*

I slowly got out of bed, trying not to wake up Nadia. I walked to the living room, and dialed a Leningrad number again—this time it was Aunt Olia's home. I knew what I was going to hear—but I had to be certain. Arkady answered the phone. It was still very early in Leningrad; I must have woken him up.

"Where is Olga Petrovna?" I asked.

"She is gone."

"???"

She was hit by a car... and died in the hospital two months later. She was fighting for her life... You know her, she was very strong... If she had gotten proper medical care, she could have survived...

"When did it happen?"

"December 15."

Olga died in the hospital on December 15, ten days before the Soviet Union was officially dissolved. Just one day after Nina. A month before her death, Nina visited Olga in the hospital; she had trouble finding her bed in an overcrowded ward with inadequate hygiene and severe shortage of medical personnel. But then Olga appeared lively; she was glad to see Nina; she tried to persuade her to take better care of herself. I am sure they talked about me, and how good it was that I had left in time...

I went back to bed. I was not crying any more. What happened was too unreal to take it seriously. It was long past midnight, but I was lying wide-awake, thinking about myself as about some third person whom I barely knew. A person that I might have read about in a book, or seen in a movie.

I remember wondering to whose funeral I would have gone if I had been in Leningrad then. Nina and Aunt Olia died one day apart, but probably were buried on the same day. The idea of choosing which funeral to attend was so ridiculous that I almost laughed at it. And suddenly, to my great surprise, I felt that I was falling asleep.

I had time to think that, when I wake up the next morning, I will at first decide that I had experienced a weird nightmare. And then I would understand that it was not a nightmare, but a horrific reality. But I *will live* with this reality. I did not know *how* I would possibly be able to live with it—but I knew I would.

And I knew one more thing:

I will never, ever be the same person again.

I will have to drag my life—maybe for many, many more years—carrying a piece of dead soul inside me.

Because it was part of me that died that night—

January 2, 1992.

* * *

I received Nina's letter. It was only three pages long, written in a rush late at night by a very tired and very sick woman who had no friends left in her country, and was married to a man who almost never talked, but was working on his computer programs all nights long.

She did give it to the person who was leaving for America—a few minutes before she fell dead on a street of the city where she and I had been born.

I have that letter—as well as all her other letters, written in less than a year of our separation. It ends with the words:

I am trying to understand why you suddenly stopped writing. I know that people change a lot when they leave. I know that many forget their old friends. But I have never believed that it could happen to you...

She was right: I did not forget. And never will.
I also was right that night:
I never was the same person again.
And never will be.

ENDNOTES

1. [PAGE 62] **Komsomol**, Russian abbreviation of *Vsesoyuzny Leninsky Kommunistichesky Soyuz Molodyozhi,* English *All-Union Leninist Communist League of Youth*, in the history of the Soviet Union, organization for young people aged 14 to 28 that was primarily a political organ for spreading Communist teachings and preparing future members of the Communist Party.

The Komsomol was organized in 1918 in order to band together various youth organizations that had previously been involved in the Russian Revolution; many of these groups had fought in the Civil War. When the military phase ended, a new purpose was set in 1922—to engage the members in health activities, sports, education, publishing activities, and various service and industrial projects. Komsomol membership reached a maximum of about 40 million in the 1970s and early '80s. All Komsomol cells were federated at levels paralleling those of the party. Reflecting the collapse of communism in the Soviet Union, the Komsomol disbanded in 1991. (*Encyclopedia Britannica*, https://www.britannica.com/topic/Komsomol)

2. [Page 163] **"Propiska"** was both a residency permit and a migration-recording tool, used in the Russian Empire before 1917 and in the Soviet Union from the 1930s. Literally, the word propiska means "inscription", alluding to the inscription in a state internal passport permitting a person to reside in a given place. For a state or third-party owned property, propiska meant a person was included in the rental contract associated with a dwelling. The propiska was documented in local police (Militsiya) registers and certified with a stamp in internal passports. (*Wikipedia*)

3. [PAGE 203] **Nikita Khrushchev** (1894–1971) led the Soviet Union during the height of the Cold War as the First Secretary of the Communist Party of the Soviet Union (CPSU) from 1953 to 1964, and as Chairman of the Council of Ministers, or Premier, from 1958 to 1964. Khrushchev was responsible for the "de-Stalinization" of the Soviet Union, for backing the progress of the early Soviet space program, and for several relatively liberal reforms in areas of domestic policy. Yet Khrushchev could be authoritarian in his own right, crushing a revolt in Hungary and approving the construction of the Berlin Wall. Though he largely pursued a policy of peaceful coexistence

with the West, the Cuban Missile Crisis began after he positioned nuclear weapons 90 miles from Florida. Khrushchev's party colleagues removed him from power in 1964, replacing him with Leonid Brezhnev as the CPSU First Secretary and Alexei Kosygin as the Premier Minister.

4. [PAGE 207]   **Perestroika** refers to the reconstruction of the political and economic system established by the Communist Party. Politically, contested elections were introduced to reflect the democratic practices of Western society and allow citizens to have a slight say in government. Economically, Perestroika called for de-monopolization and some semi-private businesses to function, ending the price controls established by the government for the past seven decades. The goal was to create a semi-free market system, reflecting successful capitalist practices in the economies of Germany, Japan, and the United States. Unfortunately, such an economy took time to thrive, and people found themselves stuck in a worn-out economy, which led to long-lines, strikes, and civil unrest.

5. [PAGE 358]   **Mikhail Gorbachev**, in full *Mikhail Sergeyevich Gorbachev*, (born March 2, 1931, Privolye, Stavropol kray, Russia, U.S.S.R.), Soviet official, the general secretary of the Communist Party of the Soviet Union (CPSU) from 1985 to 1991 and president of the Soviet Union in 1990–91. His efforts to democratize his country's political system and decentralize its economy led to the downfall of communism and the breakup of the Soviet Union in 1991. In part because he ended the Soviet Union's postwar domination of eastern Europe, Gorbachev was awarded the Nobel Prize for Peace in 1990. (*Encyclopedia Britannica.* https://www.britannica.com/biography/Mikhail-Gorbachev)

6. [PAGE 358]   The term "**Glasnost**" means "openness" and was the name for the social and political reforms to bestow more rights and freedoms upon the Soviet people. Its goals were to include more people in the political process through freedom of expression. This led to a decreased censoring of the media, which in effect allowed writers and journalists to expose news of government corruption and the depressed condition of the Soviet people. Glasnost also permitted criticism of government officials, encouraging more social freedoms like those that Western societies had already provided. Yet, the totalitarian state present since 1917 was difficult to dismantle, and when it fell apart, citizens were not accustomed to the lack of regulation and command. The outburst of information about escalating crime and crimes by the government caused popular panic. This caused an

increase in social protests in a nation used to living under the strictest government control, and went against the goals of Gorbachev.

7. [Page 444]   December 19, 1989. Several hundred Jews from all over the Soviet Union convened in Moscow on Monday for a historic conference aimed at establishing the first congress of Soviet Jewish communities and organizations. An estimated 700 Jews, representing 175 Soviet Jewish organizations from 75 Soviet cities, gathered at the Central Cinema, Moscow's equivalent of Radio City Music Hall, despite attempts by anti-Semitic demonstrators to keep them out.

About 60 members of the anti-Semitic group *Pamyat* gathered in subzero temperatures, waving placards that said, "Jews Out," and "Down with Communism and Zionism."

Several Jews testified that they had been physically assaulted, according to Israeli reporters attending the conference. The assaults took place despite the presence of a number of Soviet militia officers engaged to prevent such occurrences. They largely managed to turn away the ruffians, telling them that they were demonstrating without permission, whereas the conference was being held with a permit.

"Had it not been for the police, one cannot tell how it would have ended," a Jewish participant told Gideon Allon, a reporter for the Israeli Hebrew daily Ha'aretz.

RAISA BOROVSKY was born in Leningrad (currently St. Petersburg), Russia. She had an elite upbringing in *Akademgorodok* (Academic town) in southwestern Siberia, then the center of Soviet science. After graduating from one of the best schools in the Soviet Union, she returned to Leningrad to receive her higher education. She spent the next 12 years living in Moscow, Leningrad, and her childhood town in Siberia, moving through different social strata and changing several professions. In the 1980s (the last decade of the Cold War), she distributed underground literature and secretly learned Hebrew.

Throughout the years of Perestroika, she took active part in emerging Jewish cultural life and the movement for free emigration. She received political refugee status in the American embassy in Moscow in 1989, and moved to the USA a few months before the collapse of the Soviet Union. She currently lives in suburban Boston with her husband, her youngest daughter and her granddaughter, working as a mental health counselor and a yoga instructor.

45378643R00281

Made in the USA
Middletown, DE
18 May 2019